Student Study Guide with Selected Solutions

Barbara Bode Snyder
San Jose City College, San Jose, California

ELECTRONICS AND COMPUTER MATH

SEVENTH EDITION

Bill Deem

Prentice
Hall

Upper Saddle River, New Jersey
Columbus, Ohio

Editor in Chief: Stephen Helba
Acquistions Editor: Frank Mortimer
Production Editor: Alexandrina Benedicto Wolf
Design Coordinator: Diane Ernsberger
Production Manager: Brian Fox

This book was set in Times Roman by The Special Projects Group. It was printed and bound by Victor Graphics, Inc. The cover was printed by Phoenix Color Corp.

Pearson Education Ltd.
Pearson Education Australia Pty. Limited
Pearson Education Singapore Pte. Ltd.
Pearson Education North Asia Ltd.
Pearson Education Canada, Ltd.
Pearson Educación de Mexico, S.A. de C.V.
Pearson Education—Japan
Pearson Education Malaysia Pte. Ltd.
Pearson Education, *Upper Saddle River, New Jersey*

10 9 8 7 6 5 4 3 2 1
ISBN 0-13-048782-1

PREFACE

Mathematics is an interesting and necessary adjunct to the electronics field. This new and expanded edition contains both a Student Study Guide and a Solutions Manual, with many practical hints included throughout both parts. The combination of the text and this Study Guide / Solutions Manual can be very valuable to you as you prepare yourself for your study of electronics.

As you study each chapter of the text, work the Practice Problem Sets and the Self-Tests as you come to them. If any section is still unclear, work the End-of-Chapter Problems with the same number as that section, and then check those answers in the Solutions Manual while also reading the Notes to the Student in the Solutions Manual.

The Solutions Manual contains answers to all of the Student Quizzes and most of the End-of-Chapter Problems, along with hints on how to work many of the problems. Many problems have been worked in great detail as a guide on how to do the problems. But always try the problem yourself before looking at the solution. In many cases, more than one method of solution is possible and valid. And of course there may be several correct ways to express the answer.

You can strengthen your understanding of the material by studying the summary of the chapter in the Student Study Guide. Give yourself the Student Quiz in the Study Guide and check your answers in the Solutions Manual. These questions are designed to let you test your skill and mastery of the chapter material.

If you discover a weakness in your quiz results, go back and study the text. Work out some of the End-of-Chapter Problems for each section where you did not fully understand the material. Check those answers in the Solutions Manual. Retake the quizzes and self tests as often as needed for mastery.

Estimate the solution to each problem first by hand. Then use your scientific calculator to your advantage to work the problem, storing the answer in memory. Always prove your answers, using the calculator where possible to insert your values into the original equations to be sure your values work in the original equations.

M is you **MUST** know **MATH** for a good understanding of electronics.

A is be **ABLE** to work these problems, and electronics will be easy for you.

T is to **TAKE** the **TIME** to study math and your understanding of electronics will be easy for you.

H is to **HAVE** a good attitude towards Math and the four letter word **MATH** will lead you to a successful career in electronics.

CONTENTS

Chapter 1   **THE DECIMAL NUMBER SYSTEM**   1
      Decimal Number System   1
      Decimal Fractions   1
      Rounding Whole Numbers   2
      Rounding Non-Whole Numbers   2
      Signed Numbers   2
      Addition and Subtraction   3
      Multiplication and Division   3
      Mathematical Expressions and Terms   4
      Practical Comments   4
      Student Quiz   5

Chapter 2   **POWERS OF TEN**   9
      Positive Exponents   9
      Negative Exponents   9
      Multiplication in Powers of Ten Form   9
      Division in Powers of Ten Form   9
      Combined Multiplication and Division in Powers of Ten   10
      Scientific Notation   10
      Problems with Complex Denominators   10
      Reciprocals   11
      Powers and Roots in Base Ten   11
      Practical Comments   11
      Student Quiz   13

Chapter 3   **UNITS AND PREFIXES**   15
      Units   15
      Prefixes   15
      Applications   16
      Systems of Measurement   16
      Powers and Roots   16
      Practical Comments   17
      Student Quiz   19

Contents

Chapter 4 **FRACTIONS, DECIMALS AND PERCENTS**   **21**

    Prime Numbers and Prime Factors 21

    Reducing Fractions to Lowest Terms 21

    Multiplication and Division of Fractions 21

    Addition and Subtraction of Fractions 22

    Improper Fractions and Mixed Numbers 22

    Decimal Fractions 22

    Practical Comments 22

    Student Quiz 23

Chapter 5 **ALGEBRAIC TERMS: ROOTS AND POWERS**   **25**

    Literal and Real Numbers 25

    Algebraic Expressions and Terms 25

    Numerical Coefficients 25

    Exponents 25

    Roots 26

    Practical Comments 26

    Student Quiz 27

Chapter 6 **FRACTIONS AND LITERAL NUMBERS**   **29**

    Prime Numbers 29

    Lowest Common Multiple 29

    Multiplication and Division of Monomials 29

    Multiplication and Division of Fractions 29

    Addition and Subtraction of Fractions 29

    Practical Comments 30

    Student Quiz 31

Chapter 7 **LINEAR EQUATIONS**   **33**

    Identifying Equations 33

    Linear Equations 33

    Second-Degree Equations 34

    Applications 34

    Practical Comments 34

    Student Quiz 35

Chapter 8 **FACTORING ALGEBRAIC EQUATIONS**   **37**

    Multiplication of Polynomials by Monomials 37

    Multiplication of Binomials by Binomials 37

    Division of Polynomials 37

    Factoring Polynomials 38

    Factors of Trinomials 38

    Practical Comments 38

    Student Quiz 39

Contents

Chapter 9   **FRACTIONAL EQUATIONS**   **41**
General Equations 41
Some Real Equations 41
Quadratic Equations 42
Practical Comments 42
Student Quiz 43

Chapter 10   **DC CIRCUIT ANALYSIS: KIRCHHOFF'S LAWS**   **45**
Kirchhoff's Current Law 45
Kirchhoff's Voltage Law 45
Polarity 46
Practical Comments 46
Student Quiz 47

Chapter 11   **DC CIRCUIT ANALYSIS: OHM'S LAW**   **51**
Circuit Resistance 51
Series Circuits 51
Parallel Circuits 52
Series-Parallel Circuits 52
Practical Comments 52
Student Quiz 53

Chapter 12   **DC CIRCUIT ANALYSIS: CIRCUIT THEOREMS**   **57**
Superposition Theorem 57
Thévenin's Theorem 57
Norton's Theorem 58
Practical Comments 58
Student Quiz 59

Chapter 13   **GRAPHING**   **61**
Graphing Linear Equations 61
Slope of a Line 62
Slope-Intercept Form 62
Interpreting Graphs 62
Plotting Curves 63
Practical Comments 63
Student Quiz 65

Chapter 14   **SIMULTANEOUS LINEAR EQUATIONS**   **69**
Linear Equations in Two Unknowns: Graphical Solution 69
Linear Equations in Two Unknowns: Algebraic Solution 69
Determinants 70
Applications 70
Practical Comments 71
Student Quiz 73

Contents

Chapter 15   COMPLEX NUMBERS   **75**
        Imaginary Numbers   75
        Complex numbers   75
        Practical Comments   76
        Student Quiz   77

Chapter 16   THE RIGHT TRIANGLE   **79**
        Sides and Angles   79
        Pythagorean Theorem   79
        Trigonometric Functions   80
        Inverse Trigonometric Functions   80
        Trigonometric Equations   81
        Practical Comments   82
        Student Quiz   83

Chapter 17   TRIGONOMETRIC IDENTITIES   **85**
        Law of Sines   85
        Law of Cosines   85
        Practical Comments   85
        Student Quiz   87

Chapter 18   AC FUNDAMENTALS   **89**
        Generating Angles   89
        Generating Sine Waves   89
        Frequency and Time   90
        Angular Velocity   90
        RMS and Peak Values of Voltage and Current   90
        Phase Angle of Lead or Lag   90
        Instantaneous Values of Voltage and Current   91
        Practical Comments   92
        Student Quiz   93

Chapter 19   AC CIRCUIT ANALYSIS: SERIES CIRCUITS   **95**
        Series RC Circuits   95
        Series RL Circuits   96
        Polar to Rectangular Conversion   96
        Series Resonance   97
        Practical Comments 97
        Student Quiz   99

Contents

Chapter 20 AC CIRCUIT ANALYSIS: PARALLEL CIRCUITS **103**
    RC Circuit Analysis 103
    RL Circuit Analysis 103
    Equivalent Circuits 103
    AC Networks 104
    Practical Comments 104
    Student Quiz 105

Chapter 21 FILTERS **107**
    RC Circuit Analysis 107
    Thévenin's Theorem 107
    Band-Pass Filters 108
    Practical Comments 108
    Student Quiz 109

Chapter 22 LOGARITHMS **113**
    Logarithms Defined 113
    Common Logarithms 113
    Multiplication of Numbers by Using Logarithms 114
    Division of Numbers by Using Logarithms 114
    Raising a Number to a Power by Using Logarithms 114
    Natural Logarithms 114
    Practical Comments 114
    Student Quiz 115

Chapter 23 LOGARITHMIC EQUATIONS **117**
    Logarithmic and Exponential Forms 117
    Logarithmic Equations: Common Logs 117
    Logarithmic Equations: Natural Logs 117
    Practical Comments 117
    Student Quiz 119

Chapter 24 APPLICATIONS OF LOGARITHMS **121**
    Gain Measurement 121
    Reference Levels 121
    Frequency Response 122
    RC Circuits 123
    Practical Comments 123
    Student Quiz 125

Contents

Chapter 25   **COMPUTER NUMBER SYSTEMS**   **127**
>   Binary Number System   127
>   Octal Number System   127
>   Hexadecimal Number System   128
>   Binary to Octal to Hexadecimal Conversions   128
>   Addition   129
>   Subtraction   129
>   Practical Comments   130
>   Student Quiz   131

Chapter 26   **BOOLEAN ALGEBRA**   **133**
>   Logic Variables   133
>   The AND Function   133
>   The OR Function   134
>   The NOT Function   134
>   Boolean Expressions   134
>   Booelan Postulates and Theorems   135
>   Practical Comments   136
>   Student Quiz   137

Chapter 27   **KARNAUGH MAPS**   **141**
>   Two-Variable Expressions   141
>   Three-Variable Expressions   142
>   Four-Variable Expressions   142
>   Practical Comments   142
>   Student Quiz   143

Chapter 28   **INTRODUCTION TO STATISTICS**   **145**
>   Population, Range, Mean, Median, Mode   145
>   Standard Deviation or Sigma   145
>   Normal Distribution Curve   146
>   Statistical Analysis   147
>   Practical Comments   148
>   Student Quiz   149

**SOLUTIONS MANUAL: ANSWERS TO STUDENT QUIZZES
          IN STUDY GUIDE**   **151**

**SOLUTIONS MANUAL: ANSWERS TO SELECTED TEXT
          END OF CHAPTER PROBLEMS**   **155**

THE DECIMAL NUMBER SYSTEM

DECIMAL NUMBER SYSTEM

◆ The word *decimal* means base ten.

◆ The decimal system of numbers uses ten *digits*. A digit is a symbol for a number. We use these digits in the decimal system: 0, 1, 2, 3, 4, 5, 6, 7, 8, and 9.

◆ Each position of a digit in a number has a *place value*. This is the number's value at that place.

◆ The digit that has the greatest effect upon the value of a number is called the *most significant digit (MSD).*

◆ The *MSD* is the leftmost nonzero digit in a number.

◆ The *MSD* is never zero unless that total number is exactly equal to zero.

◆ The *least significant digit (LSD)* is the digit with a place value that has the smallest effect upon the number's value. The *LSD* is at the right of a number.

◆ The *LSD* can be (and often is) zero.

◆ There are 4 significant digits in both numbers 009820 and 009.820. The *MSD* in both numbers is 9. The *LSD* in both numbers is 0.

DECIMAL FRACTIONS

◆ A fraction has two numbers (1/2). The number above the line is called the *numerator*, and the number below the line is the *denominator*.

◆ In a fraction, the *numerator* is divided by the *denominator*.

◆ A fraction whose denominator is 10 or a multiple of ten is known as a decimal fraction.

◆ To convert from a decimal fraction to a decimal number, determine the value of the denominator and place the LSD of the numerator in that position.

◆ Conversion from a decimal number to a fraction is the reverse process.

ROUNDING WHOLE NUMBERS

◆ *Rounding* numbers to the nearest place value, which becomes the new *LSD*, is a very common method used to simplify electronic calculations.

◆ A general rule is if the digit to the right of the *new LSD* is 4 or smaller (4, 3, 2, 1, 0), replace the digits to the right of the *new LSD* with zeros.

◆ A general rule is if the digit to the right of the *new LSD* is 5 or greater (5, 6, 7, 8, 9), increase the new LSD by one and replace the digits to the right of the *new LSD* with zeros or drop digits to right and add a multiplier.

◆ In order to maintain the desired number of significant digits, truncate the number at the *new LSD* and add a times value or words so that the number of significant digits is correct. If you want 3 significant digits, then:

654321   becomes 654000   which becomes 654×1000 or 654 thousand.

3456789 becomes 3460000 which becomes 346×10000 or 346 ten thousands

ROUNDING NON-WHOLE NUMBERS

◆ Use the same system as above to round decimal numbers. The number of significant digits is independent of decimal place. If you want 4 significant digits, 0.00345678 becomes 0.003457   and 876.54321 becomes 876.5

SIGNED NUMBERS

◆ Numbers can have signs such as + or −. These numbers are called *signed numbers*.

◆ Some common symbols are < (*less than*) and > (*greater than*).
For example, 1 < 2 (1 *is less than* 2) and 6.7 > 5.2 (6.7 *is greater than* 5.2).

◆ If the value of the number is used without regard to the sign, then that value is called the *absolute value*. The absolute value of −17 and 17 is +17. The *magnitude of a number* ignores the sign. The magnitude of −17 is 17.

ADDITION AND SUBTRACTION

◆ The signs + and − indicate the sign of a number. They also indicate addition and subtraction. The magnitude of the number is the number without a sign.

◆ Adding two or more positive numbers involves just adding the magnitudes and using a plus (+) sign on the result.

◆ Adding two or more negative numbers involves just adding the magnitudes and using a negative sign (−) on the result.

◆ Adding numbers with opposite signs is a slightly different process. Add together all the positive numbers and then add together all the negative numbers. Subtract the absolute value of the lesser number from the absolute value of the greater number and place the sign of the largest number before the answer.

◆ $+4 +5 = +9 \qquad -4 -5 = -9 \qquad -4 + 5 = +1 \qquad +4 -5 = -1$

◆ The process of subtraction involves the first number called the ***minuend***, minus the second number, called the ***subtrahend***. The answer is called the difference.
The rule in subtraction is to change the sign of the subtrahend and add as before.

MULTIPLICATION AND DIVISION

◆ Symbols are used to denote multiplication and division. The symbol for multiplication is $\times$ or * or no operator given before a left paren (or a letter).
$3 \times 4 = 12$ and $3 * 4 = 12$ and $3 (4) = 12$ and $3 A = (A + A + A)$

◆ Division symbols are ÷ or / or a fraction line. Division always means to take reciprocal and then multiply.
$4/5 = 4 \div 5 = \dfrac{4}{5} = 4 \times (1/5) = 0.8 = .8$ (your choice on writing leading zero)

◆ Multiplying or dividing signed numbers requires a method of determining the sign of the result.

◆ Positive signed numbers multiplied or divided will always result in a positive answer.

◆ Multiplying or dividing an even number of negative numbers will result in a positive answer. Multiplying or dividing an odd number of negative numbers will result in a negative answer.

MATHEMATICAL EXPRESSIONS AND TERMS

◆   A mathematical term is a number preceded by a + or − sign.

◆   An ***expression*** is a group of two or more terms.

◆   Mathematical expressions are often grouped together in parenthesis ( ), brackets [ ], or braces { }. All of these are types of parentheses.

◆   The order of operation in *Please Excuse My Dear Aunt Sally*.
A mathematical expression using these groupings must be solved by first performing the calculations within each set of *parentheses*, brackets, or braces. Next do any *exponents* (*which includes powers and trig functions*).

◆   Change any number after division sign to the reciprocal and change ÷ to × since division is just a special type of multiplication.
Next do all *multiplications* (including those from reciprocals of *division*).
Lastly, do all *additions* and *subtractions*.

PRACTICAL COMMENTS

◆   You are on your way to making a career in electronics. The electronics field requires a systematic method of thinking and approaching a problem. This problem solving cannot be achieved in a short period. Time and practice are necessary. Your study of math will help you to gain the learning necessary to operate with efficiency in your work with electronic circuits.

◆   The use of math in analyzing electronic circuits will show you the way that all circuits behave under any conditions. As an example, you have just installed a new battery in your car. The engine still does not turn over fast enough to start the car. Remembering Ohm's law (which taught you the relationship between voltage, current and resistance), you speculate that if the voltage is high (because of the new battery) and the starter is almost new, then high resistance must be causing the motor to slow. Bingo, you forgot to clean the battery terminals (the source of high resistance). You clean them, and away you go. This type of logical thinking is helped by your study of math.

STUDENT QUIZ

Name _____ Date _____

1.   A mathematical expression is made up of one or more terms.
      a. true
      b. false

2.   The correct order of performing operations in an expression is +, –, ×, and ÷
      a. true
      b. false

3.   MSD means the most significant digit.
      a. true
      b. false

4.   In the place value table for the decimal number system the third place has a value of hundreds.
      a. true
      b. false

5.   Zero is not a digit in the decimal system.
      a. true
      b. false

6.   Convert 746 ten-thousandths to a decimal fraction.
      a. 4.6/10,000
      b. 746/1,000
      c. 10,000/746
      d. 746/10,000

7.   Given the number 567.89, the MSD is _____ and the LSD is _____.
      a. 9, 5
      b. 5, 8
      c. 5, 9
      d. 6, 7

8.   Convert 438 thousandths to a decimal number.
      a. 0.438
      b. 0.0438
      c. 0.00438
      d. 0.000438

9.   Convert 31/10,000 to a decimal number.
      a. 0.31
      b. 0.031
      c. 0.0031
      d. 0.00031

10.   Round the number 12,965 to the nearest hundred.
      a. 12,966
      b. 12,900
      c. 12,010
      d. 13,000

11. Round the number 7.654 to two decimal places.
     a. 7.7
     b. 7.65
     c. 7.64
     d. 7.66
12. The statement $8.9 < 9.1$ is _____
     and the statement $0.73 > 0.74$ is _____
     a. true, true
     b. true, false
     c. false, false
     d. false, true
13. The absolute value of 17.5 is _____, and of -0.56 is _____
     a. 17.5, -0.56
     b. -17.5, -0.56
     c. 17.5, 0.56
     d. none of these
14. Perform the following. $30 + (-40) - (-45) =$
     a. 35
     b. -35
     c. -55
     d. 115
15. Given this expression, $21 - (-35) - 67$. Find the absolute value of the answer.
     a. -11
     b. 11
     c. 81
     d. -81
16. Perform the following. $-67 - (-34) + (-8) - (-12) - 29 =$
     a. -29
     b. -58
     c. -55
     d. -97
17. Perform the following. $(3 - 12) + 15 / 5 - 7 \times 2 =$
     a. -2
     b. -5
     c. -20
     d. -32
18. Perform the following. $\{12 + (-3 \times -12) / (2 \times 6)\} =$
     a. 15
     b. -15
     c. 9
     d. -9

19.	Perform the following. $[64 - (4 \times 8)][84 / 7 + 12] =$
    a. 396
    b. 768
    c. −308
    d. −396

20.	Perform the following. $\{18 - 3 \times 7 + 12\} / \quad [4 \times 6 / 8] =$

	note: this is the same as $\{18 - (3 \times 7) + 12\} / \quad [4 \times 6 \times (1 / 8)] =$
    a. 21
    b. 3
    c. 0
    d. 9

POWERS OF TEN

2

POSITIVE EXPONENTS

◆ Large or small numbers can be handled easily by using a system of notation called *powers of ten*.

◆ The powers of ten refers to the *exponents of ten*. This exponent is the number of times ten is multiplied by itself. For example $10 \times 10 \times 10 \times 10 = 10^4$. The four is the exponent of ten.

◆ Exponents determine the number of places the decimal point is moved from the present decimal point toward the new decimal point. If no number is given with the power of ten, insert 1. An example is $10^3 = 1. \times 10^3 = 1000.$
$$4.56 \times 10^3 = 4560.$$
Notice the decimal point moved to right with a positive exponent.

◆ To convert from a powers of ten to a number, simply write 1 and follow it by the number of 0's in the exponent if the exponent is a positive number.

NEGATIVE EXPONENTS

◆ Numbers less than 0 are dealt with by using negative exponents.

◆ Negative exponents determine the number of places the decimal point is moved from the present decimal point towards the left to the new decimal point. An example of this is $10^{-3} = 0.001$. Also $78.9 \times 10^{-4} = .00789$

MULTIPLICATION IN POWERS OF TEN FORM

◆ Multiplication of terms with powers of 10 is simply a matter of adding the powers. $10^{-3} \times 10^3 = 10^8$

DIVISION IN POWERS OF TEN FORM

◆ Division of numbers containing powers of ten involves subtraction of the exponents. $10^3/10^2 = 10^1$

COMBINED MULTIPLICATION AND DIVISION IN POWERS OF TEN

◆　　This process is one of adding or subtracting the powers of ten as required.

◆　　The powers of ten are added or subtracted using the same rules as adding or subtracting signed numbers.

◆　　To move a power of ten from a denominator to a numerator, simply change the sign of the exponent. $1/10^3 = 10^{-3}$. The opposite change is also true.

An example is $\dfrac{10^2}{10^4} = 10^2 \times 10^{-4} = 10^{-2} = \dfrac{1}{10^2} = \dfrac{1}{100} = .01$

SCIENTIFIC NOTATION

◆　　A very convenient method of expressing the numbers we use in electronics is the use of *scientific notation*.

◆　　Scientific notion is the placing of a decimal point after the MSD and adding a power of ten. The exponent of the power of ten will be the number of places the decimal point is moved.

◆　　In the original number, count the number of decimal places the decimal point moves left. This is the positive value of the exponent.

◆　　Move the decimal point to the right and the exponent is negative. $.00567 = 5.67 \times 10^{-3}$

◆　　Use your scientific calculator to do problems involving scientific notation.

◆　　Your calculator can handle any calculations with powers of ten.

PROBLEMS WITH COMPLEX DENOMINATORS OR NUMBERATORS

◆　　If your problem has a complex denominator or numerator, the fraction line says that everything in the numerator is surrounded by imaginary parentheses and must be done first. Likewise everything in the denominator has a pair of parentheses and must be combined before the division takes place. This is also the clue on how to do this with your calculator.

$$\frac{2 + 8}{3 + 2} = \frac{(2 + 8)}{(3 + 2)} = \frac{10}{5} = 2 \qquad \text{on calculator: } (2 + 8) \div (3 + 2) = 2.$$

◆　　If you have a calculator that has a parenthesis feature, then this is a simple problem.

RECIPROCALS

◆ A *reciprocal* of a number is one divided by that number. As an example, 1/2 is the reciprocal of 2. A reciprocal of a fraction (like 2/3) is that function flipped over (for 3/2).

◆ Most calculators have a separate key to give you the reciprocal of any number in its display. The key is sometimes called 1/X and sometimes X^{-1}.

POWERS AND ROOTS IN BASE TEN

◆ To raise a power of ten to a power simply multiply the exponents. $(10^2)^{-2} = 10^{-4}$
On caclulator use $(1 \times 10^{-2})^{-2} = 1 \times 10^{-4}$. You may want to use y^x key.

◆ To find the square root of a number, raise that number to the 1/2 power.
To find the third root of a number, raise that number to the 1/3 power.
To find the nth root of a number, raise that number to the 1/n power.
Most calculators use y^x key to raise a number to a power.
For example, $(10^6)^{1/2}$ will give you the square root of $10^6 = 10^3$.

PRACTICAL COMMENTS

◆ The numbers used in the electronics field are often very large or very small. Using the powers of ten is the most convenient method of expressing these large or small numbers. For example, electrical current is often measured in milliamps, (mA). This is the same as 10^{-3} or 0.001 amperes. The other extreme is a common unit of resistance called the ohm (Ω). This value can be several thousand ohms or even several million ohms. 1,000,000 ohms is the same as 10^6 Ω. This is abbreviated as 1 Megohm or even shorter, 1 MΩ. Another electrical quantity is capacitance measured in micro farads (μF).
1 μF = 1/1,000,000 Farad or 10^{-6} F. Powers of ten will be used constantly in your chosen field of electronics.

◆ Electronic engineers and technicians have a very valuable tool constantly at hand, the calculator. Most electronic happenings in a circuit can be explained by mathematical processes. The hand held calculator excels at solving these equations easily and accurately. By the way, the calculator is very handy for checking the numbers on your pay checks.

STUDENT QUIZ

Name _____ Date _____

1. Powers of ten are a convenient way of expressing only large numbers.
   a. true
   b. false
2. The calculator is very handy in electronics math.
   a. true
   b. false
3. Powers of ten can be converted to a decimal number by moving the decimal point either to the right or left depending on the sign of the exponent.
   a. true
   b. false
4. The reciprocal of 10 is 0.01.
   a. true
   b. false
5. Scientific notation is used in electronics to simplify and shorten mathematical expressions.
   a. true
   b. false
6. Convert 10^4 to a decimal number.
   a. 1
   b. 10
   c. 100
   d. 1000
   e. 10000
7. Convert 10^{-6} to a decimal number.
   a. 0.0001
   b. 0.00001
   c. 0.000001
   d. 0.0000001
8. Convert 10^{-3} to a decimal fraction.
   a. 1/10
   b. 1/100
   c. 1/1000
   d. 1/10000
9. Convert 0.001 to a power of ten form.
   a. 10^{-2}
   b. 10^{-3}
   c. 10^{-4}
   d. 10^{-5}

10. Perform the following operation. $10^{-5} \times 10^{3} =$
    a. 10^{-2}
    b. 10^{2}
    c. 10^{-8}
    d. 10^{8}

11. Divide the following. $10^{0}/10^{3} =$
    a. 10
    b. 1
    c. 10^{3}
    d. 10^{-3}

12. Perform the following. $(10^{3} \times 10^{-1} \times 10^{5}) \div (10^{3} \times 10^{5}) =$
    a. 10^{-0}
    b. 10^{-1}
    c. 10^{-3}
    d. 10^{-5}

13. Given this number, 5855. Round this to two significant digits and express your answer in scientific notation.
    a. 5.855×10^{3}
    b. 5.86×10^{3}
    c. 5.9×10^{3}
    d. 5.9×10^{-3}

14. Solve for the value of this expression, 1/47000. Express your answer in scientific notation and round to two decimal places.
    a. 2.12×10^{-5}
    b. 2.13×10^{-5}
    c. 2.127×10^{-4}
    d. 2.1276×10^{-7}

15. Solve the following. $1/[(1/(4.7 \times 10^{3}) + 1/(2.2 \times 10^{3}))] =$
    a. 1.499×10^{3}
    b. 6.673×10^{-5}
    c. 6.9×10^{4}
    d. 1.449×10^{-5}

UNITS AND PREFIXES

3

UNITS

◆ Converting from one power of ten to another is not difficult. To change to a power of ten which is more positive, compensate by moving the decimal point in the numerical part to the left to make the numerical part smaller.

$$5.678 \times 10^2 = .5678 \times 10^3 = .05678 \times 10^4 = .0005678 \times 10^6$$

◆ To change to a power of ten which is less positive (more negative), compensate by moving the decimal point in the numerical part to the right to make the numerical part larger.

$$.0005678 \times 10^6 = .5678 \times 10^3 = 567.8 \times 10^0 = 567800 \times 10^{-3}$$

◆ A number expressed with a single digit to the left of the decimal point and times a power of ten is expressed in *scientific notation*, such as 5.23×10^4.

◆ *Engineering notation* is a number expressed in two parts, a numerical part and a power of ten where the power of ten is a multiple of 3 or –3. The decimal point can be anywhere in the numerical part, such as 45.67×10^3. The power of ten can be replaced by a prefix and still be called *engineering notation*.

◆ Converting from a number to *scientific notation* is easy. Just move the decimal point to the right of the most significant digit and add a power of ten. If you moved the decimal point left (in the negative direction) 4 places, then the exponent on the power of ten must be +4. If you moved it right (in the positive direction) 2 places, then the exponent on the power of ten must be –2.

$$47000 \ \Omega = 4.7000 \times 10^4 \ \Omega \ (\text{if you don't round it}).$$
$$.01234 \ A = 1.234 \times 10^{-2} \ A$$

PREFIXES

◆ *Engineering notation* used in electronics has abbreviations for powers of ten which are multiples of 3 and –3. The most important of these are 10^{12} = Tera, 10^9 = Giga, 10^6 = Mega, 10^3 = kilo, 10^{-3} = milli, $10^{-6} = \mu$ = micro [note: μ is the lower case Greek letter mu], 10^{-9} = nano, 10^{-12} = pico, 10^{-15} = femto.

◆ Remember that any number to zero power $= 1 = 10^0 = 2^0 = 8^0$

◆ The basic electrical quantities also have their abbreviations. A resistor used in series has resistance is expressed in Ohms (Ω) and used in parallel has conductance measured in Siemens (S). Current is expressed in amperes (A), voltage in volts (V), and power in watts (W).

APPLICATIONS

◆ Calculations involving electronic quantities are commonly expressed in engineering units and abbreviated. Be sure to keep as many significant digits as were in the original data.
For example, $2.2 \text{ mV} / 4.7 \text{ k}\Omega = 5.0 \times 10^{-7} \text{ A} = .50 \times 10^{-6} \text{ A} = .50 \, \mu \text{ A}$

SYSTEMS OF MEASUREMENT

◆ Electronics uses units to measure many quantities that are very large or very small.

◆ These units of measure are based on a system called the ***Internation System of units (SI)***.

◆ Unit names are abbreviated, as capacitance (C), current (I), conductance (G), resistance (R), electromotive force (E or V), power (P).

◆ Prefixes related to powers of ten which are multiples of 3 or −3 are used with the units to express quantities of measure such as $34.5 \times 10^{-3} \text{ V} = 34.5 \text{ mV} = .00345 \text{ V}$

POWERS AND ROOTS

◆ Exponent of 2 means square. Exponent of 1/2 means square root. Exponent of 4 means fourth power. Exponent of 1/4 means fourth root.
$9^2 = 81$ and $81^{1/2} = 9$
$3^4 = 3 \bullet 3 \bullet 3 \bullet 3 = 3^2 \bullet 3^2 = 9 \bullet 9 = 9^2 = 81$ and $81^{1/4} = 3$

PRACTICAL COMMENTS

◆   All people in electronics use abbreviations. Students new to electronics must become familiar with these new terms. Changing from amperes to milliamperes (mA), for example, is an everyday occurrence. Some of you will arrive at answers of 4.56×10^4 Ω on your calculator. While this is correct, it is more convenient to be able to express the answer in kΩ. Since $k = 10^3$, to change from 10^4 to 10^3 is to make the power of ten one less positive, so to compensate move the decimal point one place in the direction to make the numerical part more positive.

4.56×10^4 Ω $= 45.6 \times 10^3$ Ω $= 45.6$ kΩ $= 45600 \times 10^0$ Ω $= 45600$ Ω

◆   Practice these conversions well and your study of electronics will be much smoother.

◆   Series circuits use ohms (Ω) values. Parallel circuits use Siemens values. Usually Ω and Siemens are reciprocals ($1/X$ or X^{-1}) of each other. Do NOT say inverse for reciprocal.
41 Ω $= (1/41)$ S $= .02439$ S $= 24.39$ mS
47 kΩ $= 47000$ Ω $= (1/47000)$ S $= 0.00002128$ S $= 21.28$ μS

STUDENT QUIZ

Name _____ Date _____

1. Engineering notation is the expression of a number times a power of where the exponent is a multiple of 3.
   a. true
   b. false
2. Scientific notation is expressing any number times a power of ten.
   a. true
   b. false
3. Some typical electronic units are volts, ohms, and amperes.
   a. true
   b. false
4. The prefix micro = 10^{-3}.
   a. true
   b. false
5. The correct power of ten to express Mega is 10^6.
   a. true
   b. false
6. Express the number 0.0067 A as _____ mA and as _____ μA.
   a. 6.7, 0.067
   b. 67, 670
   c. 6.7, 6700
   d. 0.67, 0.67
7. Express the number 1.23 V as _____ mV and as _____ kV.
   a. 1.23, 0.123
   b. 1230, 0.00123
   c. 12.3, 0.00123
   d. 1230, 0.123
8. Change 14976, Hz to kHz.

   a. 1.4976×10^5 kHz
   b. 14.976 kHz
   c. 147.96 kHz
   d. 1497.6 kHz
9. Express the number 4.7×10^{-5} to μF and then in pF.
   a. 4.7 μF, 4700 pF
   b. 0.047 μF, 47000 pF
   c. 470 μF, 470000 pF
   d. 47 μF, 47000000 pF
10. Express 2.2 kΩ as Ω.
    a. 22Ω
    b. 220Ω
    c. 2200Ω
    d. 22000

11. Express 0.005 μF as pF.
    a. 5 pF
    b. 50 pF
    c. 500 pF
    d. 5000 pF
12. Change 14 Mhz to Hz.
    a. 14000,000 Hz
    b. 1,400,000 Hz
    c. 140,000 Hz
    d. 14,000 Hz
13. Perform the indicated calculation. 15 V/4.7 kΩ =
    a. 319 μA
    b. 319 mA
    c. 0.0319 A
    d. 3.19 mA
14. Perform the following. 1/(6.28 $\times$ 12 kHz $\times$ 0.47 μF)
    a. 28.2 Ω
    b. 28.2 kΩ
    c. 0.035 Ω
    d. 0.035 kΩ
15. Perform the following. $1/6.28(0.47 \text{ mH} \times 0.47 \mu\text{F})^{1/2}$
    a. 03.3 μHz
    b. 10.7 kHz
    c. 494 kHz
    d. 494 Hz

FRACTIONS, DECIMALS AND PERCENTS

4

PRIME NUMBERS AND PRIME FACTORS

◆ A *prime number* is a number that has no whole-number factors except one and itself.

◆ A non-prime number can be divided by prime numbers. These prime numbers are called *prime factors*. An example is that 2 and 5 are prime factors of 10.

REDUCING FRACTIONS TO LOWEST TERMS

◆ Often when adding or subtracting fractions it is convenient to find the prime numbers of two or more numbers. Finding these results in determining the *lowest common multiple (LCM)*.

◆ To find the LCM of two or more numbers, find the prime numbers of each number. The LCM is then the various prime numbers found multiplied by the number of times each prime is used. For example, to find the LCM of 10 and 12, determine the prime factors: $10 = 2 \times 5$ and $12 = 2 \times 2 \times 3$. The factors 5 and 3 occur once and 2 occurs twice. From this, multiply as follows: LCM $= 5 \times 3 \times 2 \times 2 = 60$.

◆ Cancel where you can within a fraction, or when multiplying two or more fractions together. Cross out or cancel out two identical factors where one is above fraction line and one is below the fraction line. You cannot cancel 2 factors when both are above or both are below the fraction line.

MULTIPLICATION AND DIVISION OF FRACTIONS

◆ Fractions must be reduced to the lowest terms. This occurs when there are no like factors in the numerator or denominator.

◆ To multiply fractions simply multiply the numerators together. Then multiply the denominators. Reduce the result to lowest terms.

◆ Division of fractions involves reciprocating the denominator and multiplying as above.

ADDITION AND SUBTRACTION OF FRACTIONS

◆   Two or more fractions requiring addition must have a common denominator (CD) before they can be added.

◆   If two or more fractions have a common denominator, the numerators can be added together.

◆   Subtraction of fractions is similar to addition as long as a common denominator is found.

IMPROPER FRACTIONS AND MIXED NUMBERS

◆   An *improper fraction* is a fraction where the numerator is larger than the denominator.

◆   *Mixed numbers* are numbers that have a whole number part and a fraction part, such as 4 1/3.

◆   To change an improper fraction to a mixed number, divide the numerator by the denominator to get the whole number. The remainder is the numerator of the fraction.

◆   Division or multiplication of mixed numbers requires that mixed numbers be first changed to improper fractions and then they are multiplied or divided. Be sure to cancel before you multiply out.

◆   Adding and subtracting mixed numbers is often done by changing all the numbers to improper fractions. Then it is easy to find the common denominator and proceed as above.

DECIMAL FRACTIONS

◆   The most common solution to expressing fractions as decimal fractions is to use your calculator. To convert 11/15 to a decimal fraction, divide 11 by 15 and round the answer to the desired accuracy.

PRACTICAL COMMENTS

◆   Many electronic formulas involve fractions. For example we refer again to Ohm's Law. $I = V/R$ is a fraction which shows the relationship of voltage to resistance in any circuit. If $V = 20$ V and $R = 10$ Ω, then the fraction 20 V$/10\Omega = 20/10 = 2$ Amperes. This fraction also tells us that any combination of V/R that equals the whole number 2 will always produce 2 amperes of current in the circuit.

STUDENT QUIZ

Name _____ Date _____

1. An example of a prime number is 15.
    a. true
    b. false
2. The prime factors of a non-prime number are those prime numbers that can be divided into the non-prime number.
    a. true
    b. false
3. To multiply fractions simply add the numerators and multiply the denominators together.
    a. true
    b. false
4. To divide fractions, reciprocate fraction (from word reciprocal) the denominator of second and multiply.
    a. true
    b. false
5. A mixed number has a whole number and a fraction.
    a. true
    b. false
6. Reduce the following fraction to lowest terms. 26/208 =
    a. 1/16
    b. 2/64
    c. 1/8
    d. 2/16
7. Multiply the following and reduce to the lowest terms. $2/3 \times 2/5 \times 2/7 =$
    a. 4/15
    b. 14/15
    c. 4/35
    d. 8/105
8. Divide the following and reduce to the lowest terms. $9/10 \div 4/5 =$
    a. 1 1/8
    b. 7/8
    c. 8/9
    d. 18/25
9. Change the following to a mixed number. 160/23 =
    a. 17.778
    b. 17 7/9
    c. 8 8/19
    d. 160/18
10. Change the following to an improper fraction. Reduce to the lowest terms. 6 9/16 =
    a. 8/27
    b. 27/8
    c. 105/16
    d. 3 1/8

11. Perform the following and express your answer as a mixed number. $7\ 2/5 + 3\ 3/8 =$
    a. 5 15/20
    b. 1 9/16
    c. 10 8/9
    d. 10 31/40

12. Perform the following and express your answer in decimal numbers. Round to three decimal places. $7\ 3/5 \times 9\ 2/3 =$
    a. 73.467
    b. 17.267
    c. 72.467
    d. 27.469

13. Perform the following and reduce to the lowest terms. $7/30 - 9/10 =$
    a. 21/100
    b. 1 2/15
    c. 7/27
    d. −2/3

14. Perform the following and change the answer to a mixed number. $4\ 1/8 \div 2\ 3/16 =$
    a. 1 31/35
    b. 66/35
    c. 9 2/128
    d. 1 15/16

15. Perform the following and express the answer as a mixed number. $2\ 1/8 \times 4\ 3/5 =$
    a. 6 29/40
    b. 2 19/40
    c. 9 31/40
    d. 85/184

ALGEBRAIC TERMS: ROOTS AND POWERS

5

LITERAL AND REAL NUMBERS

◆ A *real number* is the kind of number we have always dealt with, such as 17, 5.7, or –2.4.

◆ A real number can have only one value.

◆ Letters are often used to represent a variable value. These are called *literal numbers*.

ALGEBRAIC EXPRESSIONS AND TERMS

◆ An algebraic expression can contain one or several combinations of both real and literal numbers.

◆ An algebraic expression with one term is called a *monomial*.

◆ An algebraic expression containing more than one term is called a *polynomial*.

NUMERICAL COEFFICIENTS

◆ If a real number precedes an algebraic term than that number is known as the numerical coefficient. As an example, in the term 3ab, 3 is the numerical coefficient.

◆ If no number is present, then the coefficient is assumed to be 1, as in the term abc.

EXPONENTS

◆ An exponent is, as you will recall, a number that tells us how many times that number is multiplied by itself. Such as, $5^3 = 5 \times 5 \times 5 = 125$

◆ When dealing with a literal number, the value cannot be found until the value of the literal number is known. The expression $a^2 = a \times a$ cannot have a value until you know the value of a.

ROOTS

◆ The ***square root*** of a number is one of its two equal factors. $7 \times 7 = 49$ is an example, where 7 is the square root of 49.

◆ The radical sign ($\sqrt{\ }$), denotes the square root.

◆ A square root can be also expressed as an exponent, such as $\sqrt{2} = 2^{1/2}$

◆ Use a calculator for most of these types of calculations.

PRACTICAL COMMENTS

◆ The use of literal numbers is most prevalent in the field of electronics. Formulas are expressed in literal terms so that they can apply to a variety of circuit conditions. For example, Ohm's Law is expressed as $I = V/R$. If you know a value for I and R, then you can calculate for the value of V. Another example is the combination of real and literal numbers. The expression for determining the value of indictive reactance in an AC circuit is $X_L = 2\pi fL$. In this case the 2 and the π are real numbers and the f (frequency) and the L (inductance) are literal values.

STUDENT QUIZ

Name _____ Date _____

1.   In the expression 6ab, the 6 is a literal number.
      a. true
      b. false

2.   The square root of a number is that number multiplied by itself.
      a. true
      b. false

3.   The expression $a^3 = 8$ is correct if $a = 2$.
      a. true
      b. false

4.   The square root of a number can be found by raising the number to the 1/2 power, such as $2^{1/2}$.
      a. true
      b. false

5.   In the expression x^4, the 4 is known as an exponent.
      a. true
      b. false

6.   Calculate the following and round to three significant digits. $1.2^4 =$
      a. 1.44
      b. 1.73
      c. 2.07
      d. 2.49

7.   If $a = 3$, $a^5 =$
      a. 27
      b. 81
      c. 243
      d. 729

8.   If $a = 1$, $b = 2$, and $c = 3$, find the value of the expression $abc^2 =$
      a. 9
      b. 18
      c. 27
      d. 36

9.   If $a = 1$, $b = 2$, and $c = 3$, find the value of the expression $4(abc)^3 =$
      a. 108
      b. 216
      c. 432
      d. 864

10.   If $a = 1$, $b = 2$, and $c = 3$, find the value of the expression $3a^2 - b^3 + 4c^2 =$
      a. 31
      b. 19
      c. 27
      d. 42

11. Solve and round the following to three significant digits. $38^{1/2} =$
    a. 6.164
    b. 6.16
    c. 2.48
    d. 1440
12. Solve and round the following to three significant digits. $289^{1/2} =$
    a. 17.6
    b. 22
    c. 49
    d. 17
13. Solve and round the following to three significant digits. $99^{1/2} =$
    a. 9.95
    b. 9800
    c. 0.995
    d. 0.00995
14. If a = 1, b = 2, and c = 3, find the value of the expression $(a^2 + 2b^2 + 3c^2)^{1/2} =$
    a. 19
    b. 24
    c. 36
    d. 6
15. If a = 1, b = 2, and c = 3, find the value of the expression $(2a^2 + 2a^2b^2 + 2a^2b^2c^2)^{1/2} =$
    Round to three significant digits.
    a. 82
    b. 9.06
    c. 9
    d. 8.49

FRACTIONS AND LITERAL NUMBERS

6

PRIME NUMBERS

◆ A literal number is a prime number when it is raised to the first power. A literal number raised to another power is not prime. For example, y is prime while y^2 is not prime, since $y^2 = y \cdot y$

LOWEST COMMON MULTIPLE

◆ To find the LCM of two literal numbers, factor each term, find the maximum number of times a prime factor appears in any one term, and multiply the primes found. This process is similar to finding the LCM or LCD of two numbers.

MULTIPLICATION AND DIVISION OF MONOMIALS

◆ Multiplication of monomials containing literal numbers involves multiplying the real and then the literal numbers.

◆ Division of monomials containing literal numbers involves the division of the real numbers followed by division of the literals. For example $6a^2/3a = 2a$.

MULTIPLICATION AND DIVISION OF FRACTIONS

◆ To multiply fractions containing literal numbers, first cancel like factors, then multiply the numerators together and then the denominators. Cancel like factors and reduce to the lowest terms.

◆ To divide 2 fractions containing literal numbers, reciprocate the denominator of the second fraction and multiply the fractions.

ADDITION AND SUBTRACTION OF FRACTIONS

◆ If the denominators of the two fractions to be added or subtracted are equal, just add or subtract the numerators.

◆ You must find a common denominator before fractions can be added or subtracted.

◆ First find the common denominator of the real numbers as described in the previous chapter.

◆ Find the common denominator of the literal part by applying the rules above for finding the LCM.

◆ After the above steps, add or subtract the numerators.

PRACTICAL COMMENTS

◆ Fractions containing real and literal numbers are common in electronics. A good example is the formula for finding the capacitive reactance of a capacitor when applied in an AC circuit. Capacitive reactance is the opposition a capacitor offers to the flow of AC current.

It is expressed in ohms and the formula is $X_C = \dfrac{1}{2\pi fC}$

The real numbers are 1 and 2π (π is a constant value real number). The literal numbers are f and C. There are many other examples that you will come across in your study of electronics.

Remember when using your calculator for X_C, use $\qquad 1 \div (2 \times \pi \times f \times C) =$

STUDENT QUIZ

Name _____ Date _____

1. The prime factors of a literal number such as b^2 is $b \cdot b$.
    a. true
    b. false
2. To factor a number with literal terms, simply add all terms together.
    a. true
    b. false
3. To multiply monomials, multiply the real parts and then the literal parts.
    a. true
    b. false
4. Division of literal numbers sometimes involves cancelling of the same literal numbers.
    a. true
    b. false
5. It is not necessary to find a common denominator when adding fractions with different denominators.
    a. true
    b. false
6. Determine the prime factors of $36a^2b^2$.
    a. 2 2 3 3 a b
    b. 2 3 a a b b
    c. 2 3 3 3 a a b b
    d. 2 2 3 3 a a b b
7. Find the LCM of the following numbers. a^3bc, ab^2c
    a. a^2b^2c
    b. a^2bc
    c. a^2b^2c
    d. a^3b^2bc
8. Multiply the following. $3a^2b^2 \cdot 4ab^{-1}c =$
    a. $12a^2b^2c$
    b. $12a^3bc$
    c. $12a^3b^2c$
    d. $12abc$
9. Reduce the following to the lowest terms. $84a^3bc^2/12a^1c =$
    a. $7abc$
    b. $7a^2bc$
    c. $7a^2c$
    d. $7abc^2$
10. Multiply the following and reduce to the lowest terms. $(6b/11c) \cdot (4b/3c^2) =$
    a. $8b^2/11c^3$
    b. $24b^2/33c^2$
    c. $4b/11c$
    d. $6bc$

11. Divide the following. $(3a/9) \div (9a/18)$
    a. a/6
    b. 2/3
    c. 18a
    d. 2/3a

12. Perform the following and reduce to the lowest terms. $(3ab/11) + (9ab/11) - (4ab/11) =$
    a. 8ab/33
    b. 8/11
    c. 8ab/11
    d. 8b/11a

13. Perform the following and reduce to the lowest terms. $11/9a - 5/9a =$
    a. 11/9a
    b. 6/a
    c. 11/45a
    d. 2/3a

14. Perform the following and reduce to the lowest terms. $3b/4 + 3b/7 =$
    a. 33b/28
    b. 3b/28
    c. 6b/28
    d. 12b

15. Perform the following and reduce to the lowest terms. $4/3b - 7/3b =$
    a. −3/3b
    b. −1/b
    c. 1/b
    d. 3/7b

LINEAR EQUATIONS

7

IDENTIFYING EQUATIONS

◆   An *equation* is an algebraic expression separated by an equal sign (=).

◆   The equation says that the left side value must equal the right side value.

◆   An equation where the unknown is raised to the first power is called a *linear equation*.

◆   An equation with a power such as a^2 is known as a *second degree equation*.

LINEAR EQUATIONS

◆   Solving for an unknown in a linear equation is simple if you remember that you can do anything to one side of an equation as long as you do the same to the other side. This maintains the equality.

◆   Any mathematical operation can be performed on an equation as long as the equality is maintained.

INVERSE OPERATIONS

◆   Use inverse operations to undo operators in an equation.
    Use PEMDAS (Please Excuse My Dear Aunt Sally) in reverse.
    First undo Addition and Subtraction.
    Next undo Multiplication and Division.
    Next undo Exponents.
    Next undo Parnetheses.

◆   Inverse of addition is subtraction.
    $$x + 3 = 7$$
    $$x + 3 - 3 = 7 - 3$$
    $$x = 4$$

◆   Inverse of multiplication is division.
    $$3x = 7$$
    $$x = \frac{3x}{3} = \frac{7}{3}$$

◆   Inverse of square is square root. $x^2 = 81$

$$\left(x^2\right)^{1/2} = x = 81^{1/2} = 9$$

◆   Inverse of reciprocal is reciprocal. $1/x = 2/3$

$$x = 3/2$$

SECOND-DEGREE EQUATIONS

◆   A *second-degree* equation has at least one second power exponent.

◆   Second-degree equations can involve taking a square root of a number with an exponent of 2.

◆   The square root of a square of a number is that number.

◆   The square of the square root of a number is that number.

APPLICATIONS

◆   The field of electronics uses many equations to express mathematically how a circuit operates.

◆   A basic equation will state an electronic principal. It is necessary to be able to solve for any unknown in an equation. An example is Ohm's Law. The basic equation is

    $I = \dfrac{V}{R}$. The other forms are $V = IR$ and $R = \dfrac{V}{I}$ and $I = GE$.

PRACTICAL COMMENTS

◆   To achieve success in your study of electronics it will be necessary for you to be able to manipulate equations. Our example of the Ohm's Law manipulation above is a case in point. Of course, you will use the Ohm's Law equations so often that you will have them memorized. There will be many formulas that you will not use often. Under these conditions, it is far easier to remember the basic formula, and then if you need to solve a variation of the formula for a different unknown, manipulate the equation so you can solve it.

STUDENT QUIZ

Name _____ Date _____

1. The sign (=) in an equation means that each side of the equation must have an equal value.
    a. true
    b. false
2. A linear equation will have unknowns raised to a power of one only.
    a. true
    b. false
3. An equation such as $x^3 = 81$ is a second-order equation.
    a. true
    b. false
4. If you add a 7 to one side of an equation, you must subtract a 7 from the other side to maintain the equality.
    a. true
    b. false
5. This equation $(x^2)^{1/2} = x$ is
    a. true
    b. false
6. This equation $3b + 7 = 9$ is known as
    a. second-degree equation.
    b. a third-degree equation.
    c. a forth-degree equation.
    d. a linear equation.
7. In the equation, $a/3 = 4$
    a. a = 1 1/4
    b. a = 12
    c. a = 5/4
    d. a = 1 3/4
8. Solve for the unknown is this equation. Round to 3 decimal places. $8/a^2 = 4$
    a. 0.707
    b. 2
    c. 1.414
    d. 4
9. Solve for the unknown in this equation. $X^2 - 4 = 32$
    a. x = 1/6
    b. x = 6
    c. x = 0.167
    d. x = 3
10. Solve $f_c = 1/2\pi RC$ for C.
    a. $C = 1/2\pi R$
    b. $C = 2\pi f_c R$
    c. $C = 1/2\pi R f_c$
    d. $C = 2\pi/f_c R$

11.   Solve $\beta = I_C / I_B$ for I_B.
        a. $I_B = I_C / \beta$
        b. $I_B = \beta\, I_C$
        c. $I_B = \beta / I_C$
        d. $I_B = I_B + I_C$

12.   The formula for finding power is $P = I^2 R$. If $P = 10$ mW and $R = 10$ kΩ, find I.
        a. 10 36
        b. 10 mA
        c. 1 mA
        d. 0.1 mA

13.   The formula for finding the resistance of two resistors in series is $R_T = R_1 + R_2$.
        If $R_T = 4.7$ kΩ and $R_2 = 3.3$ kΩ, find R_1.
        a. 10 kΩ
        b. 8 kΩ
        c. 1.94 kΩ
        d. 1.4 kΩ

14.   A formula for finding the total resistance of two resistors in parallel is
        $R_T = (R_1 R_2)/(R_1 + R_2)$. If $R_T = 68$ kΩ and $R_1 = 100$ kΩ, find R_2.
        a. 4.7 Ω
        b. 32 kΩ
        c. 212.5 kΩ
        d. 168 kΩ

15.   The potential difference across the forward biased pn junction of a transistor is
        $V_{BE} = V_B - V_E$. If $V_{BE} = -0.7$ V and $V_E = -16$ V, find V_B.
        a. -16.7 V
        b. 16.7 V
        c. -17.7 V
        d. 17.7 V

FACTORING ALGEBRAIC EQUATIONS

8

MULTIPLICATION OF POLYNOMIALS BY MONOMIALS

◆ One way of multiplying a polynomial by a monomial is to multiply each term of the polynomial by the monomial. An example of this is the following,
$4a(3a + 5) = 12a^2 + 20$.

◆ Often like terms show up. If so, just combine them. If the result of a multiplication is $2ab - 4ab + 9ab$, then combine them into $7ab$.

◆ If a fraction is a part of the polynomial, multiply the numerator and reduce if possible.

◆ It is common practice to list your answer in descending order of the powers, such as $x^3 - x^2 - x$.

MULTIPLICATION OF BINOMIALS BY BINOMIALS

◆ Multiplying two binomials together requires that each term of one binomial be multiplied by each term of the other.

◆ An expression containing four terms will result. Sometimes a combining of terms may be necessary.

◆ The square of a binomial is the same as multiplying two like binominals. For example, $(a + 2)^2 = (a + 2)(a + 2) = a^2 + 4a + 4$. Notice that the like terms are combined.

DIVISION OF POLYNOMIALS

◆ Each term in the numerator must be divided by each term in the denominator.

◆ An example of this is $(a^2 - 3a + 12)/a = a - 3 + 12/a$.

◆ A method of long division can also be used.

FACTORING POLYNOMIALS

◆   Factoring polynomials is the opposite of multiplying polynomials by a monomial.

◆   Any group of terms can be factored by any term that is common to all of the terms. Take the term $3a^2 + 9a$. The term common to all of these terms is 3a. Dividing each of these terms by 3a gives a result of $3a(a + 3)$.

FACTORS OF TRINOMIALS

◆   Factoring a trinomial of form $ax^2 + bx + c$ requires an inspection of the real numbers to find two numbers whose product equals the last term of the trinomial and whose sum equals the second term. If $a \neq 1$ then more products are involved.

◆   Assuming $a = 1$, consider all pairs of factors which multiply together to $= c$.
$30 = 30 \times 1 = 15 \times 2 = 10 \times 3 = 6 \times 5$.

◆   An example of this type of factoring is the term $x^2 + 11x + 30$ which when factored results in $(x + 5)(x + 6)$. Note the sum of 5 and 6 is 11 and the product is 30.

◆   If sign of c is + but sign of b is –, then both factors are –.
$x^2 - 13x + 30 = (x - 3)(x - 10)$

◆   If sign of c is –, then give sign of b to larger of the 2 factors.
$x^2 + 13x - 30 = (x + 15)(x - 2)$
$x^2 - 29x - 30 = (x - 30)(x + 1)$

◆   Negative terms must be watched for the correct sign.

PRACTICAL COMMENTS

◆   In your study of electronics, factoring is a most important facet. This is especially true when studying and working with the mathematics of digital circuits. Simplifying digital circuits uses the factoring process. For example, a digital logic circuit might give you an expression $AB + B$. Using the factoring principles, this factors to $B(A + 1)$. This may not seem simpler but you will learn that in logic circuits $(A + 1) = 1$. This means that the circuit simplifies to B. You will learn to use this factoring in digital logic.

STUDENT QUIZ

Name _____ Date _____

1.   To multiply a polynomial by a monomial means adding each term of the polynomial and multiplying the sum by the monomial.
     a. true
     b. false

2.   If like terms appear as a result of a multiplication, it is usually a good idea to combine them.
     a. true
     b. false

3.   Multiplying two binomials usually results in an expression of four terms. These may be combined if possible.
     a. true
     b. false

4.   Division of a polynomial by a monomial means to divide each term by the monomial.
     a. true
     b. false

5.   Factoring of a polynomial is a very useful mathematical tool in electronics.
     a. true
     b. false

6.   Perform the indicated operation and combine any like terms. $5(x + 7) =$
     a. $5x + 2$
     b. $5x - 2$
     c. $5x - 35$
     d. $5x + 35$

7.   Perform the indicated operation and combine any like terms.
     $6a(a^2 + 4a + 6) + 2a(4a + 12) =$
     a. $6a^2 + 32a + 60$
     b. $a^3 + a^2 + a$
     c. $6a^3 + 32a^2 + 60a$
     d. $a + 24a^2 + 12$

8.   Perform the indicated operation and combine any like terms. $2a(3a + 6 + 2a^2/3) =$
     a. $6a^2 + 3a + 4a^3/3$
     b. $6a^2 + 12a + 4a^3/3$
     c. $3a^2 + 6a + 4a^3/3$
     d. $3a^2 + 9a + 4a^3/3$

9.   Perform the indicated operation and combine any like terms. $(a - 3)(a + 7) =$
     a. $a^2 + 4a - 21$
     b. $3a^2 - 4a + 21$
     c. $21a^2 + 4a - 21$
     d. $a^2 - 4a + 21$

10. Perform the indicated operation and combine any like terms. $(x + y)(2x - 3y) =$
   a. $x^2 - xy + 3y^2$
   b. $2x^2 + xy + 3y^2$
   c. $2x^2 - xy - 3y^2$
   d. $3y^2 + xy - x^2$

11. Perform the indicated operation and combine any like terms. $(x^3 - 4x^2 + 3x) \div 2x =$
   a. $2x^2 - 4x + 3$
   b. $x^2/2 + 2x - 3/2$
   c. $x^2/2 - 2x + 3/2$
   d. $x/2 - 2 + 2x/3$

12. Perform the indicated operation and combine any like terms. $(a^4 - 3a^3 + 6a^2 - a) \div a =$
   a. $a^3 + 3a^2 - 6a - 1$
   b. $a^3 - 3a^2 + 6a - 1$
   c. $a^3 - a^2 + 6a - 1$
   d. $a^3 + a^2 + 6a + 1$

13. Factor and reduce the following to the lowest terms. $9x - 3 =$
   a. $(3x - 1)$
   b. $3(9x - 1)$
   c. $3(3x + 1)$
   d. $3(3x - 1)$

14. Factor and reduce the following to the lowest terms. $28a^4b^3c^2 - 14a^3b^2c + 7a^2b^2c =$
   a. $4a^2bc - 2a + 1$
   b. $4a^2b^2c - 4ab + c$
   c. $4a^2bc^2 - 4bc + 1$
   d. $4abc - 4bc + 1$

15. Factor and reduce the following to the lowest terms. $x^2 + 2x - 63 =$
   a. $(x + 7)(x - 9)$
   b. $(x - 7)(x + 9)$
   c. $(x + 7)(x - 16)$
   d. $(x - 7)(x + 12)$

FRACTIONAL EQUATIONS

9

GENERAL EQUATIONS

◆ Polynomial equations often come with some or all of the terms in the form of a fraction.

◆ Equations with fractions must be treated as any other fraction. Find the common denominator (CD) and multiply all terms on both sides of the equation by the CD.

◆ Solve the resulting equation as before.

◆ An example is $1/3 + x/4 = 3$. The CD is 12. Multiply each term by the CD. $12/3 + 12x/4 = 36$. This then reduces to $4 + 3x = 36$. From this we get $x = \dfrac{32}{3}$. It is okay to leave answer as improper fraction. Or you can change to mixed number or decimal.

SOME REAL EQUATIONS

◆ A common equation used in electronics is $R_T = \dfrac{R_1 R_2}{R_1 + R_2}$. This gives the value of total resistance of two resistors in parallel. This equation is in the form of a fraction.

◆ Another common equation is $A_V = \dfrac{R_f}{R_{in}} + 1$. This equation is for the voltage gain of a non-inverting op-amp amplifier. It too is in the form of a fraction.

◆ These practical formulas can often be solved by the use of an electronic calculator. But you must multiply each term by CD and collect terms on paper.

QUADRATIC EQUATIONS

◆ The quadratic equation must used in electronics is in the form of $ax^2 + bx + c = 0$.

◆ A standard formula for solving these types of equations is $x = \dfrac{-b \pm \sqrt{b^2 - 4ac}}{2a}$.

◆ If the quadratic equation can be factored, factor it into the terms. Set each term to 0, and solve for each value of x.
$x^2 - x - 12 = (x - 4)(x + 3) = $ factors
$x - 4 = 0$ So $x = 4 = $ root   also $x + 3 = 0$ for $x = -3 = $ root.

◆ The equation can also be solved by placing the equation in the standard quadratic form and solving for the unknown from the above formula.

$$x = \left(-(-1) + \sqrt{\ } \, ((-1)^2 - 4(1)(-12)) \right) / 2 = 4$$

$$x = \left(-(-1) - \sqrt{\ } \, ((-1)^2 - 4(1)(-12)) \right) / 2 = -3$$

PRACTICAL COMMENTS

◆ As mentioned in a previous chapter, it is far easier to know how to manipulate a standard formula to find the various unknowns, than to remember all of the variations of each formula you will encounter.

STUDENT QUIZ

Name _____ Date _____

1. Polynomial equations will not be in fraction form.
   a. true
   b. false
2. If a polynomial equation does come in fraction form, then a common denominator must be found.
   a. true
   b. false
3. Electronics formulas often result in fractional equations.
   a. true
   b. false
4. A quadratic equation may be factored and each factor set to zero and solved.
   a. true
   b. false
5. Factoring is the only method available to solve quadratic equations.
   a. true
   b. false
6. Solve the following for the unknown: $2x/7 + 4 = 6$
   a. 14
   b. 42
   c. 7
   d. 3.5
7. Solve the following for the unknown: $R/4 - 2 = 2R/3$
   a. 5
   b. −5
   c. −24/5
   d. 5/24
8. Solve the following for R_2: $f = 1/2\pi C(R_1 + R_2)$
   a. $R_2 = (1/2\pi fC) + 1$
   b. $R_2 = (1/2\pi f) - C$
   c. $R_2 = C + 2\pi f$
   d. $R_2 = (1/2\pi fC) - R_1$
9. Solve the following for the unknown: $x^2 - x - 56 = 0$
   a. $x = -7, -8$
   b. $x = -7, 8$
   c. $x = 7, 8$
   d. $x = 56$
10. Solve the following for the unknown: $x^2 - 24x - 20 = 0$
    a. $x = 24.81, -0.805$
    b. $x = -24.81, 0.805$
    c. $x = -24.81, -0.805$
    d. $x = 24.81, 0.805$

DC CIRCUIT ANALYSIS: KIRCHHOFF'S LAWS

KIRCHHOFF'S CURRENT LAW

◆ The law known as ***Kirchhoff's current law*** states that the total current that flows into a junction must equal the total current that leaves the junction.

◆ Mathematically this can be stated as an equation, $I_{IN} = I_{OUT}$.

◆ Expressed another way $I_{IN} - I_{OUT} = 0$.

◆ Any circuit consists of three basic parts: a source, a path, and a load. The source might be a battery. The path is a piece of wire (a conductor), and the load could be a resistor or a lamp.

◆ A ***series circuit*** has only one current. The current leaving the source must equal the current entering the source.

◆ In a parallel circuit there is more than one path for the current to take in its way back to the source. Each junction point for the current will produce another parallel path.

◆ The current into a junction equals the current leaving it.

◆ A ***series-parallel or combination circuit*** has various combinations of series and parallel loads.

KIRCHHOFF'S VOLTAGE LAW

◆ Kirchhoff's voltage law states that the sum of the potential drops around any path must equal 0. For two drops this would be expressed as $V_1 + V_2 - V_T = 0$

◆ Stated another way the sum of the voltage drops around any closed loop must equal the source voltage. $V_T = V_1 + V_2 + \dots V_n$

POLARITY

◆ With electron current flow the end of a load where the current enters a negative is assigned a negative sign and the other end is positive. Look at your greatest source in a circuit. With electron current flow, the current is pictured as going through greatest sources from positive end to negative end and then through load starting at negative end of the load.

◆ Conventional current flow is just the opposite.

◆ Observe the proper polarity in going around the loop. Voltage drops are usually considered positive, while a source is negative, indicating an increase of potential.

◆ A loop may contain more than one voltage source.

PRACTICAL COMMENTS

◆ There are two schools of thought on current flow. One group sees the current flowing from the positive terminal of the source through the load and then back to the negative side. This is called conventional current flow. The opposite school sees the current flowing in the direction that the electrons must take, from the negative terminal through the load and then towards the positive. This is called electron current flow. In actuality either method can be used (and are used) to analyze current flow correctly.

◆ Kirchhoff's Voltage Law can be used all of the time to analyze circuits. In a series circuit, for example, the sum of the voltage drops must equal the source. This one fact will enable you to troubleshoot many electronic circuits.

STUDENT QUIZ

Name _____ Date _____

1.   Kirchhoff's current law states that the sum of the currents leaving a junction must be approximately equal to the currents entering that junction.
        a. true
        b. false
2.   The sum of the voltage drops in any loop must equal zero.
        a. true
        b. false
3.   There are many currents in a series circuit.
        a. true
        b. false
4.   The expression $I_T = I_1 = I_2$ is correct to express the currents in a parallel circuit.
        a. true
        b. false
5.   A series-parallel circuit can have many series and parallel loads.
        a. true
        b. false

Figure 10-1

6.   See figure 10-1. If $V_T = 17$ V and $V_2 = 12$ V, find V_1.
        a. 29 V
        b. 12 V
        c. 17 V
        d. 5 V
7.   See figure 10-1. If the current through $R_2 = 15$ mA, the current through R_1 is _____ and the total current is _____.
        a. 17 mA, 12 mA
        b. 12 mA, 17 mA
        c. 15 mA, 15 mA
        d. 30 mA, 18 mA

Figure 10-2

8.   See figure 10-2. Find I_T if I_1 = 33 mA, I_2 = 16 mA, and I_3 = 12 mA.
        a. 61 mA
        b. 20.3 mA
        c. 45 mA
        d. 67 mA

Figure 10-3

9.   See figure 10-3. If V = 50 V, V_1 = 22 V, find V_2.
        a. 50 V
        b. 22 V
        c. 72 V
        d. 28 V

10.   See figure 10-3. If V_1 = 250 mV and V_2 = 1.7 V, find V.
        a. 250 mV
        b. 1.45 V
        c. 1.95 V
        d. 1.45 V

Figure 10-4

11. See figure 10-4. Which of the following expressions is correct?
    a. $V = V_4 + V_2 + V_1$
    b. $V_4 = V - V_1 + V_2$
    c. $V_1 = V - V_4$
    d. $V_2 = V_1 + V_3$

12. See figure 10-4. Which of the following statements is correct?
    a. R_1 is in series with R_2.
    b. R_1 is in parallel with R_4.
    c. R_2 is in parallel with R_3.
    d. R_2 is in series with R_3.

Figure 10-5

13. See figure 10-5. If $V = 24$ V, $V_1 = 3$ V, $V_5 = 2$ V, and $V_4 = 1$ V, find V_3.
    a. 18 V
    b. 20 V
    c. 21 V
    d. 23 V

Figure 10-6

14.   See figure 10-6. Find the voltage from point A to ground.
        a. 3 V
        b. 5 V
        c. 8 V
        d. 4 V
15.   See figure 10-6. Find the voltage from point B to ground.
        a. 4 V
        b. 8 V
        c. 22 V
        d. 16 V

DC CIRCUIT ANALYSIS: OHM'S LAW

11

CIRCUIT RESISTANCE

◆ In a series circuit, the total resistance is equal to the sum of the individual resistances. $R_T = R_1 + R_2 + \ldots R_N$.

◆ *Conductance (G)* is the reciprocal of resistance. $G = 1/R$

◆ In a parallel circuit the total resistance is less than any of the branch resistances.

◆ The formula for finding the total resistance of resistors in parallel is
$$R_T = \frac{1}{\dfrac{1}{R_1} + \dfrac{1}{R_2} + \dfrac{1}{R_3} + \ldots + \dfrac{1}{R_N}} \text{ or } R_T = \frac{1}{G_T} = \frac{1}{G_1 + G_2 + G_3 + \ldots + G_N}$$

◆ A series-parallel circuit must be analyzed by switching from series laws to parallel laws as required.

◆ Two resistors in parallel often use the symbol ‖ to indicate that they are in parallel. For example, $R_1 \parallel R_2$.

SERIES CIRCUITS

◆ There is only one current in a series circuit.

◆ The basic form of Ohm's Law is $I = V/R$.

◆ The voltage drops across any load in a series circuit can be found by Ohm's Law. Be sure to use the values for that load if you need the drop across a particular resistor.

◆ The use of total voltage and total current will give you total resistance.

◆ Ohm's Law tells us that in any circuit, current and resistance are inversely proportional. If the resistance increases, the current decreases.

◆ Voltage and resistance are directly proportional, that is, the larger resistance will have the larger voltage drop across it.

◆ An increase in voltage will cause an increased amount of current to flow. Voltage and current are directly proportional.

PARALLEL CIRCUITS

◆ Ohm's Law applies to parallel circuits as well as all other circuits.

◆ In a parallel circuit, the voltage is constant across common branches.

◆ The current flow is greater in the branch with the least resistance.

◆ Branch currents add in a parallel circuits. $I_T = I_1 + I_2 + \ldots I_N$.

SERIES-PARALLEL CIRCUITS

◆ Analysis of these series-parallel circuits involves changing from working with series circuit laws to parallel laws as often as necessary.

◆ If a branch has series resistances, combine them.

◆ If a branch is in parallel with another resistor, then use the parallel rules to solve for the total resistance or current as required.

PRACTICAL COMMENTS

◆ Always remember to apply Ohm's Law to an individual resistor using that resistor's values. If you are considering the total circuit, then use the total values of I, V, and R. Mixing these values will cause you to get many incorrect answers.

◆ An excellent check on your calculations for the total resistance of a parallel circuit is that R_T must always be less than the resistance value of the smallest resistor in the parallel circuit. Of course this is true, because as you add parallel branches the current increases and therefore the resistance must decrease.

◆ Solving series-parallel circuits can be very easy. Just remember to draw the current paths on your diagram. These paths will show you the series combinations that can be made. Also, when you come to a branch, a parallel circuit must be present. Switch from series to parallel rules as often as needed in any order necessary.

STUDENT QUIZ

Name _____ Date _____

1.   There is only one current in a series circuit.
        a. true
        b. false
2.   The total resistance of resistors in parallel is found by $R_T = R_1 + R_2$.
        a. true
        b. false
3.   This expression is correct for finding the resistance of resistors in series.
        $R_T = R_1 R_2 / (R_1 + R_2)$
        a. true
        b. false
4.   Loads in parallel share the same voltage.
        a. true
        b. false
5.   Ohms's Law applies to all circuits.
        a. true
        b. false
6.   Which of the following expressions is *NOT* correct?
        a. V = I/R
        b. I = V/R
        c. R = V/I
        d. V = IR

Figure 11-1

7.   See figure 11-1. If V = 30 V and the three resistors equal 10 kΩ each, find the voltage across R_2.
        a. 30 V
        b. 3 V
        c. 12 V
        d. 10 V

8. See figure 11-1. If I = 10 mA, R_1 = 5 kΩ, R_2 = 3 kΩ and R_3 = 4 kΩ, find V.
    a. 50 V
    b. 30 V
    c. 40 V
    d. 120 V

Figure 11-2

9. See figure 11-2. Find R_T.
    a. 18.6 kΩ
    b. 13.9 kΩ
    c. 0.89 kΩ
    d. 0.47 kΩ

10. See figure 11-2. If I_3 = 5 mA, find V.
    a. 11 V
    b. 6.55 V
    c. 93 V
    d. 12 V

Figure 11-3

11. See figure 11-3. Find I_T.
    a. 6.98 mA
    b. 5.26 mA
    c. 11.4 mA
    d. 11.6 mA

12.   See figure 11-3. Find R_T.
      a. 4.7 kΩ
      b. 2.2 kΩ
      c. 10.3 kΩ
      d. 4.75 kΩ
13.   See figure 11-3. Find I_2.
      a. 2.60 mA
      b. 2.86 mA
      c. 5.69 mA
      d. 9.75 mA

Figure 11-4

14.   See figure 11-4. Find R_T.
      a. 10.22 kΩ
      b. 5.75 kΩ
      c. 81 kΩ
      d. 26.99 kΩ
15.   See figure 11-4. Find V_2.
      a. 4.78 V
      b. 15 V
      c. 10.22 V
      d. 12 V

DC CIRCUIT ANALYSIS: CIRCUIT THEOREMS

12

SUPERPOSITION THEOREM

◆ The *superposition theorem* is a theorem that is used to analyze a circuit that usually contains multiple voltage sources.

◆ This theorem uses a method of shorting each voltage source except one. Then the calculations are made for the current in a particular load.

◆ Each voltage is shorted out and the load current is calculated until all sources have been dealt with in a like manner.

◆ The resultant current through the load is then the algebraic sum of the currents found by the above calculations.

◆ The polarity of the currents must be watched carefully.

◆ When the load current has been found, the load voltage can then be calculated.

THÉVENIN'S THEOREM

◆ *Thévenin's theorem* states that any circuit, no matter how complex, can be represented by one series resistance and one voltage source.

◆ The *voltage source* is called $V_{OC} = V_{TH}$.

◆ The equivalent resistance is labeled R_{TH}.

◆ There are certain steps to take when applying Thévenin's Theorem. The first is to remove the load and calculate the voltage drop across the terminals of the open load. This will be called V_{OC} or open circuit voltage.

◆ Next, replace the voltage source with a short and calculate the resistance seen at the open circuit terminals. This is R_{TH}.

◆ Last, connect the load back to the output terminals of the equivalent circuit just calculated. Calculate the load current I_L by $I_L = \dfrac{V_{OC}}{R_{TH} + R_L}$

◆ Calculate the load voltage as follows: $V_L = \dfrac{V_{OC} R_L}{R_{TH} + R_L}$

NORTON'S THEOREM

◆ *Norton's theorem* states that any circuit can be represented by a single current source and a parallel resistance.

◆ To operate Norton's theorem, replace the load with a short circuit and calculate the current through the short. This is $I_{SC} = I_N$.

◆ Next, open the load short and short the voltage source. Determine the conductance at the open circuit terminals. Call this G_N.

◆ Often it is easier to find R_{TH} and then take the reciprocal to find G_N.

◆ Calculate the value of $V_L = \dfrac{I_{SC}}{G_N + G_L}$.

◆ The load current can then be found by $I_L = \dfrac{I_{SC} G_L}{G_L + G_N}$.

PRACTICAL COMMENTS

◆ The superposition theorem is very useful for finding the currents and voltages across a load when multiple voltage sources are used. Many transistor circuits are analyzed by this method because there are several DC voltage sources present. The theorem is handy; learn it and use it.

◆ Thévenin's theorem is used more than the other circuit theorems. Some types of circuits can be solved easily w58th this theorem. One such circuit is the bridge circuit. Using ordinary Ohm's law on a bridge circuit is very difficult. These bridge circuits are often found in measuring instruments and some types of transistor amplifiers.

STUDENT QUIZ

Name _____ Date _____

1.   The superposition theorem is very handy for calculating the values in the bridge type circuit.
        a. true
        b. false
2.   Thévenin's equivalent resistance is called R_{TH}.
        a. true
        b. false
3.   Thévenin's theorem states that any circuit can be reduced to one voltage source and one resistance.
        a. true
        b. false
4.   Norton's theorem states that any circuit can be reduced to several current sources and one parallel resistance.
        a. true
        b. false
5.   All of these circuit theorems require certain steps to use them properly.
        a. true
        b. false

Figure 12-1

6.   See figure 12-1. Use the superposition theorem and find the value of V_4.
        a. 22.76 V
        b. 5.17 V
        c. 17.59 V
        d. 27.97 V
7.   See figure 12-1. Use the superposition theorem and find the value of I_4.
        a. 17.24 mA
        b. 5.33 mA
        c. 6.74 mA
        d. 22.76 mA

Figure 12-2

8. See figure 12-2. Use Thévenin's theorem and find the value of V_{RL}.
    a. 15.12 V
    b. 22 V
    c. 1.26 V
    d. 18.88 V

9. See Figure 12-2. Use Thévenin's theorem and find the value of I_{RL}.
    a. 0.402 mA
    b. 1.26 mA
    c. 0.858 mA
    d. 0.456 mA

Figure 12-3

10. See figure 12-3. Use Norton's theorem to find I_L in this Norton's equivalent circuit.
    a. 26.6 μA
    b. 93.1 μA
    c. 2.66 mA
    d. 9.31 mA

GRAPHING

13

GRAPHING LINEAR EQUATIONS

◆ A *linear equation* is an equation in which each term contains only one variable and no exponents other than one.

◆ A *graph* is a picture of results of an equation as one factor changes.

◆ A graph of a linear equation must be a straight line.

◆ A system of *rectangular coordinates* is a graph where the horizontal axis (x-axis) is laid out in equal increments. The vertical axis (y-axis) is also linear.

◆ Positive values for the x-axis are plotted horizontally from the vertical axis towards the right. Negative values are plotted to the left.

◆ Positive values of y are plotted up and negative values are plotted down.

◆ The system of coordinates uses a standard notation as in (x, y) to identify a point. The x-coordinate is always first; the y-coordinate is last.

◆ A coordinate of (2, 3) means that the point is 2 spaces to the right and 3 spaces up.

◆ The x-axis is called the *abscissa*. The y-axis is called the *ordinate*.

◆ An equation such as $3x - 2y = 5$ will be a straight line, but it is safe to assume that there will be a place where the resulting graph line will intercept both the x-and y-axes.

◆ To find these intercept points, just set x to zero and solve for y. You will have the point coordinates of (0, y). Do the same for y = 0. The point coordinates will be (x,0).

SLOPE OF A LINE

◆ The *slope* of a line is a measure of how fast the line changes. Slope is as the $\frac{\text{change in y}}{\text{change in x}}$ or $\frac{\text{DELTA y}}{\text{DELTA x}}$ or $\frac{\Delta y}{\Delta x}$ or $\frac{\text{rise}}{\text{run}}$.

◆ A slope of 1/3 means that y changes 1 unit while x changes 3.

◆ We always read the graph so that x is positive.

SLOPE-INTERCEPT FORM

◆ A linear equation containing two variables can be written in the *slope-intercept form*.

◆ The slope-intercept form is $y = mx + b$.

◆ In this form, m is the slope and b is the y-intercept.

◆ Any two-variable linear equation can be rewritten in this form, and the slope and intercept are directly known.

INTERPRETING GRAPHS

◆ If a graph is a straight line, then you can find the value of the y-coordinate for any value of x.

◆ The slope can also be found.

◆ A graph may not be linear. In this case the slope must be found by finding the tangent at the point on the graph you are interested in.

◆ There are many curves that are non-linear, and they can also be used to find points or values as one axis changes.

PLOTTING CURVES

◆ The curve for the relationship between voltage and current in a series circuit with a resistor is linear. The *independent variable* is plotted on the horizontal axis. In this case it would be the value for current.

◆ The *dependent variable* is plotted on the vertical axis and is voltage. The voltage is dependent upon the current.

◆ If the current is a parallel circuit, usually the voltage is the independent variable and is graphed horizontally, while the current is the dependent variable and is graphed vertically.

◆ Look at your data and select an appropriate scale. Then plot your data.

◆ Linear graphs only require two points to plot. You should use a third point and often a fourth point to check for errors.

PRACTICAL COMMENTS

◆ Graphs are an important facet in your study of electronics. For example, a graph of the frequency response of your stereo amplifier will show how well it performs at low or high frequencies. This kind of curve is often included in the manufacturer's data on the unit.

◆ 63nother vital use of graphing principles is the trace on an oscilloscope. This trace is an instantaneous graph of the way a voltage is changing in a circuit under test. The oscilloscope has a horizontal axis of time, called the timebase. The vertical axis is the voltage present in the circuit. The resulting graph shows the varying of voltage as time changes. This important tool for electronic measurements is used frequently.

STUDENT QUIZ

Name _____ Date _____

1. A linear equation contains only one variable in a term
    a. true
    b. false
2. The coordinate of a point is expressed (y, x).
    a. true
    b. false
3. An intercept is when one variable of an equation equals zero.
    a. true
    b. false
4. The slope of a line equals (delta y)/(delta x).
    a. true
    b. false
5. In an equation in the form of y = mx + b, m is the slope and b is the intercept.
    a. true
    b. false

Figure 13-1

6. See figure 13-1. The coordinates of point A are
    a. (−1, 7)
    b. (2, 6)
    c. (−6, 0)
    d. 6, −3)
7. See figure 13-1. The coordinates of point D are
    a. (−1, 7)
    b. (2, 6)
    c. (−6, 0)
    d. (6, −3)

8. See figure 13-1. A line drawn between points C and E would have an x-intercept of
    a. (0, –2)
    b. (0, 2)
    c. (–1, 0)
    d. (0, –1)

9. See figure 13-1. A line drawn between points C and E would have a y-intercept of
    a. (0, –2)
    b. (0, 2)
    c. (–1, 0)
    d. (0, –1)

10. See Figure 13-1. Given the equation y = 2x + 2. Select two coordinate points from the figure that will fall on the graph of this equation.
    a. C, D
    b. C, E
    c. A, D
    d. A, E

11. See Figure 13-1. Given the equation y = –x/4 – 3/2. Select two coordinate points from the figure that will fall on the graph of this equation.
    a. C, D
    b. C, E
    c. A, D
    d. A, E

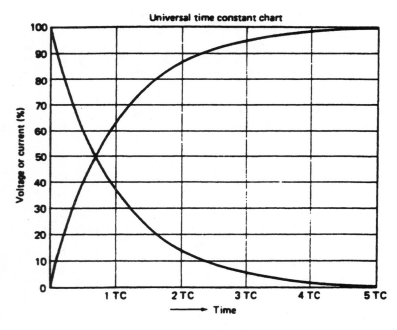

Figure 13-2

12. See Figure 13-2. If the applied voltage is 100 V, find the value of V_C at 0.707 TC.
    a. about 63 V
    b. about 50 V
    c. about 23 V
    d. about 16 V

13.   See Figure 13-2. If the applied voltage is 22 V, find the number of time constants to
       change the capacitor to 22 V
       a. 1
       b. 2
       c. 3
       d. 4
       e. 5

14.   See Figure 13-2. If the applied voltage is 25 V in an RC circuit, find the value of V_R after
       3 TC.
       a. about 15.9 V
       b. about 21.6 V
       c. about 23.5 V
       d. about 1.5 V

15.   See Figure 13-2. If the applied voltage is 12 V in an RC circuit, find the number of time
       constants required to charge the capacitor to 7.62 V.
       a. about 1
       b. about 2
       c. about 3
       d. about 4
       e. about 5

SIMULTANEOUS LINEAR EQUATIONS

14

LINEAR EQUATIONS IN TWO UNKNOWNS: GRAPHICAL SOLUTION

◆ Every linear equation in two unknowns has an unlimited number of solutions.

◆ If there are two linear equations that are plotted on the same system of rectangular coordinates, then there will be only one solution. One point will be common to each graph as long as the lines are not parallel or have the same slope.

◆ Two equations that have one common point for a solution are called *simultaneous equations.*

LINEAR EQUATIONS IN TWO UNKNOWNS: ALGEBRAIC SOLUTION

◆ It is possible to solve simultaneous equations by the *addition or subtraction method*, often called simply the addition method. Subtraction means change sign and add.

◆ Using the rules for algebra, manipulate the two equations so that the x or y terms are equal.

◆ Add or subtract the two equations. Use addition if the term signs are different, subtraction if the signs are the same.

◆ Solve for the first unknown, and then substitute in the other equation to find the other unknown.

◆ The *substitution method* of solving simultaneous equations is also used.

◆ Solve one of the equations for one unknown in terms of the other.

◆ Substitute this result in the other equation, and solve for the second unknown.

◆ The addition method can only be used with 2 equations in 2 unknowns. The substitution method is more powerful and can be used with any number of equations with any number of unknowns.

DETERMINANTS

◆ Another method to solve simultaneous equations is to use *determinants*.

◆ A determinant is an array of numbers.

◆ Arrange the two linear equations in the following general equations into this pattern:
$$a_1 x + b_1 y = k_1$$
$$a_2 x + b_2 y = k_2$$

◆ The a's and b's are the coefficients of the unknowns.

◆ The determinant of the denominator is found by cross-multiplying the coefficients of the unknowns. The general equation will be $a_1 b_2 - a_2 b_1$.

◆ The general equation of the numerator will be $k_1 b_2 - k_2 b_1$ for the unknown x, and $a_1 k_2 - a_2 k_1$ for the unknown y.

◆ Put the numerator and denominator together and solve for the unknowns.

◆ Solving three simultaneous equations using determinants is similar to the above method.

◆ If there are three coefficients in a diagonal row, arrange the coefficients in an array and multiply them.

◆ Substitute the values for the coefficients and solve for the unknowns x, y, and z.

APPLICATIONS

◆ Simultaneous equations can be used to solve circuits. The results will be the same as we discovered using the circuit theorems.

◆ An example is using Kirchhoff's voltage law in a parallel circuit. Write the two equations around each loop. If there are two loops, two equations will result.

◆ Solve these equations as simultaneous equations using one of the methods in this chapter.

◆ If the circuit under analysis has two sources, you must assume the direction of the currents. If you assume incorrectly, the values will be correct but the polarity will be negative.

PRACTICAL COMMENTS

◆   Simultaneous equations can be solved in many ways. In relatively simple electronic circuits, often the simplest method is to use Ohm's and Kirchhoff's laws. Learn to solve these equations with the method that involves the fewest steps. The fewer steps you need for a solution, the greater your chances are for an accurate solution.

71   Checking your answer is a smart procedure to learn when solving electronic circuits. Find some method for checking your answer. An example might be to use Ohm's law when you have solved for a current or voltage. Are your values correct? Will they give you the correct value of resistance that you started with? Ohm's law will give you a quick check.

◆   Always use a different method to prove or check your answers than the method used to solve the problem.

STUDENT QUIZ

Name _____ Date _____

1.   Linear simultaneous equations can not be solved by a graphical method.
      a. true
      b. false
2.   Addition and subtraction is a method for solving linear simultaneous equations.
      a. true
      b. false
3.   One method of solving simultaneous equations is by use of determinants.
      a. true
      b. false
4.   Circuit analysis can never be made using simultaneous equations.
      a. true
      b. false
5.   Substitution is a method for solving simultaneous equations.
      a. true
      b. false
6.   Given these two equations, $3x + 4y = 8$ and $x + y = 4$. Find the value of x and y that will satisfy both equations. Use the addition or subtraction method.
      a. $x = -4, y = 8$
      b. $x = 4, y = -8$
      c. $x = 8, y = -4$
      d. $x = -8, y = 4$
7.   Use the substitution method to solve these two equations. $3x + y = 12$ and $2x + 2y = 8$
      a. $x = 4, y = 16$
      b. $x = -4, y = 8$
      c. $x = 2, y = 2$
      d. $x = 4, y = 0$
8.   Use determinants to solve the following two equations. $4x + 5y = 20$ and $3x + y = 9$
      a. $x = 2\ 3/11, y = 2\ 2/11$
      b. $x = 2, y = 11$
      c. $x = -11, y = -2$
      d. $x = 11, y = 2\ 2/11$

Figure 14-1

9.   See figure 14-1. Use simultaneous equations to find voltage across R_2.
a. 26.67 V
b. 12.3 V
c. 16.67 V
d. 20 V

10.   See figure 14-1. Find the value of current through R_2.
a. 20 mA
b. 16.67 mA
c. 2.46 mA
d. 26.67 mA

COMPLEX NUMBERS

IMAGINARY NUMBERS

♦   The square root of a negative number is an *imaginary* number.

♦   It is usual to signify the square root of a negative number as $(-36)^{1/2} = 6(-1)^{1/2}$. The number 6 is real and the $(-1)^{1/2}$ is the imaginary part.

♦   In electronics we shorten the imaginary to *j*. $j = (-1)^{1/2}$. Also $j^2 = -1$.

♦   The real part of a complex or rectangular number is graphed horizontally on the real axis. The j part is graphed vertically on the j axis or imaginary axis. The total number is graphed as a rectangle, which is why these numbers are often called rectangular numbers.

♦   Numbers on the real axis have j part = 0 as in 3 + j0 or –5 + j0. Numbers on the j axis have real part = 0 as in 0 + j7 or 0 – j9.

COMPLEX NUMBERS

♦   A *complex number* consists of a number with a real and an imaginary part, such as 3 + j6. The 3 is real and the j6 is imaginary.

♦   Real numbers can be combined. Imaginary numbers can also be combined. An example is 3 + 4 + j3 + j4 = 7 + j7.

♦   Addition and subtraction of complex numbers consists of adding (or subtracting) the real parts and then doing the same for the imaginary parts.

♦   For example, (3 + j5) + (6 + j2) = 9 + j7.

♦   Most scientific calculators will perform these calculations for you.

♦   To multiply complex number, use the rules of algebra. Remember that $j \cdot j = j^2 = -1$.

♦   The *conjugate* of a complex number is that same number with the sign of the imaginary part changed.

◆ To divide 2 complex numbers such as (a + jb) / (c + jd), we multiply the fraction by a second fraction where both numerator and denominator equal conjugate of the denominator of the first fraction.

◆ Again the use of the calculator is very handy.

◆ A rectangular number is properly graphed by drawing a rectangle with one corner on a point such as the origin, 0 + j 0, and the opposite corner at the designated number, such as 3 + j 4 where the horizontal part of the rectangle is 3 units long and the vertical part is 4 units high. This rectangle contains 12 square units.

◆ An arrow (called a vector) can be drawn along the diagonal of the rectangle formed by the rectangular number a + j b. The starting point of the arrow is at the origin (0 + j 0) and extends directly up to the opposite point, such as a + j b. This vector is usually given using polar numbers of the form $c\angle\theta$ where c is the length of the diagonal line and θ is the angle which is the arctangent of b/a.

PRACTICAL COMMENTS

◆ Other math books use i for imaginary numbers. However in electronics the i is used for current. The next letter in the alphabet after i is j, so j is used in electronics.

◆ Imaginary or rectangular numbers are used extensively in the analysis of AC circuits. The j represents the phase angle θ between the voltage and the current of a circuit which contains R or G or C or L. Of course DC circuits do not have a differing phase relationship because when the voltage increases, the current increases at the same time. In AC circuits, Ohm's Law still works but with a different twist which includes j.

◆ The answer to any problem with rectangular numbers must be in the form of $\pm a \pm j b$ where a is clearly separated from b.
$$\frac{-4 + j\,5}{3} = \frac{-4}{3} + j\,\frac{5}{3} \text{ so a} = \frac{-4}{3} \text{ and b} = \frac{5}{3}$$

◆ Always replace j^2 with -1 as soon as you get it.

◆ Never leave j in the denominator.
$$\frac{7}{j2} = \frac{7 \times j}{j2 \times j} = \frac{j\,7}{-2} = -j\,\frac{7}{2}$$

◆ To get rid of j in a denominator of form a + 76 b, multiply the entire fraction by a fraction with numerator and denominator equal to the complex conjugate of the denominator: $a - j\,b$.
$$\frac{4 - j\,1}{3 + j\,2} = \frac{(4 - j\,1)(3 - j\,2)}{(3 + j\,2)(3 - j\,2)} = \frac{12 - j8 - j3 + j^2 2}{9 - j^2 4} = \frac{10}{13} - j\,\frac{11}{13}$$

STUDENT QUIZ

Name _____ Date _____

1.　The solution to x = $(-6)^{1/2}$ is an real number.
　　a. true
　　b. false
2.　The term j is used to signify imaginary numbers.
　　a. true
　　b. false
3.　Imaginary numbers can be combined similar to real numbers.
　　a. true
　　b. false
4.　The graph of a complex number can be called a vector.
　　a. true
　　b. false
5.　When it comes to complex numbers, calculators are not useful.
　　a. true
　　b. false
6.　Perform the following. $j^2 \cdot j^3 3 \cdot j^2 6 =$
　　a. j6
　　b. −j6
　　c. 18j2
　　d. −j18
7.　Perform the following. (15 + j3) + (−1 + j3) =
　　a. −15 + j6
　　b. 14 − j
　　c. 14 + j6
　　d. 15 − j6
8.　Perform the following. (2 − j3) − (6 + j4) =
　　a. 4 − j7
　　b. −4 + j7
　　c. −4 − j7
　　d. 4 + j
9.　Perform the following. (2 + j3)(3 − j9) =
　　a. 33 + j9
　　b. −33 + j9
　　c. 33 − j9
　　d. 6 + 18j
10.　Perform the following. (3 − j2) ÷ (3 + j2) =
　　a. 0.923 − j0.385
　　b. 0.385 − j0.923
　　c. −1.08 + j1.08
　　d. −1j

THE RIGHT TRIANGLE

16

SIDES AND ANGLES

◆ A *right triangle* is a triangle where one angle is 90° or a right angle.

◆ The longest side of a right triangle is called the *hypotenuse*.

◆ The angles are often labeled A, B, and C, where C is the right angle.

◆ The hypotenuse is the longest side and is opposite the right angle.

◆ The side opposite to the angle A is also called the *side adjacent to B*.

◆ The *adjacent side* to the angle A is the side closest to the angle A and is opposite to angle B.

◆ The angle A is often called *theta (θ)* in electronics, assuming that A is next to the horizontal axis.

◆ The angle B is called phi *(Φ)*, assuming that A is next to horizontal axis.

◆ The sum of the angles θ and Φ is 90°.

◆ In the electronics field the hypotenuse is often called Z for impedance, the adjacent side is R for resistance, and the opposite side is X for reactance in an ohms triangle.

◆ Another convenient way to label the sides is to make side a along the horizontal axis, where a is positive, and then make side b vertical into either quadrant I or IV. Then the triangle conforms to the notation for rectangular numbers, where $a + j b = c\angle\theta$.

PYTHAGOREAN THEOREM

◆ The Pythagorean theorem states that the sum of the squares of the sides equals the square of the hypotenuse or $c^2 = a^2 + b^2$. A more convenient form is $c = \sqrt{a^2 + b^2}$.

◆ If any two sides of a right triangle are known, then the third side can be found by applying the Pythagorean theorem.

◆ An AC circuit will apply this theorem as $Z = \sqrt{R^2 + X^2}$.

◆ The calculator is again very useful for doing this type of calculation.

◆ The Pythagorean theorem is useful for finding the length of a side of a right triangle where knowing the value of an angle is not required.

TRIGONOMETRIC FUNCTIONS

◆ The sides of a right triangle in relationship to one another are discussed in ratios known as *trigonometric functions*.

◆ The functions we will work with are called the *sine, cosine,* and *tangent*.

◆ The sine of an angle $\theta = \dfrac{opposite\ side\ to\ \theta}{hypotenuse}$ *or* $\sin\theta = \dfrac{o}{h}$

◆ The cosine of an angle $\theta = \dfrac{adjacent\ side\ to\ \theta}{hypotenuse}$ *or* $\cos\theta = \dfrac{a}{h}$

◆ The tangent of an angle $\theta = \dfrac{opposite\ side\ to\ \theta}{adjacent\ side\ to\ \theta}$ *or* $\tan\theta = \dfrac{o}{a}$

◆ The three basic trigonometric functions for various angles are listed in a table called a *trig table*.

◆ The trig values are more easily found by your calculator.

INVERSE TRIGONOMETRIC FUNCTIONS

◆ The inverses of trigonometric functions are called arcfunctions (arcsine, arccosine, arctangent), and they get you to the angle which produced that number as a result of using a sine, cosine, or tangent. The result of an arcfunction is always an angle.

The inverse of sine is arcsine (abbreviated arcsin or $\sin^{-1}$).
The inverse of cosine is arccosine (abbreviated arccos or $\cos^{-1}$).
The inverse of tangent is arctangent (abbreviated arctan or $\tan^{-1}$).

θ = arcsin(opposite side to θ / hypotenuse) = $\sin^{-1}$(opposite side to θ / hypotenuse)

θ = arccos(adjacent side to θ / hypotenuse) = $\cos^{-1}$(adjacent side to θ / hypotenuse)

θ = arctan(opposite side to θ / adjacent side to θ)

   = $\tan^{-1}$(opposite side to θ /adjacent side to θ)

◆   Most calculators require 2 keystrokes to use an arcfunction. An arcsin usually requires you to tap 2nd key or shift key or INV key followed by sin key. Often the key itself has sin written on it, and in another color directly over the key is written $\sin^{-1}$ which is said as arcsin. Make it a habit to say to yourself "arc" when you tap 2nd key (or shift key or INV key) and then "sine" when you tap the sin key.

◆   Any inverse returns you to what you started with.
The inverse of addition is subtraction. $A + B - B = A$
Read this as Anything plus Blank minus Blank returns you to original Anything.
The inverse of multiplication is division. $A \times B / B = A$
The inverse of raising to a power is a root. $\sqrt{(A^2)} = A$
The inverse of a root is a power. $(\sqrt{(A)})^2 = A$
The inverse of (1/X) is (1/X). $1 / (1 / A) = A$

◆   Be sure you understand that in general an inverse is NOT a reciprocal unless you are specifically talking about reciprocals. If you enter 2 into your calculator, take reciprocal (1/X) to get .5, then take reciprocal again to get 2. A reciprocal can be written with an exponent of -1, but this is the only time it means reciprocal; an exponent of -1 next to any function really means the inverse.

$A^{-1} = 1 / A$ $1 / A^{-1} = A$
arcsin $(\sin A) = \sin^{-1}(\sin A) = A$ $\sin(\text{arcsin } A) = \sin(\sin^{-1} A) = A$
arccos $(\cos A) = \cos^{-1}(\cos A) = A$ $\cos(\text{arccos } A) = \cos(\cos^{-1} A) = A$
arctan $(\tan A) = \tan^{-1}(\tan A) = A$ $\tan(\text{arctan } A) = \tan(\tan^{-1} A) = A$

TRIGONOMETRIC EQUATIONS

◆   The trig relationships are actually formulas you can manipulate to obtain other unknowns. For example, tan θ = o/a is the basic tangent function. Also o = atanθ, and a = o/tanθ.

◆   The calculator is again a useful tool.

PRACTICAL COMMENTS

◆   A easy way to remember the trig functions is to use a convenient mnemonic. Here is one.

$$\sin = \frac{opposite}{hypotenuse} = \frac{\underline{O}scar}{\underline{H}ad}$$

$$\cos = \frac{adjacent}{hypotenuse} = \frac{\underline{A}}{\underline{H}and}$$

$$\tan = \frac{opposite}{adjacent} = \frac{\underline{O}ut}{\underline{A}gain}$$

STUDENT QUIZ

Name _____ Date _____

1.   The sum of the three angles in a right triangle is 90°.
      a. true
      b. false
2.   The longest side of a right triangle is called the hypotenuse.
      a. true
      b. false
3.   The Pythagorean theorem is useful for finding the angles in a right triangle.
      a. true
      b. false
4.   Trig functions are simply the ratios of various sides.
      a. true
      b. false
5.   The sides of a right triangle are often called R, X, and Z in electronic circuits.
      a. true
      b. false

Figure 16-1

6.   See figure 16-1. If $\theta = 42°$ find angle Φ.
      a. 138°
      b. 90°
      c. 48°
      d. 42°
7.   See figure 16-1. Which side is adjacent to angle Φ?
      a. Z
      b. R
      c. X
8.   See figure 16-1. If R = 22 kΩ and X = 90 kΩ, find Z.
      a. 92.6 kΩ
      b. 2.65 kΩ
      c. 24.6 kΩ
      d. not enough data to calculate

9.   See figure 16-1. If Z = 100 kΩ and R = 47 kΩ, find X.
        a. 147 kΩ
        b. 88.3 kΩ
        c. 110.5 kΩ
        d. 53 kΩ

10.   See figure 16-1. If Z = 57.4 Ω and X = 12 Ω, find R.
        a. 69.4 Ω
        b. 45.4 Ω
        c. 58.6 Ω
        d. 56.1 Ω

11.   See figure 16-1. If X = 12 Ω and R = 12 Ω, find the angle θ.
        a. 45°
        b. 90°
        c. 0°
        d. 22.5°

12.   See figure 16-1. If θ = 33.5° and R = 4.7 kΩ, find Z.
        a. 0.55 kΩ
        b. 0.66 kΩ
        c. 5.64 kΩ
        d. 6.61 kΩ

13.   See figure 16-1. If θ = 67° and Z = 88 kΩ, find R.
        a. 34.4 kΩ
        b. 0.39 kΩ
        c. 2.35 kΩ
        d. 53.6 kΩ

14.   Determine tan 17.25°.
        a. 0.297
        b. 0.955
        c. 0.311
        d. 3.221

15.   Find $\sin^{-1}$ 0.9814.
        a. 0.999°
        b. 0.017°
        c. 79.8°
        d. 78.9°

TRIGONOMETRIC IDENTITIES

17

LAW OF SINES

◆ The *Law of Sines* enables us to calculate sides or angles of oblique triangles.

◆ If we know two sides and the included angle or if we know two angles and the side opposite one of them, the Law of Sines will let us solve for any other side or angle.

◆ There are three general equations in this law. Angle A is opposite side a.
  $\sin C/c = \sin B/b$
  $\sin C/c = \sin A/a$
  $\sin A/a = \sin B/b$

◆ Each of these equations can be used depending on the unknown and known values.

LAW OF COSINES

◆ The *Law of Cosines* will let us solve for sides or angles of triangles that the Law of Sines prevents, including finding the angles when only the sides are know.

◆ The three equations in this law are as follows.
  $a^2 = b^2 + c^2 - 2bc \cos A$
  $b^2 = a^2 + c^2 - 2ac \cos B$
  $c^2 = a^2 + b^2 - 2ab \cos C$

◆ Arranging any of these equations will enable you to solve for unknowns in a triangle.

PRACTICAL COMMENTS

◆ The need to solve these oblique triangles arise in your study of phase relationships in certain electronic and power circuits. Work with many types of filter circuits involves using these laws to properly design the circuits frequency response.

STUDENT QUIZ

Name _____ Date _____

1.   The easiest law to apply to solve a right triangle if you only need to know the sides is the Pythagorean Law.
     a. true
     b. false

2.   If you know two angles and the included sides of an oblique (not right) triangle, then you should apply the Law of Cosines.
     a. true
     b. false

3.   The Law of Sines is valuable when you need to know an angle but you only have the three sides given.
     a. true
     b. false

4.   The sum of the angles in any triangle is 180°.
     a. true
     b. false

5.   An oblique triangle can have one angle larger than 90°.
     a. true
     b. false

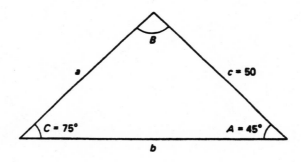

Figure 17-1

6.   See figure 17-1. Find side b.
     a. 70.7
     b. 14.14
     c. 36.6
     d. 44.8

7.   See figure 17-1. Find side a.
     a. 36.6
     b. 29.89
     c. 14.14
     d. 70.7

8.   Given a triangle with a = 40, b = 50, and c = 80. Find the angle A.
       a. 155.85°
       b. 65.85°
       c. 24.15°
       d. 22.71°

9.   Given a triangle with a = 40, b = 50, and c =80. Find the angle B.
       a. 24.15°
       b. 22.71°
       c. 125.1°
       d. 30.75°

10.   Given a triangle with a = 40, b = 50, and c = 80. Find the angle C.
       a. 24.15°
       b. 22.71°
       c. 125.1°
       d. 30.75°

AC FUNDAMENTALS

18

GENERATING ANGLES

♦ Our previous study of rectangular coordinates gave us a method of plotting any point.

♦ We can plot a line in the horizontal direction on the horizontal axis starting with origin and going to right. This line is a base line and it has an angle of 0°.

♦ The vertical axis represents an angle of 90°.

♦ The negative horizontal axis has an angle of 180° and the negative vertical axis an angle of 270° or −90°.

♦ It is customary to consider a line as rotating in a positive counterclockwise direction. A clockwise rotation will produce a negative angle.

♦ The line that is rotated is called a *vector*, and can represent a voltage or current in an AC circuit.

♦ The angle between the base and our graph line is called *theta (θ)*.

♦ This angle is measured in degrees or *radians*. A radian = 57.3° = 180°/π.

♦ To convert an angle in degrees to radians, divide the angle by 57.3 or multiply the angle by π/180°.

♦ The opposite conversion from radians to degrees, just multiply the angle in radians by 57.3° or multiply R radians × 180°/π to get degrees.

GENERATING SINE WAVES

♦ If we rotate a vector through 360°, the end of the vector will produce a sine wave.

♦ The positive peak value will be at 90°. The negative peak value will occur at 270°.

♦ The value will be zero at 0° and 180° rotation.

♦ The value of the output voltage can be found at any point by $v = V_{pk}\sin \omega t$.

FREQUENCY AND TIME

◆ The length of time used to generate one complete sine wave is called the **Period** (T). Lower case t is used to indicate any time.

◆ **Frequency** (f) is the number of complete cycles of sine waves generated in a specific amount of time.

◆ **Period** and **frequency** are reciprocals of each other. That is, $f = 1 / T$ and $T = 1/ f$

ANGULAR VELOCITY

◆ If the sine wave is generated at a constant rate of rotation, that rate of rotation is called **angular velocity** (ω).

$\omega = 360°f$ if you want the answer to be in degrees.

$\omega = 2 \pi f$ if you want the answer to be in radians.

$\omega = 400_g f$ if you want the answer to be in gons or grads.

RMS AND PEAK VALUES OF VOLTAGE AND CURRENT

◆ The peak or maximum value of the sine wave is at 90°
The RMS or effective value is at 45° and equals peak value / $\sqrt{2}$
$I_{RMS} = I_{eff} = I_{pk} \sin 45° = I_{pk} / \sqrt{2} = .707 I_{pk}$
If $V_{pk} = 8 V_{pk}$, then $V_{RMS} = 8 V_{pk}/ \sqrt{2} = 5.657 V_{RMS} = 5.657 V_{eff} = 5.657 V$

◆ A value given without a subscript is assumed to be RMS. $9 V = 9 V_{RMS}$

◆ The peak or max value equals RMS value x $\sqrt{2}$
$5.6 mA = 5.6 mA_{RMS} = 5.6 mA_{eff} = 7.92 mA_{pk} = 7.92 mA_{max} = 15.84 mA_{pp}$

PHASE ANGLE OF LEAD OR LAG

◆ In an AC circuit with just a resistance, current and voltage are in phase which means $\theta = 0°$.

◆ $|\theta|$ means absolute value of θ which means the result is always positive. $|-42°| = 42°$ and $|+42°| = 42°$

◆ An AC circuit which includes a capacitor and/or inductor has voltage and current out of phase with each other by phase shift of $|\theta|$.

◆ The voltage leads the current in any inductive circuit by θ.

The current leads the voltage in any capacitive circuit by θ.

◆ In a series DC circuit, the current is constant. In a series AC circuit, the current is the reference, and its vector is always graphed initially on the horizontal axis. The voltage will then either lead or lag or be in phase with the current, and its vector will be offset by θ from vector for current.

◆ In a parallel DC circuit, the voltage is constant. In a parallel AC circuit, the voltage is the reference and its vector is always graphed initially on the horizontal axis. The current will then either lead or lag or be in phase with the voltage and its vector will be offset by θ from vector for voltage.

INSTANTANEOUS VALUES OF VOLTAGE AND CURRENT

◆ Lower case letters are used for instantaneous values of voltage and current and time. Be sure to include a subscript of t after the unit to show instantaneous (4.56 V_t or 7.89 mA_t) or subscripts of RMS, eff, pk, max, pp.

◆ The formula for instantaneous current is: $i = I_{pk} \sin(\omega t \pm |\theta|)$ and for instantaneous voltage is: $v = V_{pk} \sin(\omega t \pm |\theta|)$

◆ Assume a parallel inductive circuit with given values of V = 12 V, I = 5 mA, frequency = 450 Hz, t = 2 m sec, $\theta = -40°$

voltage is the reference so $\theta = 0°$ in voltage equation.

voltage leads current by 40° so $\theta = -40°$ in current equation.

The general formulas for instantaneous current and voltage are:

$i = 5 \times \sqrt{2}\ mA_{pk} \sin(\omega t - 40°) = 7.071\ mA^{pk} \sin(\omega t - 40°)$

$v = 12 \times \sqrt{2}\ V_{pk} \sin(\omega t + 0°) = 16.97\ V^{pk} \sin(\omega t)$

Notice that ωt is left as ωt in general equations.

$\omega = 360°f = 2\pi f = 400_g f$

Since θ is given in degrees, calculate ωt in degrees.

$$\omega t = \frac{360°}{cycle} \times \frac{450\ cycles}{sec} \times 2\ msec = 324°$$

$i = 7.071\ mA_{pk} \sin(324° - 40°) = -6.861\ mA_t$

$v = 16.97\ V_{pk} \sin(324°) = -9.975\ V_t$

PRACTICAL COMMENTS

◆   The oscilloscope is nothing more than a graph showing the instantaneous voltage in a circuit. Now you can begin to see how the scope can be useful. While the scope does not measure current directly, it can give an indication of the current in an AC circuit. Properly connected, the scope can show the instantaneous voltage and current in any AC circuit. If the circuit has only resistance, then the traces on a dual trace scope will be in phase. Using a capacitor or inductor will enable you to see and measure the phase difference between the voltage and the current.

◆   Be sure to use proper subscripts (RMS, eff, pk, max, pp, t) on units so there is no question which is which.

STUDENT QUIZ

Name _____ Date _____

1. A rotating constant vector quantity will produce a sine wave.
    a. true
    b. false
2. There are 5.35°/radian.
    a. true
    b. false
3. The instantaneous value of voltage in an AC circuit can be calculated by $v = 2\pi f$.
    a. true
    b. false
4. The voltage and current in an AC circuit that includes a capacitor are out of phase.
    a. true
    b. false
5. The statement $V_{pk} = 0.707\ V_{RMS}$ is
    a. true
    b. false
6. If the period equals 15 μs, find f.
    a. 15 kHz
    b. 258 Hz
    c. 66.6 kHz
    d. 66.6 Hz
7. Convert 28° to radians.
    a. 1604 radians
    b. 0.489 radians
    c. 60 radians
    d. 0.017 radians
8. Convert 2.75 radians to degrees.
    a. 11145°
    b. 0.412°
    c. 1705°
    d. 158°
9. Find the angular velocity in degrees per second for a frequency of 37.5 Hz.
    a. 13500°/s
    b. 235°/s
    c. 15000°/s
    d. 9.6°/s
10. Find the frequency if the angular velocity is 4000°/s.
    a. 0.09 Hz
    b. 11.1 Hz
    c. 111 Hz
    d. 1.11 Hz

11. If $V = 20$ V_{pk9} and $f = 2$ kHz, find the instantaneous voltage, v after 25 μs.
     a. 0.309 V
     b. 3.09 V
     c. 6.18 V
     d. 13.8 V

12. An AC voltage is 18 V_{RMS}. Convert this to V_{pk}.
     a. 50.92 V_{pk}
     b. 25.5 V_{pk}
     c. 17.73 V_{pk}
     d. 5.56 V_{pk}

13. An AC voltage is 369 V_{p-p}. Convert this to RMS.
     a. 284 V_{RMS}
     b. 521 V_{RMS}
     c. 65 V_{RMS}
     d. 130 V_{RMS}

14. An AC current is 700 mA. Convert this to I_{pk}.
     a. 990 mA
     b. 495 mA
     c. 248 mA
     d. 124 mA

15. An AC voltage is 125 V_{pk}. Convert this to V_{p-p}.
     a. 177 V
     b. 88.4 V
     c. 353 V
     d. 250 V

AC CIRCUIT ANALYSIS: SERIES CIRCUIT

19

SERIES RC CIRCUITS

◆ Every RC circuit has some resistance and some capacitance.

◆ In a series circuit the current is the same in all parts of the circuit.

◆ The voltage across the resistor and current through it are in phase with each other.

◆ The voltage across the capacitor and the current through the capacitor are not in phase. The capacitor current leads the voltage by 90°.

◆ Drawing a vector diagram of the current in the circuit, we draw its vector horizontally. This vector represents I and V_R.

◆ The vector for V_C is drawn down at 90°, actually called –90°.

◆ The resultant is the source voltage V. The *phase angle (θ)* is the angle between the source V and current I.

◆ The phase angle can be calculated using trig functions.

◆ Since there is only one current in the circuit, the same vectors can represent the resistance, reactance, and impedance.

◆ The capacitor offers an opposition to the flow of AC current. This is called *capacitive reactance (X_c)*.

◆ Capacitive reactance is found by $X_C = \dfrac{1}{2\pi f C}$. The unit is ohms.

SERIES RL CIRCUITS

◆ In a circuit with an inductor and resistor in series, the inductance causes the voltage to lead the current.

◆ We plot the current and V_R along the x-axis. The voltage across the inductor leads the current by 90°.

◆ The resultant of these two vectors is the source voltage.

◆ The source voltage leads the current by the phase angle θ.

◆ The resulting right triangle can be solved using the Pythagorean theorem and trig functions.

◆ The opposition to the flow of current in an inductor is called *inductive reactance (X_L)*. The unit is ohms.

◆ The formula for finding inductive reactance is $X_L = 2\pi fL$.

◆ There is an important ratio used with inductance. This ratio is called *Q*. The ratio is shown as follows: $Q = X_L/R$.

POLAR TO RECTANGULAR CONVERSION

◆ The vector for V_S is expressed with a magnitude and the phase angle. In polar form the vector might be 45/–30°. In rectangular form it might be 38.97 – j22.50.

◆ A calculator is used to convert from polar to rectangular and vice versa.
45/–30° = 45 × cos (–30°) + j45 × sin (–30°) = 38.97 – j22.50
38.97 –j22.50 = $(38.97^2 + 22.50^2)^{1/2}$/arctan (–22.50/38.97) = 45/–30°

◆ Vectors which lie along the same plane can be added or subtracted directly.

◆ To add vectors which are not in the same plane, convert the vectors to rectangular form, then add these coordinates and convert back to polar form.

◆ Subtraction follows a similar pattern.

◆ Series RLC circuits can be combined using addition of the rectangular coordinates. Remember the L and C vectors are in the same plane but opposite in polarity.

SERIES RESONANCE

◆ In a series RLC circuit there is a frequency where $X_L = X_C$. This condition is called *resonance*.

◆ At resonance, $\theta = 0°$ and $Z = R$. The impedance is minimum and the current is maximum.

◆ The *resonant frequency (f_r)* is found by $f_r = \dfrac{1}{2\pi\sqrt{LC}}$.

◆ The ratio Q is useful in determining V_C and V_L as follows: $Q = V_c/V_s$ or $V_C = QV_s$. Also $V_L = QV_s$.

PRACTICAL COMMENTS

◆ The use of vector diagrams to represent the voltages or currents in an AC circuit saves time and will give you a good understanding of AC circuit theory. The phase relationships between the voltage and current in series RLC circuits are used extensively in the design and maintenance of such circuits as filters, transmitters, television, and medical equipment. Communication circuits of all kinds use the principle of resonance to operate.

STUDENT QUIZ

Name _____ Date _____

1. The phase angle in a series circuit is the angle between the resistance and the source voltage.
    a. true
    b. false
2. Vectors can be expressed in polar or rectangular form.
    a. true
    b. false
3. At resonance, a series RLC circuit has $X_L = X_C$.
    a. true
    b. false
4. The vector sum of the voltage drops around a series RC circuit is the source voltage.
    a. true
    b. false
5. Any series AC circuit can be simplified into a circuit containing a resistance and either an inductance or capacitance.
    a. true
    b. false

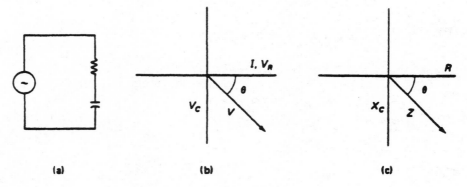

Figure 19-1

6. See figure 19-1. If $V_R = 18$ V and $V_C = 12$ V, find V_T and θ.
    a. 21.63 V, 56.3°
    b. 36 V, 33.7°
    c. 21.63 V, 33.7°
    d. 56.3 V, 33.7°
7. See figure 19-1. If $V = 60$ V and $\theta = 22°$, find V_R and V_C.
    a. 30 v, 45 V
    b. 58.9 V, 32 V
    c. 55.6 V, 22.5 V
    d. 22.5 V, 55.6 V

8. See figure 19-1. If R = 47 kΩ, C = 0.022 μF, and f = 300 Hz, find Z
    a. 52.8 kΩ
    b. 5.8 kΩ
    c. 5.28 kΩ
    d. 5.28 MΩ

9. See figure 19-1. If R = 68 kΩ, C = 2500 pF, f = 22 kHz, and V = 18 V, find I.
    a. 26.4 mA
    b. 68.1 mA
    c. 0.264 mA
    d. 28.95 mA

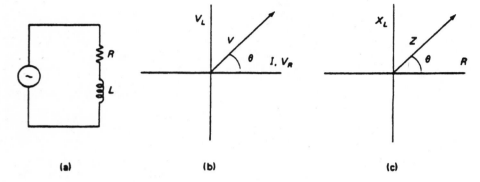

Figure 19-2

10. See figure 19-2. If V_R = 18 V and V_L = 20 V, find V.
    a. 26.9 V
    b. 38 V
    c. 12 V
    d. 12.1 V

11. See figure 19-2. If θ = 26° and V = 35 V, find V_L.
    a. 31.45 V
    b. 15.34 V
    c. 44.79 V
    d. 16.11 V

12. See figure 19-2. If X_L = 680 Ω and θ = 27°, find Z.
    a. 1335 Ω
    b. 680 Ω
    c. 1498 Ω
    d. 655 Ω

13. What is the result of adding the following impedances:
    Z_1 = 4.7/25° kΩ, Z_2 = 6.8/32° kΩ.
    a. 10.01/32° kΩ
    b. 11.47/5° kΩ
    c. 5.59/10.23° kΩ
    d. 11.48/29.14° kΩ

14. Express $5.765 - j9.2$ in polar form.
    a. $10.9\underline{/45.7°}$
    b. $10.9\underline{/57.9°}$
    c. $10.9\underline{/-57.9°}$101
    d. $57.9\underline{/-10.9°}$
15. Express $9.76\underline{/34°}$ in rectangular form.
    a. $8.09 - j5.46$
    b. $8.09 + j5.46$
    c. $5.46 - j8.09$
    d. $5.46 + j8.09$

AC CIRCUIT ANALYSIS: PARALLEL CIRCUITS

20

RC CIRCUIT ANALYSIS

◆ In a parallel circuit the voltage across each branch is equal.

◆ The voltage across and the current through the resistor are plotted along the horizontal axis.

◆ The current through the capacitor is plotted along the positive y-axis.

◆ The total current is the vector sum of I_L and I_R.

◆ X_C, Z, and R are not usually plotted for a parallel circuit; however their reciprocals are often plotted. The reciprocal of X_C is *susceptance (B)*. The reciprocal of impedance is *admittance (Y)*. The reciprocal of resistance is *conductance (G)*.

RL CIRCUIT ANALYSIS

◆ As in an RC circuit, the source voltage and resistor current, in an RL circuit, are plotted horizontally.

◆ The current through the inductor is plotted down at −90°.

EQUIVALENT CIRCUITS

◆ To multiply or divide vectors they must be in polar form.

◆ Multiply or divide the magnitudes. Add the angles if you are multiplying; subtract the angles if you are dividing.

◆ A parallel circuit can be converted to an equivalent series circuit.

◆ The admittance of the parallel circuit is the reciprocal of the impedance of the series circuit. Make the conversion. Find R and X_C.

AC NETWORKS

◆ In many complex series-parallel circuits it is necessary to make many conversions between series and parallel.

◆ A group of formulas is often used which are called *transforms*.

◆ The transforms from series to parallel are $G = \dfrac{R}{R^2 + X^2}$ and $B = \dfrac{X}{R^2 + X^2}$.

◆ To convert from parallel to series, the transforms become $R = \dfrac{G}{G^2 + B^2}$ and $X = \dfrac{B}{G^2 + B^2}$.

◆ These transform equations give absolute values. The correct signs must be added.

◆ Another way to convert is to start with Z in rectangular form and convert to Z polar. Reciprocate Z polar to get Y polar. Then convert Y polar to Y rectangular to get G + jB.

PRACTICAL COMMENTS

◆ Currents can be added in parallel circuits because the voltage is a constant or a reference. It is easy to calculate for the total current in a parallel circuit and then use that value to solve for the circuit's impedance using Ohm's law. This method is often less prone to errors that to use B and Y in a parallel circuit. Either method will result in the correct answer. Use the method that will be simpler and less work for you. The easier method will result in more correct answers.

STUDENT QUIZ

Name _____ Date _____

1.　In a parallel RC circuit the vector for the voltage and the I_T is drawn in the same plane.
　　a. true
　　b. false
2.　A parallel RL circuit has the voltage and the current through the resistor in phase.
　　a. true
　　b. false
3.　To divide vectors they must be in rectangular form.
　　a. true
　　b. false
4.　To multiply vectors, the angles are added.
　　a. true
　　b. false
5.　Transform formulas are used to convert from series to parallel equivalent circuits.
　　a. true
　　b. false

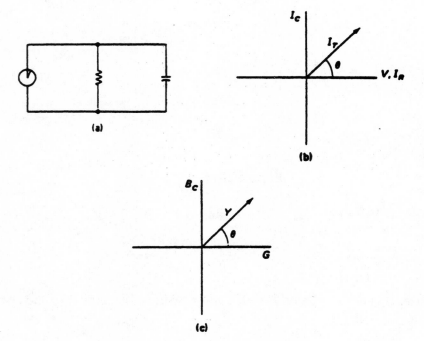

Figure 20-1

6.　See figure 20-1. If I_T = 4.7 mA and θ = 42.5°, find I_C.
　　a. 3.47 mA
　　b. 1.52 mA
　　c. 1.23 mA
　　d. 3.18 mA

7. See figure 20-1. If I_R = 22.57 mA and I_C = 32 mA, find θ.
    a. 35.2°
    b. 44.9°
    c. 54.8°
    d. 74.9°

8. See figure 20-1. If I_R = 23 mA, I_C = 12.8 mA, and V_T = 18 V, find Z.
    a. 1.46 kΩ
    b. 0.68 kΩ
    c. 780 Ω
    d. 1.41 kΩ

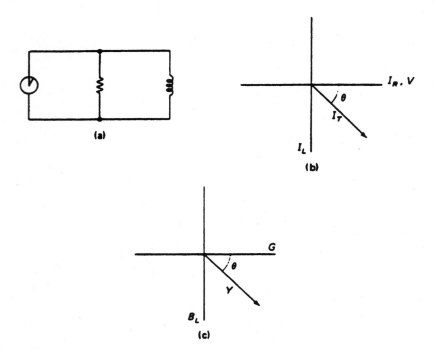

(a)

(b)

(c)

Figure 20-2

9. See figure 20-2. If V_T = 12 V, I_T = 75 mA, and θ = –19°, find Z.
    a. 160 Ω
    b. 737 Ω
    c. 253 Ω
    d. 229 Ω

10. See figure 20-2. If G = 492 μS and B = 250 μS, find the resistance R of the equivalent series circuit.
    a. 2033 Ω
    b. 4000 Ω
    c. 1615 Ω
    d. 1234 Ω

FILTERS

21

RC CIRCUIT ANALYSIS

♦ A *low-pass filter* is a circuit that passes low frequencies easily and attenuates higher frequencies.

♦ A *high-pass filter* passes high frequencies easily and attenuates low frequencies.

♦ To attenuate means to reduce the amplitude or peak-to-peak value of the voltage.

♦ A low pass filter can consist of an RC circuit (a resistor in series with a capacitor) where the output is taken across the capacitor or of an RL circuit (a resistor in series with an inductor) where the output voltage V_O is taken across the resistor.

♦ A high pass filter can consist of an RC circuit where V_O is taken across the resistor or of an RL circuit where V_O is taken across the inductor.

♦ There is a frequency called the cutoff frequency where $X_C = R$ for an RC circuit or where $X_L = R$ for an RL circuit.

♦ The cutoff frequency is found by $f_{co} = 1/2\pi RC$ for an RC circuit or $f_{co} = \dfrac{R}{2\pi L}$ for an RL circuit.

♦ V_O at the cutoff frequency equals $0.707V_{in}$. $V_O = 0.707V_{in}$.

♦ The phase angle θ is 45° at f_{co}.

♦ The power is $P = 0.5 \, P_{max}$.

THÉVENIN'S THEOREM

♦ Thévenin's theorem can be used to solve some AC filter circuits.

♦ A low-pass filter with several resistors may require this theorem to actually find the equivalent resistance. You can then proceed to find the necessary values.

♦ Norton's theorem can also be used in solving filter circuits.

BAND-PASS FILTERS

◆ A *band-pass filter* passes a band of frequencies easily but rejects all frequencies above and below the *pass-band*.

◆ The pass-band is that group of frequencies between the upper and lower cut off frequencies.

◆ A band-pass filter can consist of a high-pass filter circuit followed by a low-pass circuit. Putting the filters in opposite positions will also produce a band-pass result.

◆ Thévenin's and Norton's theorems can be used to find values at the cut off frequencies.

◆ A band-pass filter can also be made using an RLC circuit.

◆ An inductor and capacitor connected in series can form a resonant circuit when frequency is such that $X_L = X_C$. The output would be taken across the series resistance.

◆ The *bandwidth (BW)* is the same as the pass-band. It is found as follows $BW = f_2 - f_1$.

◆ The resonant frequency falls essentially in the middle of the band so $f_1 = f_r - BW/2$ and $f_2 = f_r + BW/2$.

◆ There is also a relationship between f_r, BW, and Q. It is $BW = f_r/Q$.

◆ A *band-stop* filter is a filter that will reject frequencies in a band and pass the frequencies above and below the cutoff frequencies.

◆ Another name for a band-stop filter is *band-reject*.

◆ A band-reject filter usually has a parallel resonant circuit in series with a resistance. V_o is taken across the resistance.

PRACTICAL COMMENTS

◆ A band-pass RC filter can have either section first in the signal path; however it is good design procedure to have the low-pass section first. Loading effects are minimized with this configuration. RC filters are usually used at audio frequencies. Filters that operate at radio frequencies are usually of the LC type.

STUDENT QUIZ

Name _____ Date _____

1. A filter that passes low frequencies easily is called a low-pass filter.
   a. true
   b. false
2. A high-pass filter attenuates high frequencies.
   a. true
   b. false
3. The BW of a band-pass filter is found by $f_2 - f_1$.
   a. true
   b. false
4. A band-reject filter passes all frequencies between the two cutoff frequencies.
   a. true
   b. false
5. At the cutoff frequency of a low-pass filter $X_C = R$.
   a. true
   b. false

Figure 21-1

6. See figure 21-1. This represents the frequency response curve of the output from a
   a. high-pass filter.
   b. low-pass filter.
   c. band-reject filter.
   d. band-pass filter.

Figure 21-2

7.   See figure 21-2. This represents the frequency response curve of the output from a
     a. high-pass filter.
     b. low-pass filter.
     c. band-reject filter.
     d. band-pass filter.

Figure 21-3

8.   See figure 21-3. This represents the frequency response curve of the output from a
     a. high-pass filter.
     b. low-pass filter.
     c. band-reject filter.
     d. band-pass filter.

Figure 21-4

9.   See figure 21-4. This represents the frequency response curve of the output from a
     a. high-pass filter.
     b. low-pass filter.
     c. band-reject filter.
     d. band-pass filter.

Figure 21-5

10. See figure 21-5. If R = 47 kΩ and C = 256 pF, find f_{co}.
    a. 13.2 kHz
    b. 132 kHz
    c. 1320 Hz
    d. 132 Hz

11. See figure 21-5. If R = 520 kΩ, find the value of C that will give an f_{co} of 100 kHz.
    a. 3.06 μF
    b. 1.59 μF
    c. 3.06 pF
    d. 1.59 pF

12. See figure 21-5. If R = 10 kΩ, C = 22 μF, and V_{in} = 17 V, find V_{out} at f_c.
    a. 12 V
    b. 17 V
    c. 9.25 V
    d. 7.12 V

Figure 21-6

13. See figure 21-6. This circuit is known as a
    a. low-pass filter,
    b. high-pass filter.
    c. band-pass filter.
    d. band-reject filter.

14. See figure 21-6. Find f_1.
    a. 1.12 MHz
    b. 27.5 Hz
    c. 5.55 kHz
    d. 74.4 Hz

15. See figure 21-6. Find f_2.
    a. 1.12 MHz
    b. 27.5 Hz
    c. 5.55 kHz
    d. 74.4 Hz

LOGARITHMS

LOGARITHMS DEFINED

◆ Remember that $10^3 = 1000$. The base is 10 and the exponent is 3. The ***logarithm*** of the expression is the exponent 3.

◆ A logarithm is an exponent to which a base must be raised to equal a number.

◆ $\text{Log}_B M = N$ means $B^N = M$

COMMON LOGARITHMS

◆ Common logarithms use the base of 10.

◆ A common logarithm is written log 1000 = 3.

◆ The expression $10^3 = 1000$ is an ***exponential expression***.

◆ A ***logarithmic expression*** would be log 1000 = 3.

◆ Common logarithms of numbers between 1 and 10 can be found in a table of common logarithms. Your scientific calculator can also present these values.
Be sure to use 4 or 5 or 6 significant digits when working with logarithms. Then round your final answer. On your calculator, log and 10^x are usually on same key since 10^x = antilog = the inverse of log.

◆ Common logarithms of any number can easily be found on your calculator. Try this one: what is the log of 75? Your calculator should show that the log 75 = 1.875.

◆ If the number is a decimal, the logarthm is a negative exponent. For example, log 0.075 = –2.125.

MULTIPLICATION OF NUMBERS BY USING LOGARITHMS

◆ Since a common logarithm is an exponent of the common base 10, the exponents are added to multiply the numbers.

◆ An example is as follows:
$102 \times 75 = \log 102 + \log 75 = 2.0086 + 1.8751 = 3.8837$ and $10^{3.8837} = 7650$.
Be sure to show logarithms when showing your work.

DIVISION OF NUMBERS BY USING LOGARITHMS

◆ Division of numbers using logarithms involves subtracting the exponents. Here is an example: $102/75 = \log 102 - \log 75 = 2.0086 - 1.8751 = .13354$ and $10^{.13354} = 1.36$

RAISING A NUMBER TO A POWER BY USING LOGARITHMS

◆ This process involves multiplying the exponents. An example of this is
$6^3 = 3 \log 6 = 3 (.77815) = 2.3345$ and $10^{2.3345} = 216$.

NATURAL LOGARITHMS

◆ A *natural logarithm* is an exponent where the base is (e).

◆ The numerical value of e is rounded to 2.72.

◆ Natural logarithms can easily be found using your calculator.

◆ The abbreviation for natural logarithms is ln.

◆ On calculator, ln and e^x are usually on the same key since they are inverses of each other.

◆ In summary:
$\log_B M = N$ means $B^N = M$
$\log_B (MN) = \log_B M + \log_B N$
$\log_B (M/N) = \log_B M - \log_B N$
$\log_B (M^N) = N \log_B M$

PRACTICAL COMMENTS

◆ Logarithms are a convenient method of doing calculations by hand. With the advent of the calculator, the hand method has gone out of style. Logs, as they are abbreviated, are used extensively in electronic work, as you will see in the next chapter.

STUDENT QUIZ

Name _____ Date _____

1. This expression log 0.0089 = –2.05 is a logarithmic expression
   a. true
   b. false
2. Logarithms are exponents.
   a. true
   b. false
3. The addition of logs will produce a division of the numbers.
   a. true
   b. false
4. If the log is negative, the number must be greater than one.
   a. true
   b. false
5. Natural logarithms are to the base e.
   a. true
   b. false
6. Find the common logarithm of 32.765.
   a. 3.489
   b. 5.82×10^{32}
   c. 1.515
   d. 0.644
7. Perform the following using logarithms: 28.9×54.6
   a. 345.03
   b. 584.36
   c. 0529
   d. 1577.94
8. Perform the following using logarithms: 1234/19.56
   a. 24137
   b. 63.088
   c. 41.44
   d. 1.799
9. Perform the following using logarithms: $0.00345^{-1.9}$
   a. 47659
   b. 19.764
   c. –19.764
   d. 4.678
1150. Find the number whose natural logarithm is 0.693.
   a. –0.159
   b. 9.18
   c. 2
   d. 1.765

LOGARITHMIC EQUATIONS

LOGARITHMIC AND EXPONENTIAL FORMS

◆ The two forms of equations used are the exponential and the logarithmic.

◆ The basic logarithmic equation is log $N = x$ or ln $a = b$.

◆ An exponential equivalent would be $10^x = N$ and $e^b = a$.

LOGARITHMIC EQUATIONS: COMMON LOGS

◆ An example of solving a logarithmic equation is $x = $ log 750. Finding log 750 = 2.875, we know that $x = 2.875$.

◆ The exponential form of the same is log $a = 2.875$. The solution is 7.5×10^2.

◆ An equation such as, $x = 9.3^{1.2}$ can be solved by taking the log of both sides of the equation as follows, log $x = 1.2$ log $9.3 = 1.162$ and $10^{1.162} = 14.53 = x$
Remember that $\log_B (M^N) = N \log_B M$.

LOGARITHMIC EQUATIONS: NATURAL LOGS

◆ Logarithmic equations can use natural logs. An example is: $e^{2.1} = x$. This can be solved by taking the inverse natural log of 2.1 which $= e^{2.1} = 8.166$.

◆ The calculator is invaluable in these types of problems.

PRACTICAL COMMENTS

◆ Many types of electronic circuits operate on a logarithmic response. An example is the use of decibels, a unit to measure power level changes. Another type of circuit is the curve that results when you charge a capacitor. The increase in voltage across the capacitor follows a natural log curve.

STUDENT QUIZ

Name _____ Date _____

1.   An equation in logarithmic form is written x = log N.
     a. true
     b. false
2.   An equation written in exponential form is $x = a^2 + b$.
     a. true
     b. false
3.   Common logarithms have a base of 10.
     a. true
     b. false
4.   Natural logarithms have a base of x.
     a. true
     b. false
5.   A logarithmic equation must be solved using the same rules as any equation.
     a. true
     b. false
6.   Solve the following equation: log x = 0.375
     a. x = 7.32
     b. x = –0981
     c. x = 0.019
     d. x = 2.37
7.   Solve the following equation: log 0.06753 = y
     a. y = –2.695
     b. y = –1.171
     c. y = 1.168
     d. y = 0.155
8.   Solve the following equation: $x = 10^{1.2}$
     a. x = 15.85
     b. x = –15.85
     c. x = 3.32
     d. x = –3.32
9.   Solve the following equation: 5 = log (x/75)
     a. $x = 1.33 \times 10^{-7}$
     b. $x = 7.5 \times 10^6$
     c. x = 6.875
     d. $x = -7.5 \times 10^{-6}$
10. Solve the following equation: ln y = 1.50
     a. y = 31.6
     b. y = –31.6
     c. y = 4.48
     d. y = 2.72

APPLICATIONS OF LOGARITHMS

24

GAIN MEASUREMENTS

◆ An important parameter in many electronic circuits is *gain*.

◆ There are several types of gain: *voltage gain (A_V), current gain (A_I), and power gain (A_P).*

◆ Gain is the ratio of output/input. It can be expressed as a ratio; for example, the voltage gain is 17, which is an expression of the ratio 17/1.

◆ Power and other gains are is often expressed in *decibels (dB).*

◆ The formula for power gain in dB is $A_P (dB) = 10 \log \dfrac{P_{OUT}}{P_{IN}}$

◆ Voltage gain is also expressed in dB: $A_V (dB) = 20 \log \dfrac{V_{out}}{V_{in}}$

◆ The formula for current gain is $A_I (dB) = 20 \log \dfrac{I_{out}}{I_{in}}$.

◆ These gain formulas can be solved using logarithmic and algebraic methods previously covered.

◆ A typical example is the equation $20 \text{ dB} = 10 \log (P_{out}/500 \ \mu\text{W})$. To solve this, divide both sides of the equation by 10, change the form to exponential, and solve using algebra. $P_{out} = 0.05$ W is the answer.

◆ If the dB figure is a loss (−), then the answer will indicate that P_{out} is smaller than P_{in}.

121

REFERENCE LEVELS

◆ A very common reference level for power gain measurement is to use a reference level of l mW. This reference level is called a *dBm*.

◆ Using dBm's will give you actual power levels.

FREQUENCY RESPONSE

◆ Most systems have a response that varies as the frequency of operation is changed.

◆ A *Bode plot* is a graph of the frequency response of a filter.

◆ The Bode plot shows how gain varies with frequency.

◆ This graph is plotted on semilog paper with frequency on the horizontal axis and gain on the vertical axis.

◆ The Bode plot assumes that the gain falls off or increases at a rate of *6 dB per octave or 20 dB per decade.*

◆ An octave is a doubling or halving of the frequency.

◆ A decade changes the frequency by a factor of 10.

◆ Plot the points on your Bode plot starting at the cutoff frequency. Recall that $f_{co} = 1/2\pi RC$.

◆ The gain will drop by 20 dB for each decade of frequency change.

◆ Connect each two points with a straight line. The result is a Bode plot.

◆ There is some error in the Bode plot especially close to the cutoff frequency, but very little.

RC CIRCUITS

◆ In an earlier chapter we used the universal time constant curve to determine the voltage across a capacitor as it charges.

◆ The actual formula for this curve is given by $v_C = V(1 - e^{-t/RC})$. v_c is the voltage across the capacitor, V is the source voltage, t is the time in seconds, and R and C are the values of the components.

◆ A similar formula for the voltage across the resistance is $v_R = Ve^{-t/RC}$.
Notice that at any time t, $v_R + v_R = V$

PRACTICAL COMMENTS

◆ The fact that a capacitor exhibits the effect of taking time to charge after a voltage is applied is paramount in the operation of countless electronic circuits. All of our circuits that provide communications rely on this effect. These include radio, tv, satellite communications, and many others. Telephone systems are a large user of filters for squeezing many conversations onto one pair of wires. In fact it is hard to find some electronic circuits that do not use this capacitance effect, especially since all AC-DC power supplies use capacitors to filter and smooth the pulsating AC to DC, and most electronic equipment uses power supplies of one type or another. Capacitors are in all of them.

STUDENT QUIZ

Name _____ Date _____

1. A measure of the performance of an amplifier is often the voltage gain.
    a. true
    b. false
2. Amplifier gains must be expressed in decibels.
    a. true
    b. false
3. Power gain is the product of the voltage and current gains.
    a. true
    b. false
4. A Bode plot is a graphical representation of the frequency response of a filter.
    a. true
    b. false
5. Decibels are a convenient method of expressing the power in-out functions of a filter.
    a. true
    b. false
6. An amplifier has a P_{in} = 3 mW. It's P_{out} = 13 W. Find the power gain in dB.
    a. 72.7 dB
    b. 26.4 dB
    c. 36.4 dB
    d. 83.7 dB
7. An amplifier's A_p = 35 dB and its P_{in} = 75 mW. Find P_{out}.
    a. 118.5 W
    b. 237 mW
    c. 4.77 W
    d. 237 W
8. An amplifier has a power gain of 16 dBm. Find P_{out}.
    a. 39.8 mW
    b. 79.6 mW
    c. 39.8 W
    d. 14 mW
9. An amplifier has R_{out} = R_{in}. V_{in} = 500 mV and V_{out} = 12 V. Find A_v in dB.
    a. 55.21 dB
    b. 32.4 dB
    c. 27.6 dB
    d. 13.8 dB
10. If a filter's total response is –23 dB at the second decade frequency, find the response at the cutoff frequency.
    a. –6 dB
    b. –3 dB
    c. –20 dB
    d. –26 dB

COMPUTER NUMBER SYSTEMS

25

BINARY NUMBER SYSTEM

◆ The *binary number system* has only two digits, 0 and 1.

◆ In the decimal system the LSD has a value of 10^0. The next least significant digit is 10^1, and so on. The binary system follows the same system. The base is two instead of the decimal's 10.

◆ The place values for the binary places are $2^0 = 1$, $2^1 = 2$, $2^2 = 4$, and $2^3 = 8$ and so on.

◆ Binary digits are called *bits*.

◆ In the binary system we have the *least significant bit (LSB)* and the *most significant bit (MSB)* and a binary point (like a decimal point).

◆ To convert from a binary number to a decimal number, add the place values of each place where the binary digit is 1. As an example, $1101_2 = 8 + 4 + 0 + 1 = 13_{10}$.

◆ Conversion from decimal to binary uses a continual divide-by-2 method. Divide the decimal number by 2. The remainder if any will be a 1. The remainder of 0 or 1 is the LSB of the binary number. Divide the whole number, answer to your first division above by two. If the remainder is 1, that is the next bit. If there is no remainder, then 0 will be the bit. Continue dividing the answers to previous divisions until no further divisions can be made.

OCTAL NUMBER SYSTEM

◆ Another number system that finds some use in digital circuits is the *octal number system.*

◆ The base of this system is 8.

◆ The octal digits are 0, 1, 2, 3, 4, 5, 6, and 7.

◆ The octal system has, as we have seen before, an LSD of 8^0 which equals 1. The next digit's place value is $8^1 = 8$ and so on.

◆ Reading an octal number, such as, 160_8 is one-six-zero not one hundred and sixty.

◆ Converting from octal to decimal involves the corresponding place value table we used in binary to decimal conversion.

◆ Multiply the octal digit's place value by the octal number and add the results. For example,
$734_8 = (7 \times 8^2) + (3 \times 8^1) + (4 \times 8^0) = 448 + 24 + 4 = 476_{10}$.

◆ Decimal to octal conversion can be done by dividing successively by 8 with the remainder being the octal number. Remember the first division will produce the octal LSD.

HEXADECIMAL NUMBER SYSTEM

◆ A number system with a base of 16 is the *hexadecimal number system*.

◆ This system is often abbreviated hex.

◆ The hex system has 16 digits 0, 1-9, and A, B, C, D, E, and F.

◆ Hex to decimal and decimal to hex conversions are similar to our other conversions.

◆ Hex subscripts can be written as 16 or as H. $B_H = B_{16} = 1011_2 = 13_8 = 11_{10}$

BINARY TO OCTAL TO HEXADECIMAL CONVERSIONS

◆ Binary to octal conversions are made by starting at the LSB of the binary number and dividing the bits into groups or nybbles of 3. A Byte has 8 bits; an octal nybble is a little Byte of 3 bits. A hex nybble has 4 bits. Then write the octal digits for each binary group. If the binary number to be converted is 10110111011, the rightmost 3 bits = 3, the next group of 3 bits = 7, the next group of 3 bits = 6, and the left most 2 bits = 2. The result, therefore is 2673_8.

◆ Conversions from binary to hexadecimal is a similar process. Divide the binary number into groups of four bits. Be sure to start at the LSB. Substitute the hex digit for each group.

   $101\ 1011\ 1011_2 = 5BB_H = 10\ 110\ 111\ 011_2 = 2673_8$

◆ Conversions between any two of our systems can be accomplished by use of a calculator designed for this operation. Calculators have a limit on the size of numbers they can store. This is especially true of the binary system since large numbers expressed in binary use the most digits.

ADDITION

◆ Adding decimal numbers involves an operation known as the carry. That is, when the sum of a column is greater than 9 a carry is placed in the next column.

◆ Octal numbers can also be added with a carry value of 8. This carry value must be subtracted from the column sum. This subtracted answer is the octal place value. Of course, you then carry a 1 to the next column.

◆ Hexadecimal numbers are added by using a carry value of 16. This is similar to binary and octal addition.

SUBTRACTION

◆ Decimal numbers are sometimes subtracted by using the borrow. Many of us are familiar with this system.

◆ Subtracting octal numbers involves the same borrow procedure. The value of the borrow is 8.

◆ Hexadecimal numbers use a borrow of 16.

◆ Binary numbers can also be subtracted by using the borrow process.

◆ The use of the *one's complement* method of subtracting binary numbers is generally easier than using the borrow method.

◆ Finding a one's complement of a binary number is simply changing all the 1's to 0's and vice versa.

◆ A one's complement is used to subtract as follows. Change the subtrahend (what you are subtracting) to a one's complement. Add the one's complement to the minuend (what you are subtracting from). Perform an end around carry and add again. An end-around carry is adding the final MSB carry.

◆ The use of a *two's complement* to subtract binary numbers is very popular in computers.

◆ A two's complement is one's complement plus a 1. For example, the one's complement of 101_2 is 010. By adding a one you get the two's complement: $010 + 1 = 011 = 011$ which is the two's complement of 101_2.

◆ To subtract using the two's complement, add the two's complement of the subtrahend to the minuend and ignore the carry.

PRACTICAL COMMENTS

◆ A very simple way of converting hex130or octal to decimal is to convert each number to binary. Then a conversion to decimal is easy. Unless you regularly make a lot of conversions you will remember this system longer than any other method. Fewer mistakes are made by students using this shortcut.

◆ Use the calculator every chance you get to do these types of calculations. You need to know the manual methods but later when you go into the working world, the calculator will be your quick solution. However, you may not have that calculator with you, so know how to do these manually.

◆ The main points are:

$$0 + 0 = 0 \text{ in any number system}$$
$$0 + 1 = 1 \text{ in any number system}$$
$$1 + 1 = 10_2 \text{ in binary}$$
$$7 + 1 = 10_8 \text{ in octal}$$
$$9 + 1 = 10 \text{ in decimal}$$
$$F + 1 = 10_H = 10_{16} \text{ in hexadecimal}$$

STUDENT QUIZ

Name _____ Date _____

1. The binary number system uses two digits, 0 and 1.
    a. true
    b. false
2. The octal system uses the digits 1, 2, 3, 4, 5, 6, 7, and 8.
    a. true
    b. false
3. Hexadecimal numbers are commonly used in computer systems because they have fewer digits.
    a. true
    b. false
4. The two's complement method is a way to add binary numbers.
    a. true
    b. false
5. The digits used in the hexadecimal number system include those used in the decimal system plus A, B, C, D, and E.
    a. true
    b. false
6. Convert this number, 10010110_2 to decimal.
    a. 151_{10}
    b. 51_{10}
    c. 150_{10}
    d. 351_{10}
7. Convert the number 245_{10} to binary.
    a. 101100011_2
    b. 110011010_2
    c. 110000111_2
    d. 11110101_2
8. Convert 245_8 to base 10.
    a. 165_{10}
    b. 821_{10}
    c. 220_{10}
    d. 123_{10}
9. The hexadecimal number, $2C80_{16}$ expressed as a binary number is
    a. $0010\ 1110\ 1000\ 0000_2$
    b. $0001\ 1100\ 1000\ 0000_2$
    c. $0010\ 1100\ 1000\ 0000_2$
    d. $0000\ 1000\ 1100\ 0010_2$
10. Convert the following binary number, 110001110010_2 to an octal number.
    a. 6161_8
    b. 6162_8
    c. 2616_8
    d. 6261_8

11. Add the following $1100110_2 + 101010_2 =$
  a. 10010000_2
  b. 10010010_2
  c. 10001110_2
  d. 10011101_2

12. Add the following. $ABCD_{16} + 10C5_{16} =$
  a. $ABD3_{16}$
  b. $CDE7_{16}$
  c. $BCD2_{16}$
  d. $BC92_{16}$

13. Find the two's complement of $10010010_2 =$
  a. 01101101
  b. 01101110
  c. 10011001
  d. 01101001

14. Perform the following. $1100110_2 - 10110_2 =$
  a. 1010000_2
  b. 1111100_2
  c. 1011100_2
  d. 1010_2

15. Perform the following. $8B4C_{16} - 10FC_{16} =$
  a. $F4A0_{16}$
  b. $9C48_{16}$
  c. 3418_{16}
  d. $7A50_{16}$

BOOLEAN ALGEBRA

LOGIC VARIABLES

◆   *Boolean algebra* is the mathematics of digital logic circuits.

◆   This algebra provides a system of manipulating *logic variables*.

◆   Logic variables consist of states where a statement is either true or false. No other states are allowed.

◆   These logic states are usually called a high (logic 1) or a low (logic 0).

◆   In Boolean algebra we deal only with variables which are 1's or 0's.

THE AND FUNCTION

◆   A basic function can be simulated by connecting two switches in series with a light and a source. You can see that the only way to turn the light on is to have both switches on.

◆   This type of function is called *AND logic*. The symbol for AN<u>D</u> looks like upper case D.

◆   A table showing the various combinations of logic inputs and the outputs from an AND logic circuit is called a *truth table*.

◆   Two inputs A and B are ANDed together to form an output A•B.

◆   We can also say that A and B = AB. Note: A AND B is a product operation.

◆   These logic circuits are called *gates*. Thus we have an AND gate.

◆   An AND gate can have several inputs. The expression for the output is ABC if there are three inputs. Inputs are always on the left in a logic diagram, and outputs are always on the right. The output will be high only if all inputs are high.

THE OR FUNCTION

◆　Another basic gate is the *OR gate*. The symbol has) on left and 2 curves on right, no straight lines.

◆　This gate has the logic that if any input is a logic high, then the output will be a logic high. The only time a logic low output will occur is if all the inputs are low.

◆　If there are two inputs A and B and they are ORed together, the output is A + B. The mathematical operation is one of addition, but we say A is ORed with B.

◆　As with the AND gate, an OR gate can have several inputs.

THE NOT FUNCTION

◆　A logic function that produces a *complement* of a single input is called a *NOT function*.

◆　The logic circuit that will produce this is called an *inverter*. The symbol is a tilted triangle with vertical straight line on left of triangle. There must always be a bubble either to left or right of the triangle. Without the bubble, the tilted triangle often means an amplifier.

◆　Since the output is not equal to the input, but is the complement of it, it is called "not A" or simply $\overline{A}$.

BOOLEAN EXPRESSIONS

◆　These three logic gates, AND, OR, and NOT comprise the major parts of a logic circuit.

◆　A logic circuit can have several variables denoting the operation desired in a logic circuit. Examples of these are $BC + DE + B\overline{A}$ and $A\overline{B}CD\overline{E}$.

◆　The Boolean expression can be used to draw a logic circuit to perform some desired operation

◆　Keep in mind the type of mathematical operation the various gates will perform.

◆　A Boolean expression may also be written from a logic circuit.

BOOLEAN POSTULATES AND THEOREMS

◆   A *postulate* is a self-evident truth. An example of this is as follows: if $A = 1$ then $\overline{A} = 0$.

◆   These postulates can be summarized as follows.

Postulates	
$A = 1$ (if $A \neq 0$)	$A = 0$ (if $A \neq 1$)
$0 \cdot 0 = 0$	$1 \cdot 1 = 1$
$1 \cdot 1 = 1$	$1 + 1 = 1$
$1 \cdot 0 = 0$	$1 + 0 = 1$
$\overline{1} = 0$	$\overline{0} = 1$

Table 26-1

◆   Some algebraic properties also apply to Boolean expressions.

The commutative property:	$AB = BA$	or	$A + B = B + A$.
The associative property:	$A(BC) = AB(C)$	or	$A + (B + C) = (A + B) + C$.
The distributive property:	$A(B + C) = AB + AC$.	or	$A + BC = (A+B)(A + C)$

◆   There are several Boolean theorems that are used to simplify logic circuits. These theorems are summarized in Table 26-2.

Theorems	
$A \cdot 0 = 0$	$A + 0 = A$
$A \cdot 1 = A$	$A + 1 = 1$
$A \cdot A = A$	$A + A = A$
$A \cdot \overline{A} = 0$	$A + \overline{A} = 1$
$\overline{\overline{A}} = A$	$\overline{\overline{A}} = A$

Table 26-2

◆   These theorems combined with the postulates are used to simplify a logic circuit into its simplest form. This means one must find a combination which performs the desired logic with the fewest gates.

◆ *DeMorgan's theorem* gives us a very valuable tool for simplifying logic circuits. This theorem tells us that $\overline{A}\ \overline{B} = \overline{A + B}$. This also tells us that $\overline{AB} = \overline{A} + \overline{B}$.

◆ DeMorgan's theorem can be simplified to add a bar to each variable and to the total expression and either change AND to OR or change OR to AND. If the result is a double bar, break or delete the bar.

For instance $AB = \overline{\overline{A} + \overline{B}}$ also $\overline{A} + B = \overline{\overline{\overline{A}}\ \overline{B}} = \overline{A}\ \overline{B}$

◆ The *absorption theorem* gives us some very common substitutions us136ful in simplifying Boolean expressions. These are shown in Table 26-3.

Absorption Theorem	
$A\,(A + B) = A$	$A + AB = A$
$A\,(\overline{A} + B) = AB$	$A + \overline{A}B = A + B$

Table 26-3

PRACTICAL COMMENTS

◆ The study of Boolean algebra will be invaluable for your applications of your knowledge of electronics to the digital world. These days the state of the art in electronics is digital signal processing. Since these logic circuits can become very large, involving dozens of gates, is it incumbent upon the technician or engineer to be able to design and construct the simplest circuit. Boolean algebra gives you this ability.

◆ A great advantage Boolean algebra gives the designer is the ability to design the logic in a formula, rather than use an experimental approach. The computer has greatly simplified this approach. Many CAD (computer aided design) programs exist today that are most helpful in simulating the logic functions for a particular application. Your study of this fascinating subject will prepare you well for your future in electronics.

STUDENT QUIZ

Name _____ Date _____

1. The Boolean expression for the output of an AND gate is A + B.
   a. true
   b. false
2. An inverter gate has the output complemented from the input.
   a. true
   b. false
3. An OR gate has an output of 1 if any input is 1.
   a. true
   b. false
4. Boolean postulates and theorems seldom help to simplify a circuit.
   a. true
   b. false
5. The Boolean expression ABC is the output from an OR gate.
   a. true
   b. false
6. See figure 26-1 (a). Select the correct Boolean expression for the output of this circuit.
   a. $A + B + C$
   b. $\overline{(A + B)}\,\overline{(B + C)}$
   c. $\overline{\overline{A} + B + \overline{C}}$
   d. $\overline{ABC}$
7. See figure 26-1 (b). Select the correct Boolean expression for the output of this circuit.
   a. $A + B + C$
   b. $\overline{(A + B)}\,\overline{(B + C)}$
   c. $\overline{\overline{A} + B + \overline{C}}$
   d. $\overline{ABC}$
8. See figure 26-1 (c). Select the correct Boolean expression for the output of this circuit.
   a. $A + B + C$
   b. $\overline{(A + B)}\,\overline{(B + C)}$
   c. $\overline{\overline{A} + B + \overline{C}}$
   d. $\overline{ABC}$
9. See figure 26-1 (d). Select the correct Boolean expression for the output of this circuit.
   a. $A + B + C$
   b. $\overline{(A + B)}\,\overline{(B + C)}$
   c. $\overline{\overline{A} + B + \overline{C}}$
   d. $\overline{ABC}$

10.   See Figure 26-1 (e). Select the correct Boolean expression for the output of this circuit.
a. $A + B + C$
b. $\overline{(A + B)} \; \overline{(B + C)}$
c. $\overline{A} + B + \overline{C}$
d. $\overline{\overline{ABC}}$

Figure 26-1

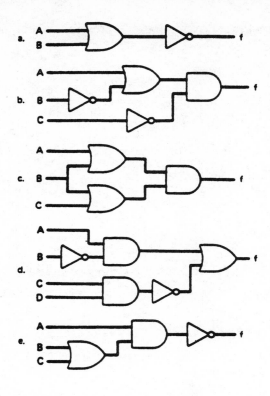

Figure 26-2

11.   See figure 26-2-a. Given the <u>following</u> logic expression, select the logic circuit which
      will implement it correctly. $\overline{A + B}$
      a. A
      b. B
      c. C
      d. D
      e. E

12.   See figure 26-2-b. Given the following logic expression, select the logic circuit which
      will implement it correctly. (A + B)(B + C)
      a. A
      b. B
      c. C
      d. D
      e. E

13. See figure 26-2-c. Given the following logic expression, select the logic circuit which will implement it correctly. $\overline{A(B + C)}$
   a. A
   b. B
   c. C
   d. D
   e. E

14. See figure 26-2-d. Given the following logic expression, select the logic circuit which will implement it correctly. $\overline{C} (A + \overline{B})$
   a. A
   b. B
   c. C
   d. D
   e. E

15. See figure 26-2-e. Given the following logic expression, select the logic circuit which will implement it correctly. $A\overline{B} + \overline{CD}$
   a. A
   b. B
   c. C
   d. D
   e. E

KARNAUGH MAPS

27

TWO-VARIABLE EXPRESSION

◆ Designing complex digital circuits requires the process of simplification.

◆ One process of simplifying digital circuits is to use Boolean theorems and postulates.

◆ Another system of making digital circuits less complex is to use **Karnaugh maps**.

◆ A Karnaugh map is a group of squares which represent the logic functions desired.

◆ These maps can have 2, 4, or more squares. The number of squares depends upon the quantity of variables. Two variables will require 4 squares, 3 variables will require 8, and so on.

◆ Take the data from a truth table and place it in the Karnaugh map squares.

◆ Allow only one change in variables as you go from square to square. The change must be from a complement to an uncomplement. As an example, start in the upper left square with $\overline{A}\,\overline{B}$. The next square to the right would be $A\,\overline{B}$. The next square is AB.

◆ Fill in the value for the bottom row.

◆ It is usual to only fill in the squares where the value is a 1. Look for adjacent pairs of squares where a variable does not change.

◆ OR the variables in the squares. The result is a Karnaugh map expression for the logic desired.

◆ If two horizontal or vertical squares have as an ORed expression $A\,\overline{B} + AB$, for example, simplify it to A. Note: Only the common value A remains.

THREE-VARIABLE EXPRESSION

◆ A truth table for a three-input circuit will have 8 possible combinations. The Karnaugh map will also have 8 squares.

◆ These squares may be in a 4 × 2 or 2 × 4 arrangement.

◆ A single square represents a three-variable term.

◆ Any two adjacent squares are combined to represent a two-variable term.

◆ A combination of four adjacent squares will represent one variable.

◆ Proceed to fill in the squares and OR the correct combinations together.

◆ Look for a wrap-around combination of squares at the ends of rows combining with the squares at the other end. These are valid combinations.

FOUR-VARIABLE EXPRESSIONS

◆ The rule for a four-variable combination is similar in nature to those above.
    A four-variable term is represented by one square.
    A three-variable term is represented by 2 adjacent squares.
    A two-variable term is represented by 4 adjacent squares.
    A single term is represented by 8 adjacent squares.

◆ Use the same procedure to combine the terms. OR the combinations where the terms are the same.

PRACTICAL COMMENTS

◆ Practice simplifying with Karnaugh maps. This system can be of importance to you, because it is a technique that works. You can actually visualize the Boolean expression. This will help you in your design problems. It is also important to become proficient in Boolean theorems which will, in combination with your Karnaugh map techniques, make you very adept at solving digital circuits.

◆ Karnaugh mapping techniques will be handy to use for designing such circuits as counters, multiplexers, flip-flop circuits, and many others.

STUDENT QUIZ

Name _____ Date _____

1. A Karnaugh map is useful for simplifying logic circuits.
    a. true
    b. false
2. A Boolean expression containing three terms will require a Karnaugh map with four squares.
    a. true
    b. false
3. Digital design dictates using the most complex circuits.
    a. true
    b. false
4. Karnaugh maps will have only one variable change from square to square, either vertically or horizontally.
    a. true
    b. false
5. Boolean simplification combined with Karnaugh mapping techniques are an effective design tool.
    a. true
    b. false
6. Use Karnaugh mapping to simplify the following expression: $\overline{A}\,\overline{B}C + \overline{A}\,\overline{B}\,\overline{C} + \overline{A}B\overline{C}$
    a. $\overline{A}$
    b. $\overline{AB}\overline{C} + \overline{C}$
    c. $\overline{A}\,\overline{B} + \overline{A}\,\overline{C}$
    d. $AB + BC$
    e. AC
7. Use Karnaugh mapping to simplify the following expression: $A\overline{B}C + ABC$
    a. $\overline{A}$
    b. $\overline{AB}\overline{C} + \overline{C}$
    c. $\overline{A}\,\overline{B} + \overline{A}\,\overline{C}$
    d. $AB + BC$
    e. AC
8. Use Karnaugh mapping to simplify the following expression: $\overline{A}\,\overline{B} + \overline{A}B$
    a. $\overline{A}$
    b. $\overline{AB}\overline{C} + \overline{C}$
    c. $\overline{A}\,\overline{B} + \overline{A}\,\overline{C}$
    d. $AB + BC$
    e. AC

9. Use Karnaugh mapping to simplify the following expression: $\overline{A}BC + AB\overline{C} + ABC$
   a. $\overline{A}$
   b. $\overline{AB}\overline{C} + \overline{C}$
   c. $\overline{A}\,\overline{B} + \overline{A}\,\overline{C}$
   d. $AB + BC$
   e. AC

10. Use Karnaugh mapping to simplify the following expression:
    $$\overline{AB}C + \overline{A}\overline{B}C + ABC + A\overline{B}C$$
    a. $\overline{A}$
    b. $\overline{AB}\overline{C} + \overline{C}$
    c. $\overline{A}\,\overline{B} + \overline{A}\,\overline{C}$
    d. $AB + BC$
    e. AC

INTRODUCTION TO STATISTICS

28

POPULATION, RANGE, MEAN, MEDIAN, MODE

◆ The entire set of data to be tested is a *population.* We usually test a *random sample* of the *population* which means each item in the *population* has an equal chance of being selected.

◆ A *frequency distribution table* tells how many items are in a study and how often each appears. These data are often shown using a *histogram* or *bar graph*.

◆ The *range* in a set of data is the difference between the extremes of data, between the largest (upper boundary number) and the smallest (lower boundary) numbers in the set.

◆ The *midpoint* or *median* of a set of numbers is the middle value if there are an odd number of data items or is the average of the two middle values if there are an even number of data items. Half the data values are greater than the *median* and half are less.

◆ The *mean* is the average or $\bar{x}$ of the set of data values. Add up all of the values and divide by the number of data items.

◆ The *mode* is the data that occurs most frequently.

STANDARD DEVIATION or SIGMA

◆ The *standard deviation* (symbolized with lower case sigma, σ, or σ_n on calculator) is a measure of the distance any piece of data is from the *mean.*

◆ The sample sigma, σ_{n-1} or S_x, in used more often than the population sigma, σ_n. The sample sigma is slightly larger than the population sigma.

NORMAL DISTRIBUTION CURVE

◆ In a normal distribution of values, the **mean** and the **median** and the **mode** occur at the same point.

◆ When data with normal distribution are graphed in a histogram and the high points form a curve then:
- the curve is bell shaped with only one peak, which is center
- shapes are same on both sides of the peak, which means the data value are NOT skewed (heavy on one side of mid-point)
- **mean** and **median** and **mode** occur at the peak
- 68% of values fall within ± one σ of the **mean**
- 95% of values fall within ± two σ of the **mean**
- 99.7% of values fall within ± three σ of the **mean**

◆ When analyzing data, the number of items sampled, **n**, can be very important. A beautifully done analysis with a small number of data points might not be very meaningful.

◆ The size of the σ is very important to any analysis. If you are manufacturing something, it is important to keep the σ within acceptable limits to be sure that the product meets manufacturing specifications.

STATISTICAL ANALYSIS

A histogram gives:

```
      X                           X
      X                           X
X     X     X     X     X     X     X     X     X     X
62    71    77    79    80    81    85    91    94    99
```

A better histogram
gives:

```
            X           X
            X   X   X   X   X
            X   X   X   X   X   X
      60  65  70  75  80  85  90  95  100
       1   0   3   2   2   3   2   1   0
```
intervals in sets of five: 60 = from 60 to 64.5

◆ The extreme values are 99 and 62. The data range is 99 − 62 = 37.

◆ The number of data items is 14, an even number.
The two middle numbers are 80 and 81. **median** = (80 + 81) / 2 = 80.5

◆ The most often given scores are 71 and 85, each of which is a **mode**
This set is **bimodal** since there are two **modes**

◆ Mode and median are not usually obtained by calculator but by observing the data.

◆ The **mean** or average value is the sum / number of data items or
(62 +71 +71 +71 +77 +79 +80 +81 +85 +85 +85 +91 +94 +99) / 14 = 1131 / 14 = 80.79

◆ The standard deviation or sigma or σ or σ_n is 9.72

◆ The one σ range is (**mean** ± σ) and should include 68% of data. (80.79 − 9.72 = 71.07) to
(80.79 + 9.72 = 90.51) includes 10 out of the 14 or 71%, assuming 71 ≈ 71.07 is in the
range.

◆ The two σ range is (**mean** ± 2σ) and should include 95% of data. (71.07 − 9.72 = 61.35)
to (90.51 + 9.72 = 100.23) includes all of the data.

◆ If you use sample sigma, $\sigma_{n-1} = S_x$, instead of population σ_n, σ_{n-1} = 10.09
one σ range is (80.79 − 10.09 = 70.70) to (80.79 + 10.09 = 90.88)
two σ range is (70.70 − 10.09 = 60.61) to (90.88 + 10.09 = 100.97)
Then 11 of 14 or 71% of scores are in 1−σ range.
Then 14 of 14 or all of scores are in 2-σ range.

147

PRACTICAL COMMENTS

◆ A histogram or bar graph is a convenient way of showing how many items were in each category. The histogram gives a visual idea of the relative sizes of the numbers without having to read the individual numbers in a list or table. A line drawn across top of bars gives an idea of how the different items are distributed.

◆ A histogram can be made using equal sized blocks (as on grid paper) or by using X (or any letter or symbol) with one letter for each block. The idea is to visually show the relative sizes of data items.

◆ If the number of data values is small, use a separate bar for each type of data. If the number is larger, then group the data into similar sizes or shapes or numbers for each interval. Be sure to label the intervals you choose, because two people may choose different intervals and both can be correct.

◆ Before you start analyzing data, arrange them in order. Then determine the median and modes by just observing the arranged data. You can't do this with your calculator.

◆ Statistical measurements can be calculated using formulas or almost automatically with many algebraic calculators. You just have to change the calculator to statistical mode, enter the data, then use the function keys to give you the mean and the sigmas (standard deviation).

◆ This population sigma, σ_n, is not used as often as the sample sigma, given on calculator as σ_{n-1} or S_x.

◆ Combine mean and sigma to give you the range.

◆ Calculate your own grades in this class so far this semester. What grade do you think you have earned so far?

STUDENT QUIZ

Name _____ Date _____

1.   The average of a set of data is called the:
        a. median   b. mean   c. mode   d. sigma   e. standard deviation

2.   Which percentage of data items in a set should fall within one σ range of the mean:
        a. 50%   b. 60%   c. 68%   d. 70%   e. 99%

3.   In a normal distribution of values, the mean and the median and the mode occur at the same point.
        a. true   b. false

        Assume these percentage scores are given in a test:
        58   63   63   68   72   72   76   78   84   84   84   92

4.   The mean is:
        a. 9.93   b. 34   c. 58   d. 63   e. 68   f. 72   g. 74
        h. 74.5   i. 75.4   j. 76   k. 78   l. 84   m. 92   n. 19.9

5.   The median is:
        a. 9.93   b. 34   c. 58   d. 63   e. 68   f. 72   g. 74
        h. 74.5   i. 75.4   j. 76   k. 78   l. 84   m. 92   n. 19.9

6.   The mode is:
        a. 9.93   b. 34   c. 58   d. 63   e. 68   f. 72   g. 74
        h. 74.5   i. 75.4   j. 76   k. 78   l. 84   m. 92   n. 19.9

7.   The standard deviation or sigma is:
        a. 9.93   b. 34   c. 58   d. 63   e. 68   f. 72   g. 74
        h. 74.5   i. 75.4   j. 76   k. 78   l. 84   m. 92   n. 9.93

8.   The size of the range is:
        a. 9.93   b. 34   c. 58   d. 63   e. 68   f. 72   g. 74
        h. 74.5   i. 75.4   j. 76   k. 78   l. 84   m. 92   n. 19.9

9.   The number of data points within one σ is:
        a. 4   b. 5   c. 6   d. 7   e. 8   f. 9   g. 10

10.   The number of data points within two σ is:
        a. 6   b. 7   c. 8   d. 9   e. 10   f. 11   g. 12

11. These data are distributed in a normal distribution.
     a. true   b. false
12. If the number of data items is odd, the median is the average of the two middle values, and if the number is even then the median is the middle value itself.
     a. true   b. false

SOLUTIONS MANUAL
ANSWERS TO STUDENT QUIZZES IN STUDY GUIDE

ANSWERS TO STUDY GUIDE STUDENT QUIZ FOR CHAPTER 1

1	2	3	4	5	6	7	8	9	10	11	12	13	14	15
A	B	A	A	B	D	C	A	C	D	B	B	C	A	B

16	17	18	19	20
B	C	A	B	B

ANSWERS TO STUDY GUIDE STUDENT QUIZ FOR CHAPTER 2

1	2	3	4	5	6	7	8	9	10	11	12	13	14	15
B	A	A	B	A	E	C	C	B	A	D	B	C	B	A

ANSWERS TO STUDY GUIDE STUDENT QUIZ FOR CHAPTER 3

1	2	3	4	5	6	7	8	9	10	11	12	13	14	15
A	B	A	B	A	C	B	B	D	C	D	A	B	A	B

ANSWERS TO STUDY GUIDE STUDENT QUIZ FOR CHAPTER 4

1	2	3	4	5	6	7	8	9	10	11	12	13	14	15
B	A	B	A	A	C	D	A	B	C	D	A	D	A	C

ANSWERS TO STUDY GUIDE STUDENT QUIZ FOR CHAPTER 5

1	2	3	4	5	6	7	8	9	10	11	12	13	14	15
B	B	A	A	A	C	C	B	D	A	B	D	A	D	B

ANSWERS TO STUDY GUIDE STUDENT QUIZ FOR CHAPTER 6

1	2	3	4	5	6	7	8	9	10	11	12	13	14	15
A	B	A	A	B	D	C	B	C	A	B	C	D	A	B

ANSWERS TO STUDY GUIDE STUDENT QUIZ FOR CHAPTER 7

1	2	3	4	5		6	7	8	9	10		11	12	13	14	15
A	A	B	B	A		D	B	C	B	C		A	C	D	C	A

ANSWERS TO STUDY GUIDE STUDENT QUIZ FOR CHAPTER 8

1	2	3	4	5		6	7	8	9	10		11	12	13	14	15
B	A	A	A	A		D	C	B	A	C		C	B	D	A	B

ANSWERS TO STUDY GUIDE STUDENT QUIZ FOR CHAPTER 9

1	2	3	4	5		6	7	8	9	10
B	A	A	A	B		C	C	D	B	A

ANSWERS TO STUDY GUIDE STUDENT QUIZ FOR CHAPTER 10

1	2	3	4	5		6	7	8	9	10		11	12	13	14	15
B	A	B	B	A		D	C	A	D	C		C	D	A	C	C

ANSWERS TO STUDY GUIDE STUDENT QUIZ FOR CHAPTER 11

1	2	3	4	5		6	7	8	9	10		11	12	13	14	15
A	B	B	A	A		A	D	D	C	A		B	D	B	A	C

ANSWERS TO STUDY GUIDE STUDENT QUIZ FOR CHAPTER 12

1	2	3	4	5		6	7	8	9	10
B	A	A	B	A		C	B	D	A	C

ANSWERS TO STUDY GUIDE STUDENT QUIZ FOR CHAPTER 13

1	2	3	4	5		6	7	8	9	10		11	12	13	14	15
A	B	A	A	A		C	D	B	C	B		C	B	E	D	A

ANSWERS TO STUDY GUIDE STUDENT QUIZ FOR CHAPTER 14

1	2	3	4	5		6	7	8	9	10
B	A	A	B	A		C	D	A	B	C

ANSWERS TO STUDY GUIDE STUDENT QUIZ FOR CHAPTER 15

1	2	3	4	5		6	7	8	9	10
B	A	A	A	B		D	C	C	C	B

ANSWERS TO STUDY GUIDE STUDENT QUIZ FOR CHAPTER 16

1	2	3	4	5		6	7	8	9	10		11	12	13	14	15
B	A	B	A	A		C	C	A	B	D		A	C	A	C	D

ANSWERS TO STUDY GUIDE STUDENT QUIZ FOR CHAPTER 17

1	2	3	4	5		6	7	8	9	10
A	B	B	A	A		D	A	C	D	C

ANSWERS TO STUDY GUIDE STUDENT QUIZ FOR CHAPTER 18

1	2	3	4	5		6	7	8	9	10		11	12	13	14	15
A	B	B	A	B		C	B	D	A	B		C	B	D	A	D

ANSWERS TO STUDY GUIDE STUDENT QUIZ FOR CHAPTER 19

1	2	3	4	5		6	7	8	9	10		11	12	13	14	15
B	A	A	A	A		C	C	A	C	A		B	C	D	C	B

ANSWERS TO STUDY GUIDE STUDENT QUIZ FOR CHAPTER 20

1	2	3	4	5		6	7	8	9	10
B	A	B	A	A		D	C	B	A	C

ANSWERS TO STUDY GUIDE STUDENT QUIZ FOR CHAPTER 21

1	2	3	4	5		6	7	8	9	10		11	12	13	14	15
A	B	A	B	A		B	A	D	C	A		C	A	C	B	A

ANSWERS TO STUDY GUIDE STUDENT QUIZ FOR CHAPTER 22

1	2	3	4	5		6	7	8	9	10
A	A	B	B	A		C	D	B	A	C

ANSWERS TO STUDY GUIDE STUDENT QUIZ FOR CHAPTER 23

1	2	3	4	5	6	7	8	9	10
A	B	A	B	A	D	B	A	B	C

ANSWERS TO STUDY GUIDE STUDENT QUIZ FOR CHAPTER 24

1	2	3	4	5	6	7	8	9	10
A	B	A	A	A	C	D	A	C	D

ANSWERS TO STUDY GUIDE STUDENT QUIZ FOR CHAPTER 25

1	2	3	4	5	6	7	8	9	10	11	12	13	14	15
A	B	A	B	B	C	D	A	C	B	A	D	B	A	D

ANSWERS TO STUDY GUIDE STUDENT QUIZ FOR CHAPTER 26

1	2	3	4	5	6	7	8	9	10	11	12	13	14	15
B	A	A	B	B	C	D	B	A	A	A	C	E	B	D

ANSWERS TO STUDY GUIDE STUDENT QUIZ FOR CHAPTER 27

1	2	3	4	5	6	7	8	9	10
A	B	B	A	A	C	E	A	D	B

ANSWERS TO STUDY GUIDE STUDENT QUIZ FOR CHAPTER 28

1	2	3	4	5	6	7	8	9	10	11	12
B	C	A	H	G	L	A	N	E	G	B	B

SOLUTIONS MANUAL
ANSWERS TO SELECTED TEXT
END OF CHAPTER PROBLEMS

END OF CHAPTER I PROBLEMS

End of Chapter Problems 1–1

Note To Student: Many people, including those who speak French or German or Spanish, use a comma as a decimal point and a point or period to divide numbers into sets for readability, while those speaking English use the reverse.

Commas for grouping are usually omitted in this book to reduce confusion.

The decimal point is never optional, so it is always included and will always be used in this book as a point or period, never a comma.

Modern universal notation uses spaces in place of comma or point to denote grouping into sets for readability; this grouping is optional anyway.

1. In the number 8 042, (a) 8 is the MSD (b) 2 is the LSD (c) 0 occupies the hundreds position (d) 2 occupies the units position (e) the 8 has a weight of 8 000 (f) there are 4 tens.

3. In the number 67 403, (a) 6 is the MSD (b) 3 is the LSD (c) 4 occupies the thousands position (d) 0 occupies the tens position (e) the 7 has the weight of 7000 (f) there are 4 hundreds.

5. In the number 894 307, (a) 8 is the MSD (b) 7 is the LSD (c) 3 occupies the hundreds position (d) 9 occupies the ten-thousands position (e) the 8 has the weight of (f) there are 0 thousands.

End of Chapter Problems 1–2

Note To Student: A fraction can be expressed using either a horizontal line or a slanted line. Since you need to start thinking in terms of what your calculator or computer will accept, most fractions are given in this book with the fraction line expressed as a slanted line. Spaces are used in the place of commas to make reading easier. You may continue to use commas if you prefer a comma to a space. A leading zero is by personal preference; it is not required.

1. (a) $3 / 10 = 0.30$ (b) $16 / 1\ 000 = 0.016$ (c) $278 / 100\ 000 = 0.00278 = .00278$
   (d) $1763 / 10\ 000 = 0.1763$ (e) $435 / 1\ 000 = 0.435$ (f) $2060 / 10\ 000 = 0.206 = .206$

3. (a) $0.007 = 7 / 1\ 000$ (b) $0.0432 = 432 / 10\ 000$ (c) $0.074 = 74 / 1\ 000$
   (d) $0.\ 00\ 0065 = 65 / 1\ 000\ 000$ (e) $0.00\ 16 = 16 / 10\ 000$

5. (a) 17 thousandths $= 17/1000 = 0.017$
   (b) 4 hundredths $= 4/100 = 0.04$
   (c) 460 ten-thousandths $= 460 / 10\ 000 = 0.0046$
   (d) 27 millionths $= 27 / 1\ 000\ 000 = 0.00\ 002\ 7$
   (e) 1780 hundred-thousandths $= 1780 / 100\ 000 = 0.01\ 780$
   (f) 65 thousandths $= 65 / 1\ 000 = 0.0065$

7. In the number 0.00 164 2:
   (a) the one appears in the thousandths place
   (b) the two appears in the millionths place
   (c) the six appears in the ten-thousandths place

9. In the number 0.50 874 3:
   (a) the seven appears in the ten-thousandths place
   (b) the three appears in the millionths place
   (c) the zero appears in the hundredths place
11. (a) 0.006 = six thousandths
    (b) 0.147 = one hundred forty-seven thousandths
    (c) 0.00 092 = ninety-two hundred thousandths
    (d) 0.00 000 7 = seven millionths
    (e) 0.0413 = four hundred thirteen ten-thousandths

End of Chapter Problems 1–3

1. (a) $7.14 = 7\frac{14}{100}$ (b) $50.02 = 50\frac{2}{100}$ (c) $710.143 = 710\frac{143}{1000}$

   (d) $9.099 = 9\frac{99}{1000}$ (e) $73.653 = 73\frac{653}{1000}$ (f) $207.7834 = 207\frac{7834}{10,000}$

   (g) $28.00736 = 28\frac{736}{100,000}$ (h) $8.0706 = 8\frac{706}{10,000}$

3. (a) $5\frac{68}{100} = 5.68$ (b) $25\frac{7}{1000} = 25.007$ (c) $7\frac{165}{10,000} = 7.0165$

   (d) $70\frac{4}{10} = 70.4$ (e) $473\frac{25}{1000} = 473.025$ (f) $80\frac{743}{100,000} = 80.00743$

   (g) $2475\frac{35}{1,000,000} = 2475.000035$ (h) $307\frac{8}{100,000} = 307.00008$

5. (a) Ninety-three and seven tenths = $93.7 = 93\frac{7}{10}$

   (b) Thirty and four hundredths = $30.04 = 30\frac{4}{100}$

   (c) Eleven and one ten-thousandths = $11.001 = 11\frac{1}{10,000}$

   (d) Two hundred seventy-three and twenty-five hundred-thousandths = $273.00025 = 273\frac{25}{100,000}$

   (e) Seven hundred four and seven hundred four millionths = $704.000704 = 704\frac{704}{1,000,000}$

   (f) Three and thirty-three thousandths = $3.033 = 3\frac{33}{1000}$

End of Chapter Problems 1–4

	Original Number	Rounded to Nearest 10	Rounded to Nearest 100	Rounded to Nearest 1000
1.	17	20		
3.	45	50		
5.	64	60		
7.	127	130		
9.	874	870		
11.	273	270	300	
13.	356	360	400	

	Original Number	Rounded to Nearest 10	Rounded to Nearest 100	Rounded to Nearest 1000
15.	1377	1380	1400	
17.	1407	1410	1400	
19.	8706	8710	8700	
21.	4817	4820	4800	5000
23.	85468	85470	85500	85000
25.	78673	78670	78700	79000
27.	2784	2780	2800	3000
29.	35486	35490	35500	36000
31.	68448	68450	68400	68000
33.	73654	73650	73700	74000
35.	465432	465430	465400	465000

35. 465432 = 470,000 to the nearest ten thousand

End of Chapter Problems 1–5

	Original Number	Rounded to Nearest 100th	Rounded to Nearest 10th	Rounded to Nearest Unit	Rounded to Nearest 10
1.	163.782	163.78	163.8	164	160
3.	9.464	9.46	9.5	9	10
5.	88.888	88.89	88.9	89	90
7.	749.493	749.49	749.5	749	750
9.	39.278	39.28	39.3	39	40
11.	63.7478	63.75	63.7	64	60
13.	478.6706	478.67	478.7	479	480
15.	47.474	47.47	47.5	47	50
17.	16.545	16.55	16.5	17	20
19.	76.746	76.75	76.7	77	80

End of Chapter Problems 1-6

1. (a) 5   (b) 4   (c) 4   (d) 4   (e) 3   (f) 4
3. In number 8042   (a) 8 is the MSD   (b) 2 is the LSD
5. In number 67,403   (a) 6 is the MSD   (b) 3 is the LSD
7. In number 894,307   (a) 8 is the MSD   (b) 7 is the LSD

End of Chapter Problems 1–7

1. $12 - (+4) + (-3) = 12 - 4 - 3 = 5$ 3. $16 + 4 + (-6) = 16 + 4 - 6 = 14$

5. $-20 - (-4) - (-10) = -20 + 4 + 10 = -6$ 7. $30 + (-3) + 7 = 30 - 3 + 7 = 34$

9. $-10 - (+4) + (-14) = -10 - 4 - 14 = -28$ 11. $7 - (-7) - (+7) = 7 + 7 - 7 = 7$

13. $-5 - (-3) - (+12) = -5 + 3 - 12 = -14$ 15. $14 + (-3) - (-7) = 14 - 3 + 7 = 18$

17. $9 - (-4) - (-8) = 9 + 4 + 8 = 21$ 19. $-20 - (+6) + (-7) = -20 - 6 - 7 = -33$

End of Chapter Problems 1–8

1. $14 \times (-3) = -42$
3. $-9 \times (-6) = 54$
5. $-12 \times 7 = -84$
7. $-45 \times (-5) = 225$
9. $-310 \times (-3) = 930$
11. $28 \div (-4) = -7$
13. $-144 \div 6 = -24$
15. $-72 \div (-6) = 12$
17. $512 \div (-16) = -32$
19. $-700 \div (-25) = 28$

End of Chapter Problems 1–9

Note To Student: The division operator can be given by "÷" or by slash " / ". Yes, the slash also means a fraction line, but a fraction line means division. Since the division operator "÷" can be easily confused with "+" when reading a problem, that sign is usually replaced in this book with the slash " / " to mean division.

1. $(-7) \times 3 + 4 = -21 + 4 = -17$
3. $6 \times (-3) - 6 \times (-3) = -18 - (-18) = 0$
5. $-6 + 3 \times 5 - 4 = 6 + 15 - 4 = 17$
7. $6 \times 4 - 6 \div 2 = 24 - 3 = 21$
9. $(-7) - (-4) \times 6 + 1 = -7 - (-24) + 1 = 18$
11. $-2 - (-2) \times 4 - 5 \times (-4) = -2 + 8 + 20 = 26$
13. $16 \div (-4) - 7 \times 3 + 4 = -4 - 21 + 4 = -21$
15. $-4 \times (-5) - 3 + 15 \div (-3) = 20 - 3 - 5 = 12$
17. $(-35) \div 5 + 4 + 3 \times 6 = -7 + 4 + 18 = 15$
19. $7 \times (-3) - 4 \times (-5) + 6 \times (-3) = -21 + 20 - 18 = -19$

End of Chapter Problems 1–10

1. $-4 - (-2) + 6(6 - 3) = -4 + 2 + 6(3) = -4 + 2 + 18 = 16$
3. $7(-3) - [4(-7)] = -21 - (-28) = -21 + 28 = 7$
5. $(5 + 4)(-6 + 2) = (9)(-4) = -36$
7. $5 - 2 - 3[4(3 + 4)] - 2 = 3 - 3(28) - 2 = 3 - 84 - 2 = -83$
9. $4[24 \div (-8 + 4)] + 7 \times 4 = 4(-6) + 28 = -24 + 28 = 4$
11. $15 - 4[(-3 + 6)(9 - 12)] = 15 - 4[(3)(-3)] = 15 - 4(-9) = 15 + 36 = 51$
13. $5[6 - (-4) + 3 - 7)(2 - 6)] = 5[10 + (-4)(-4)] = 5(10 + 16) = 5(26) = 130$
15. $4[-6 - (-3)(4)] + 7 \times 3 = 4(-6 + 12) + 21 = 4(6) + 21 = 24 + 21 = 45$
17. $[9 + (3 \times -7)][18 - (2 \times 3)] = (9 - 21)(18 - 6) = (-12)(12) = -144$
19. $14 - [(-3) \times 4] + [3(4 - 5)(7 - 3) + 6] = 14 - (-12) + [3(-1)(4) + 6]$
    $= 14 + 12 + [3(-4) + 6] = 14 + 12 - 6 = 20$

END OF CHAPTER 2 PROBLEMS

End of Chapter Problems 2–1

1. $10 = 10^1$ 3. $1000 = 10^3$ 5. $100 = 10^2$

End of Chapter Problems 2–2

1. $10^3 = 1000$ 3. $10^0 = 1$ 5. $10^6 = 1,000,000$

End of Chapter Problems 2–3

1. $10^{-2} = 1 / 100 = 0.01$ 3. $10^{-3} = 1 / 1000 = 0.001$ 5. $10^{-1} = 1 / 10 = 0.1$

End of Chapter Problems 2–4

1. $0.00\ 01 = 10^{-4}$ 3. $0.00\ 000\ 1 = 10^{-6}$ 5. $1 / 10\ 000 = 10^{-4}$ 7. $1 / 1000 = 10^{-3}$

End of Chapter Problems 2–5

1. $10^4 \times 10^6 = 10^{10}$ 3. $10^2 \times 10^4 = 10^6$ 5. $10^5 \times 10^{-1} = 10^4$
7. $10^3 \times 10^{-7} = 10^{-4}$ 9. $10^{-1} \times 10^4 = 10^3$ 11. $10^{-6} \times 10^{-4} = 10^{-10}$
13. $10^{-3} \times 10^{-9} = 10^{-12}$ 15. $10^{-4} \times 10^{-5} = 10^{-9}$

End of Chapter Problems 2–6

1. 10^4 3. 10^{-5} 5. 10^8 7. 10^{12}
9. 10^7 11. 10^{-3} 13. 10^{-6} 15. 10^{-7}
17. 10^3 19. 10^{-4}

End of Chapter Problems 2–7

1. 10^{-7} 3. 10^{-7} 5. 10^{11} 7. 10^{-10}
9. 10^{-12} 11. 10^8 13. 10^{13} 15. 10^{-4}
17. 10^{-36}

End of Chapter Problems 2–8

		(a)	(b)	(c)
1.	$475 =$	$4.75 \times 10^2 =$	$0.0475 \times 10^4 =$	0.000475×10^6
3.	$65.9 =$	$0.0659 \times 10^2 =$	$0.00659 \times 10^4 =$	0.0000659×10^6
5.	$93400 =$	$934 \times 10^2 =$	$9.34 \times 10^4 =$	0.0934×10^6
7.	$4780 =$	$47.8 \times 10^2 =$	$0.478 \times 10^4 =$	0.00478×10^6
9.	$41800 =$	$418 \times 10^2 =$	$4.18 \times 10^4 =$	$.0418 \times 10^6$
11.	$0.00465 =$	$0.465 \times 10^{-2} =$	$0.46.5 \times 10^{-4} =$	4650×10^{-6}
13.	$0.00000555 =$	$0.000555 \times 10^{-2} =$	$0.0555 \times 10^{-4} =$	5.55×10^{-6}
15.	$0.000673 =$	$0.0673 \times 10^{-2} =$	$6.73 \times 10^{-4} =$	673×10^{-6}
17.	$0.0000000108 =$	$0.00000108 \times 10^{-2} =$	$0.000108 \times 10^{-4} =$	0.0108×10^{-6}
19.	$0.00\,000\,0233 =$	$.0000233 \times 10^{-2} =$	$.00233 \times 10^{-4} =$	$.233 \times 10^{-6}$
21.	$325 =$	$0.325 \times 10^3 =$	325000×10^{-3}	
23.	$4.75 =$	$0.00475 \times 10^3 =$	4750×10^{-3}	
25.	$2700 =$	$2.70 \times 10^3 =$	$2700\,000 \times 10^{-3}$	
27.	$180 =$	$.180 \times 10^3 =$	$180\,000 \times 10^{-3}$	
29.	$0.00450 =$	$0.00\,000450 \times 10^3 =$	4.50×10^{-3}	

End of Chapter Problems 2–9

1.	2.76×10^4	3.	4.78×10^1	5.	1.77×10^6
7.	2.73×10^2	9.	1.73×10^5	11.	7.89×10^1
13.	1.67×10^6	15.	5.79×10^4	17.	8.10×10^4
19.	4.71×10^5				

End of Chapter Problems 2–10

1.	$0.004783 = 4.79 \times 10^{-3}$	3.	$0.7474 = 7.47 \times 10^{-1}$	5.	$0.01637 = 1.64 \times 10^{-2}$
7.	$0.0045446 = 4.54 \times 10^{-3}$	9.	$0.000050085 = 5.01 \times 10^{-5}$	11.	$0.25465 = 2.55 \times 10^{-1}$
13.	$0.04\,0045 = 4.00 \times 10^{-2}$	15.	$0.00\,089\,64 = 8.96 \times 10^{-4}$	17.	$0.01\,709\,83 = 1.71 \times 10^{-2}$
19.	$0.00\,000\,2778 = 2.78 \times 10^{-6}$				

End of Chapter Problems 2–11

1.	2.13×10^4	3.	1.28×10^1	5.	1.05×10^4	7.	6.13×10^0
9.	2.99×10^0	11.	1.31×10^{-3}	13.	1.23×10^{10}	15.	2.18×10^{-6}
17.	6.70×10^0	19.	1.82×10^{-2}	21.	9.41×10^{-5}	23.	2.59×10^6

End of Chapter Problems 2–12

1.	1.10×10^4	3.	2.00×10^{-1}	5.	3.86×10^3	7.	4.82×10^5
9.	2.88×10^{-1}	11.	3.87×10^{-2}	13.	9.93×10^4	15.	4.26×10^5

End of Chapter Problems 2-13

1. $7 \times 10^2 \times 5 \times 10^1 = 35 \times 10^3 = 3.5 \times 10^4$ $737 \times 53.9 = 3.97 \times 10^4$
3. $6 \times 10^{-3} \times 6 \times 10^{-3} = 36 \times 10^{-6} = 3.6 \times 10^{-5}$ $0.0059 \times 0.005892 = 3.48 \times 10^{-5}$
5. $6 \times 10^3 \times 1 \times 10^{-2} = 6 \times 10^1$ $5957.32 \times 0.01317 = 7.85 \times 10^1$
7. $6 \times 10^2 \times 3 \times 10^2 \times 2 \times 10^2 = 36 \times 10^6 = 3.6 \times 10^7$ $620 \times 270 \times 190 = 3.18 \times 10^7$
9. $3 \times 10^4 / 3 \times 10^{-1} = 1 \times 10^5$ $32572 / 0.329 = 9.90 \times 10^4$
11. $1 \times 10^{-1} / 5 \times 10^{-3} = .2 \times 10^2 = 2 \times 10^1$ $0.0987 / 0.00475 = 2.08 \times 10^1$
13. $4 \times 10^2 / 8 \times 10^3 = .5 \times 10^{-1} = 5 \times 10^{-2}$ $392.73 / 8388.2 = 4.68 \times 10^{-2}$
15. $3 \times 10^2 \times 4 \times 10^2 / 5 \times 10^2 = 2.4 \times 10^2$ $283 \times 489 / 511 = 2.71 \times 10^2$

End of Chapter Problems 2–14

Note To Student: When setting up your calculator sequence, use a pair of parens around the entire numerator if there is more than one term in the numerator. Use another pair around the entire denominator if there is more than one term.

1. 1.09×10^1 3. 4.55×10^0 5. 1.48×10^1 7. 2.23×10^1
9. 1.07×10^1 11. 1.39×10^0 13. 1.74×10^0 15. 1.09×10^0
17. 2.53×10^0 19. 1.03×10^{-2} 21. 6.75×10^{-3}

End of Chapter Problems 2–15

1. 1.06×10^2 3. 1.27×10^{-4} 5. 3.26×10^{-3} 7. 1.67×10^{-3}
9. 3.91×10^{-5} 11. 5.16×10^{-6} 13. 1.10×10^{-4} 15. 2.56×10^3
17. 8.46×10^1 19. 3.07×10^4 21. 2.44×10^3

End of Chapter Problems 2–16

1. 10^6 3. 10^{10} 5. 10^{-12} 7. 10^{-8} 9. 10^{-8}

End of Chapter Problems 2–17

1. 10^3 3. 10^{-2} 5. 10^{-2} 7. 10^{+5} 9. 10^3

End of Chapter Problems 2–18

1. 6.29×10^3 3. 3.17×10^6 5. 2.26×10^{-3} 7. 7.62×10^{-3}
9. 2.03×10^9 11. 9.00×10^{10} 13. 8.76×10^{-8} 15. 8.15×10^{-9}
17. 6.76×10^0 19. 2.17×10^{01}

End of Chapter Problems 2–19

1. 9.64×10^0 3. 1.54×10^1 5. 8.40×10^{-2} 7. 1.02×10^{-2}
9. 5.20×10^3 11. 6.71×10^3 13. 3.04×10^{-3} 15. 5.88×10^0
17. 1.07×10^{-2} 19. 7.96×10^3 21. 1.58×10^4

END OF CHAPTER 3 PROBLEMS

End of Chapter Problems 3–1

1. $56 \times 10^3 = 0.056 \times 10^6$
3. $220 \times 10^3 = 0.22 \times 10^6$
5. $390 \times 10^3 = 0.39 \times 10^6$
7. $180 \times 10^3 = 0.18 \times 10^6$
9. $43 \times 10^3 = 0.043 \times 10^6$
11. $0.22 \times 10^{-3} = 220 \times 10^{-6}$
13. $2.13 \times 10^{-3} = 2130 \times 10^{-6}$
15. $0.0556 \times 10^{-3} = 55.6 \times 10^{-6}$
17. $0.122 \times 10^{-3} = 122 \times 10^{-}$
19. $0.256 \times 10^{-3} = 256 \times 10^{-6}$
21. $667 \times 10^{-9} = 667,000 \times 10^{-12}$
23. $17.9 \times 10^{-9} = 17,900 \times 10^{-12}$
25. $6.74 \times 10^{-9} = 6740 \times 10^{-12}$
27. $0.0177 \times 10^{-9} = 17.7 \times 10^{-12}$
29. $70 \times 10^{-9} = 70,000 \times 10^{-12}$
31. $7.3 = 7300 \times 10^{-3} = 0.0073 \times 10^3$
33. $5.67 = 5670 \times 10^{-3} = 0.00567 \times 10^3$
35. $0.0178 = 17.8 \times 10^{-3} = 0.0000178 \times 10^3$
37. $78.3 = 78,300 \times 10^{-3} = 0.0783 \times 10^3$
39. $845 = 845,000 \times 10^{-3} = 0.845 \times 10^3$

End of Chapter Problems 3–2

1. 0.26 mA $= 260$ μA
3. 0.632 mS $= 632$ μS
5. 7.63 k$\Omega = 0.00763$ MΩ
7. 17.3 mA $= 17,300$ μA
9. 713 k$\Omega = 0.713$ MΩ
11. 5630 kHz $= 5.63$ Mhz
13. 2000 k$\Omega = 2$ MΩ
15. 0.237 mS $= 237$ μS
17. 0.3 μF $= 300$ nF
19. 0.062 mA $= 62$ μA

End of Chapter Problems 3–3

1. 0.8 A
3. 0.0025 S
5. $33,000$ Ω
7. 470 Ω
9. $12,500$ Hz
11. 0.0001 F
13. 0.00025 A
15. 0.0009 S
17. $750,000$ Ω
19. 0.03 A

End of Chapter Problems 3–4

1. 0.26 mA $= 260$ μA
3. 0.00632 mS $= 6.32$ μS
5. 56.2 mS $= 56,200$ μS
7. 0.613 mS $= 613$ μS
9. 7.63 k$\Omega = 0.00763$ MΩ
11. 470 k$\Omega = 0.47$ MΩ
13. 127 kHz $= 0.127$ MHz
15. 713 k$\Omega = 0.713$ M
17. $46,300$ μA $= 0.0463$ μA
19. 0.00005 μF $= 50$ pF
21. 3200 $\Omega = 0.0032$ MΩ
23. 0.27 M$\Omega = 270,000$ Ω
25. 0.000403 S $= 0.403$ mS
27. $1,030,000$ Hz $= 1030$ kHz
29. 1430 pF $= 0.00143$ μF
31. 5.5 mS $= 5500$ μS
33. 0.00106 μF $= 1060$ pF
35. $463,000$ $\Omega = 0.463$ MΩ
37. 96.3 kHz $= 0.0963$ MHz
39. 7.8 mA $= 7800$ μA
41. 0.176 V $= 176,000$ μV
43. 1730 mW $= 0.00173$ kW

45. 25 mH = 25,000 μH

47. 0.173 S = 173,000 μS

49. 2.5 μF = 2500 nF

End of Chapter Problems 3–5

1. 2.04 mA = 2040 μA

3. 0.0957 mA = 95.7 μA

5. 0.167 mS = 167 μS

7. 0.0582 mS = 58.2 μS

9. 1.42 mS = 1420 μS

11. 964 Ω = 0.964 kΩ

13. 68700 Ω = 68.7kΩ = 0.0687 MΩ

15. 6850 Ω = 6.85 kΩ = 0.00685 MΩ

17. 115 Ω = 0.115 kΩ

19. 4690 Ω = 4.69 kΩ

21. 2.30 mS = 2300 μS

23. 0.273 mA = 273 μA

25. 70,000 Ω = 70 kΩ

27. 0.042 mA = 41.7 μA

29. 9.52 V = 9520 mV

31. 4.476 V = 4476 mV

33. 84926 Ω = 84.9 kΩ

35. 318 Ω = 0.318 kΩ

37. 0.0049 μF = 4.91 nF

39. 919 Hz = 0.919 kHz

To calculate total resistance for two resistors in parallel, you can use either

$$R_T = \frac{R_1 R_2}{R_1 + R_2}$$

or you can use $G_T = G_1 + G_2$ and then $R_T = 1 / G_T$.

On your calculator, this means $R_T = (R_1^{-1} + R_2^{-1})^{-1}$ or $R_1 (1/X) + R_2 (1/X) = (1/X)$.

41. 5000 Ω = 5 kΩ With equal resistances, result is half value of one.

43. 9990 Ω = 9.99 kΩ With different resistances, result is less than lowest one.

To calculate total resistance for three resistors in parallel, you can use either

$$R_T = \frac{R_1 R_2 R_3}{R_1 R_2 + R_1 R_2 + R_1 R_2}$$

or you can use $G_T = G_1 + G_2 + G_3$ and then $R_T = 1 / G_T$.

On your calculator, use $R_T = (R_1^{-1} + R_2^{-1} + R_3^{-1})^{-1}$ or $R_1(1/X) + R_2(1/X) + R_3(1/X) = (1/X)$.

45. 2500 Ω = 2.5 kΩ

47. 571 Ω = 0.571 kΩ

End of Chapter Problems 3–6

1. 1 cm = 0.3937 in: 100 cm $\times$ 0.3937 = 39.37 in

3. 40 cm = 40 $\times$ 0.3937 = 15.75 in

5. 1 m = 39.37 in: 2.3 m = 2.3 $\times$ 39.37 = 90.55 in
   1 m = 1.094 yd: 2.3 m = 2.3 $\times$ 1.094 = 2.156 yd

7. 10 m = 10.94 yd

9. 10,000 m = 10,940 yd; 1 km = 0.6214 mi;   10 km = 10 $\times$ 0.6214 = 6.214 mi

11. 1 in = 2.54 cm: 10 in = 10 $\times$ 2.54 = 25.4 cm

13. 35.6 in = 90.42 cm

15. 1 yd = 0.9141 m or 0.0009141 km; 880 yds = 880 $\times$ 0.9141 = 804.4 m or 0.8044 km

17. 1 mi/hr = 1.609 km/h: 55 mi/h $\times$ 1.609 = 88.50 km/h

19. 100 mi/h = 160.9 km/h

21. $500 \text{ m/s} \times 3.281 \text{ ft/s} = 1640 \text{ ft/s}$

23. $100 \text{ m/s} = 328.1 \text{ ft/s}$

25. $1 \text{ g} = 0.03527 \text{ oz}$: $60 \text{ g} \times 0.03527 = 2.116 \text{ oz}$

27. $150 \text{ g} = 5.291 \text{ oz}$

29. $800 \text{ g} = 28.22 \text{ oz}$; $1 \text{ kg} = 2.205 \text{ lb}$: $800 \text{ g} = 0.8 \text{ kg}$: $0.8 \text{ kg} \times 2.205 = 1.764 \text{ lb}$

31. $5 \text{ kg} = 176.4 \text{ oz}$ or 11.03 lb

33. $1 \text{ lb.} = 0.4536 \text{ kg}$: $1.35 \text{ lb} \times 0.4536 = 0.6124 \text{ kg}$

35. $1 \text{ oz} = 28.35 \text{ g}$: $4 \text{ oz} \times 28.35 = 113.4 \text{ g}$

37. $0.275 \text{ oz} = 7.796 \text{ g}$

END OF CHAPTER 4 PROBLEMS

End of Chapter Problems 4–1

1. $18 = 2 \cdot 3 \cdot 3$
3. $44 = 2 \cdot 2 \cdot 11$
5. $63 = 3 \cdot 3 \cdot 7$
7. $92 = 2 \cdot 2 \cdot 23$
9. $231 = 3 \cdot 7 \cdot 11$
11. $56 = 2 \cdot 2 \cdot 2 \cdot 7$
13. $147 = 3 \cdot 7 \cdot 7$
15. $84 = 2 \cdot 2 \cdot 3 \cdot 7$
17. $210 = 2 \cdot 3 \cdot 5 \cdot 7$
19. $455 = 5 \cdot 7 \cdot 13$

End of Chapter Problems 4–2

1. $\dfrac{3}{3 \cdot 7} = \dfrac{1}{7}$

3. $\dfrac{5}{2 \cdot 2 \cdot 2} = \dfrac{5}{8}$

5. $\dfrac{11 \cdot 2}{4 \cdot 4 \cdot 2} = \dfrac{11}{16}$

7. $\dfrac{2 \cdot 2 \cdot 3 \cdot 3}{3 \cdot 3 \cdot 5} = \dfrac{2}{5}$

9. $\dfrac{3 \cdot 7}{4 \cdot 2 \cdot 5} = \dfrac{21}{40}$

11. $\dfrac{2 \cdot 11 \cdot 3}{2 \cdot 11 \cdot 5} = \dfrac{3}{5}$

13. $\dfrac{2 \cdot 7 \cdot 13}{3 \cdot 5 \cdot 13} = \dfrac{14}{15}$

15. $\dfrac{3 \cdot 7 \cdot 13}{3 \cdot 3 \cdot 7 \cdot 7} = \dfrac{13}{21}$

17. $\dfrac{7 \cdot 7 \cdot 2 \cdot 3}{5 \cdot 11 \cdot 2 \cdot 3} = \dfrac{49}{55}$

19. $\dfrac{5 \cdot 2 \cdot 119}{5 \cdot 2 \cdot 3 \cdot 119} = \dfrac{1}{3}$

End of Chapter Problems 4–3

1. $\dfrac{1}{2} \times \dfrac{1}{3} = \dfrac{1}{6}$

3. $\dfrac{3}{8} \times \dfrac{2}{9} = \dfrac{2 \cdot 3}{2 \cdot 2 \cdot 2 \cdot 3 \cdot 3} = \dfrac{1}{12}$

5. $\dfrac{9}{16} \times \dfrac{8}{15} = \dfrac{2 \cdot 2 \cdot 2 \cdot 3 \cdot 3}{2 \cdot 2 \cdot 2 \cdot 2 \cdot 3 \cdot 5} = \dfrac{3}{10}$

7. $\dfrac{22}{33} \times \dfrac{15}{28} = \dfrac{2 \cdot 3 \cdot 5 \cdot 11}{2 \cdot 2 \cdot 3 \cdot 7 \cdot 11} = \dfrac{5}{14}$

9. $\dfrac{3}{4} \times \dfrac{7}{8} = \dfrac{21}{32}$

11. $\dfrac{3}{8} \times \dfrac{4}{9} \times \dfrac{2}{3} = \dfrac{2 \cdot 2 \cdot 2 \cdot 3}{2 \cdot 2 \cdot 2 \cdot 3 \cdot 3 \cdot 3} = \dfrac{1}{9}$

13. $\dfrac{1}{3} \times \dfrac{1}{4} \times \dfrac{2}{5} = \dfrac{2}{2 \cdot 2 \cdot 3 \cdot 5} = \dfrac{1}{30}$

15. $\dfrac{1}{5} \times \dfrac{4}{7} \times \dfrac{1}{2} = \dfrac{2 \cdot 2}{2 \cdot 5 \cdot 7} = \dfrac{2}{35}$

17. $\dfrac{6}{35} \times \dfrac{14}{15} \times \dfrac{5}{12} = \dfrac{2 \cdot 2 \cdot 3 \cdot 5 \cdot 7}{2 \cdot 2 \cdot 3 \cdot 3 \cdot 5 \cdot 5 \cdot 7} = \dfrac{1}{15}$

19. $\dfrac{8}{15} \times \dfrac{5}{16} \times \dfrac{22}{25} = \dfrac{\cancel{2} \cdot \cancel{2} \cdot \cancel{2} \cdot \cancel{2} \cdot \cancel{5} \cdot 11}{\cancel{2} \cdot \cancel{2} \cdot \cancel{2} \cdot \cancel{2} \cdot 3 \cdot \cancel{5} \cdot 5 \cdot 5} = \dfrac{11}{75}$

End of Chapter Problems 4–4

1. $\dfrac{9}{16} \div \dfrac{3}{4} = \dfrac{9}{16} \times \dfrac{4}{3} = \dfrac{3}{4}$

3. $\dfrac{3}{16} \div \dfrac{7}{8} = \dfrac{3}{16} \times \dfrac{8}{7} = \dfrac{3}{14}$

5. $\dfrac{5}{9} \div \dfrac{2}{3} = \dfrac{5}{9} \times \dfrac{3}{2} = \dfrac{5}{6}$

7. $\dfrac{9}{16} \div \dfrac{21}{32} = \dfrac{9}{16} \times \dfrac{32}{21} = \dfrac{6}{7}$

9. $\dfrac{8}{25} \div \dfrac{16}{35} = \dfrac{8}{25} \times \dfrac{35}{16} = \dfrac{7}{10}$

11. $\dfrac{5}{36} \times \dfrac{54}{15} = \dfrac{1}{2}$

13. $\dfrac{7}{16} \div \dfrac{15}{32} = \dfrac{7}{16} \times \dfrac{32}{15} = \dfrac{14}{15}$

15. $\dfrac{35}{64} \times \dfrac{32}{15} = 1\dfrac{1}{6}$

17. $\dfrac{23}{225} \div \dfrac{92}{175} = \dfrac{23}{225} \times \dfrac{175}{92} = \dfrac{1}{9} \times \dfrac{7}{4} = \dfrac{7}{36}$

19. $\dfrac{105}{121} \times \dfrac{363}{320} = \dfrac{63}{64}$

End of Chapter Problems 4–5

1. $\dfrac{1}{8} + \dfrac{3}{8} = \dfrac{4}{8} = \dfrac{1}{2}$

3. $\dfrac{2}{7} + \dfrac{3}{7} = \dfrac{5}{7}$

5. $\dfrac{11}{12} - \dfrac{5}{12} = \dfrac{6}{12} = \dfrac{1}{2}$

7. $\dfrac{9}{14} - \dfrac{5}{14} = \dfrac{4}{14} = \dfrac{2}{7}$

9. $\dfrac{5}{12} + \dfrac{7}{12} + \dfrac{11}{12} = \dfrac{23}{12} = 1\dfrac{11}{12}$

11. $\dfrac{3}{16} - \dfrac{5}{16} + \dfrac{7}{16} = \dfrac{5}{16}$

13. $\dfrac{7}{24} + \dfrac{11}{24} - \dfrac{5}{24} = \dfrac{13}{24}$

15. $\dfrac{7}{9} - \dfrac{5}{9} - \dfrac{4}{9} = -\dfrac{2}{9}$

17. $\dfrac{11}{16} + \dfrac{5}{16} - \dfrac{7}{16} = \dfrac{9}{16}$

19. $\dfrac{17}{18} - \dfrac{11}{18} + \dfrac{5}{18} = \dfrac{11}{18}$

End of Chapter Problems 4–6

1. $6 = 2 \cdot 3$ and $15 = 3 \cdot 5$ so LCM = is 30

3. $55 = 5 \cdot 11$ and $65 = 5 \cdot 13$ so LCM = $5 \cdot 11 \cdot 13 = 715$

5. $84 = 2 \cdot 2 \cdot 3 \cdot 7$ and $90 = 2 \cdot 3 \cdot 3 \cdot 5$ so LCM = $2 \cdot 2 \cdot 3 \cdot 3 \cdot 5 \cdot 7$

7. $22 = 2 \cdot 11$ and $26 = 2 \cdot 13$ so LCM = $2 \cdot 11 \cdot 13 = 286$

9. $8 = 2 \cdot 2 \cdot 2$ and $24 = 2 \cdot 2 \cdot 2 \cdot 3$ and $36 = 2 \cdot 2 \cdot 3 \cdot 3$ so LCM = $2 \cdot 2 \cdot 2 \cdot 3 \cdot 3$

11. $63 = 3 \cdot 3 \cdot 7$ and $75 = 3 \cdot 5 \cdot 5$ and $105 = 3 \cdot 5 \cdot 7$ so LCM = $3 \cdot 3 \cdot 5 \cdot 5 \cdot 7$

13. $18 = 2 \cdot 3 \cdot 3$ and $36 = 2 \cdot 2 \cdot 3 \cdot 3$ and $72 = 2 \cdot 2 \cdot 2 \cdot 3 \cdot 3$
so LCM = $2 \cdot 2 \cdot 2 \cdot 3 \cdot 3 = 72$

15. $20 = 2 \cdot 2 \cdot 5$ and $52 = 2 \cdot 2 \cdot 13$ and $65 = 5 \cdot 13$
so LCM = $2 \cdot 2 \cdot 2 \cdot 5 \cdot 13 = 260$

17. $50 = 2 \cdot 5 \cdot 5$ and $70 = 2 \cdot 5 \cdot 7$ and $175 = 5 \cdot 5 \cdot 7$ so LCM = $2 \cdot 5 \cdot 5 \cdot 7 = 350$

19. $45 = 3 \cdot 3 \cdot 5$ and $75 = 3 \cdot 5 \cdot 5$ and $225 = 3 \cdot 3 \cdot 5 \cdot 5$ so LCM = $3 \cdot 3 \cdot 5 \cdot 5 = 225$

End of Chapter Problems 4–7

1. $\dfrac{1}{4} + \dfrac{1}{6} = \dfrac{3}{12} + \dfrac{2}{12} = \dfrac{5}{12}$

3. $\dfrac{2}{5} + \dfrac{4}{15} = \dfrac{6}{15} + \dfrac{4}{15} + \dfrac{10}{15} = \dfrac{2}{3}$

5. $\dfrac{2}{3} - \dfrac{1}{6} = \dfrac{4}{6} - \dfrac{1}{6} = \dfrac{3}{6} = \dfrac{1}{2}$

7. $\dfrac{7}{8} - \dfrac{3}{16} = \dfrac{14}{16} - \dfrac{3}{16} = \dfrac{11}{16}$

9. $\dfrac{17}{24} - \dfrac{5}{6} = \dfrac{17}{24} - \dfrac{20}{24} = -\dfrac{3}{24} = -\dfrac{1}{8}$

11. $\dfrac{5}{12} - \dfrac{13}{16} = \dfrac{20}{48} - \dfrac{39}{48} = -\dfrac{19}{48}$

13. $\dfrac{2}{3} + \dfrac{1}{6} + \dfrac{1}{12} = \dfrac{8}{12} + \dfrac{2}{12} + \dfrac{1}{12} = \dfrac{11}{12}$

15. $\dfrac{4}{15} + \dfrac{3}{25} + \dfrac{1}{3} = \dfrac{20}{75} + \dfrac{9}{75} + \dfrac{25}{75} = \dfrac{54}{75} = \dfrac{18}{25}$

17. $\dfrac{11}{42} + \dfrac{2}{3} - \dfrac{5}{28} = \dfrac{22}{84} + \dfrac{56}{84} - \dfrac{15}{84} = \dfrac{63}{84} = \dfrac{3}{4}$

19. $\dfrac{9}{56} - \dfrac{13}{42} - \dfrac{1}{21} = \dfrac{27}{168} - \dfrac{52}{168} - \dfrac{8}{168} = -\dfrac{33}{168} = -\dfrac{11}{56}$

21. $\dfrac{4}{55} - \dfrac{3}{25} + \dfrac{3}{5} = \dfrac{20}{275} - \dfrac{33}{275} + \dfrac{165}{275} = \dfrac{152}{275}$

23. $\dfrac{3}{65} + \dfrac{2}{15} - \dfrac{4}{39} = \dfrac{9}{195} + \dfrac{26}{195} - \dfrac{20}{195} = \dfrac{15}{195} = \dfrac{1}{13}$

End of Chapter Problems 4–8

1. $\dfrac{17}{2} = 8\dfrac{1}{2}$

3. $\dfrac{37}{4} = 9\dfrac{1}{4}$

5. $\dfrac{19}{5} = 3\dfrac{4}{5}$

7. $\dfrac{43}{7} = 6\dfrac{1}{7}$

9. $\dfrac{27}{4} = 6\dfrac{3}{4}$

11. $\dfrac{67}{7} = 9\dfrac{4}{7}$

13. $\dfrac{87}{16} = 5\dfrac{7}{16}$

15. $\dfrac{89}{12} = 7\dfrac{5}{12}$

17. $\dfrac{60}{9} = 6\dfrac{6}{9} = 6\dfrac{2}{3}$

19. $\dfrac{37}{15} = 2\dfrac{7}{15}$

21. $10\dfrac{1}{2} = \dfrac{21}{2}$

23. $4\dfrac{3}{16} = \dfrac{67}{16}$

25. $3\dfrac{5}{8} = \dfrac{29}{8}$

27. $9\dfrac{1}{3} = \dfrac{28}{3}$

29. $5\dfrac{1}{6} = \dfrac{31}{6}$

31. $8\dfrac{7}{8} = \dfrac{71}{8}$

33. $12\dfrac{1}{3} = \dfrac{37}{3}$

35. $7\dfrac{1}{3} = \dfrac{22}{3}$

37. $10\dfrac{3}{5} = \dfrac{53}{5}$

39. $7\dfrac{5}{8} = \dfrac{61}{8}$

End of Chapter Problems 4–9

1. $\dfrac{3}{4} \times \dfrac{10}{3} = \dfrac{30}{24} = 1\dfrac{6}{24} = 1\dfrac{1}{4}$

3. $\dfrac{3}{4} \times \dfrac{8}{5} = \dfrac{24}{20} = 1\dfrac{4}{20} = 1\dfrac{1}{5}$

5. $\dfrac{3}{8} \times \dfrac{5}{3} = \dfrac{15}{24} = \dfrac{5}{8}$

7. $\dfrac{9}{4} \times 2\dfrac{1}{5} = \dfrac{9}{4} \times \dfrac{11}{5} = \dfrac{99}{20} = 4\dfrac{19}{20}$

9. $\quad 3 \times 3\dfrac{1}{4} = 3 \times \dfrac{13}{4} = \dfrac{39}{4} = 9\dfrac{3}{4}$

11. $\quad 2\dfrac{1}{3} \times 3\dfrac{1}{4} = \dfrac{7}{3} \times \dfrac{13}{4} = \dfrac{91}{12} = 7\dfrac{7}{12}$

13. $\quad 3\dfrac{1}{3} \times 4\dfrac{1}{5} = \dfrac{10}{3} \times \dfrac{21}{5} = \dfrac{210}{15} = 14$

15. $\quad 3\dfrac{3}{8} \times 6\dfrac{1}{3} = \dfrac{27}{8} \times \dfrac{19}{3} = \dfrac{513}{24} = 21\dfrac{9}{24} = 21\dfrac{3}{8}$

17. $\quad 2\dfrac{5}{6} \times 3\dfrac{2}{3} = \dfrac{17}{3} \times \dfrac{11}{2} = \dfrac{187}{18} = 10\dfrac{7}{8}$

19. $\quad 5\dfrac{5}{6} \times 4\dfrac{2}{5} = \dfrac{35}{6} \times \dfrac{22}{5} = \dfrac{770}{30} = 25\dfrac{20}{30} = 25\dfrac{2}{3}$

21. $\quad \dfrac{7}{2} \div \dfrac{4}{3} = \dfrac{7}{2} \times \dfrac{3}{4} = \dfrac{21}{8} = 2\dfrac{5}{8}$

23. $\quad \dfrac{7}{16} \div \dfrac{1}{4} = \dfrac{7}{16} \times 4 = \dfrac{28}{16} = 1\dfrac{12}{16} = 1\dfrac{3}{4}$

25. $\quad 3 \div \dfrac{7}{5} = 3 \times \dfrac{5}{7} = \dfrac{15}{7} = 2\dfrac{1}{7}$

27. $\quad 6 \div \dfrac{5}{8} = 6 \times \dfrac{8}{5} = \dfrac{48}{5} = 9\dfrac{3}{5}$

29. $\quad \dfrac{9}{4} \div 1\dfrac{2}{3} = \dfrac{9}{4} \div \dfrac{5}{3} = \dfrac{9}{4} \times \dfrac{3}{5} = \dfrac{27}{20} = 1\dfrac{7}{20}$

31. $\quad \dfrac{7}{4} \div 2\dfrac{4}{5} = \dfrac{7}{4} \div \dfrac{14}{5} = \dfrac{7}{4} \times \dfrac{5}{14} = \dfrac{35}{56} = \dfrac{5}{8}$

33. $\quad 3\dfrac{1}{2} \div 4\dfrac{1}{3} = \dfrac{7}{2} \div \dfrac{13}{3} = \dfrac{7}{2} \times \dfrac{3}{13} = \dfrac{21}{26}$

35. $\quad 2\dfrac{1}{3} \div 6\dfrac{1}{2} = \dfrac{7}{3} \div \dfrac{13}{2} = \dfrac{7}{3} \times \dfrac{2}{13} = \dfrac{14}{39}$

37. $\quad 5\dfrac{3}{5} \div 3\dfrac{1}{3} = \dfrac{28}{5} \div \dfrac{10}{3} = \dfrac{28}{5} \times \dfrac{3}{10} = \dfrac{84}{50} = 1\dfrac{34}{50} = 1\dfrac{17}{25}$

39. $\quad 4\dfrac{2}{5} \div 1\dfrac{8}{25} = \dfrac{22}{5} \div \dfrac{33}{25} = \dfrac{22}{5} \times \dfrac{25}{33} = \dfrac{550}{165} = 3\dfrac{55}{165} = 3\dfrac{1}{3}$

End of Chapter Problems 4–10

1. $\quad \dfrac{16}{5} + \dfrac{10}{3} = \dfrac{48}{15} + \dfrac{50}{15} = \dfrac{98}{15} = 6\dfrac{8}{15}$

3. $\quad 4\dfrac{5}{6} + \dfrac{5}{7} = \dfrac{29}{6} + \dfrac{5}{7} = \dfrac{203}{42} + \dfrac{30}{42} = \dfrac{233}{42} = 5\dfrac{23}{42}$

5. $\quad 2\dfrac{1}{3} + \dfrac{9}{5} = \dfrac{7}{3} + \dfrac{9}{5} = \dfrac{35}{15} + \dfrac{27}{15} = \dfrac{62}{15} = 4\dfrac{2}{15}$

7. $\quad 3\dfrac{7}{8} + 4\dfrac{1}{2} = \dfrac{31}{8} + \dfrac{9}{2} = \dfrac{31}{8} + \dfrac{36}{8} = \dfrac{67}{8} = 8\dfrac{3}{8}$

9. $\quad \dfrac{7}{8} - \dfrac{7}{32} = \dfrac{28}{32} - \dfrac{7}{32} = \dfrac{21}{32}$

11. $\quad \dfrac{10}{3} - \dfrac{1}{4} = \dfrac{40}{12} - \dfrac{3}{12} = \dfrac{37}{12} = 3\dfrac{1}{12}$

13. $3\dfrac{5}{6} - \dfrac{9}{4} = \dfrac{23}{6} - \dfrac{9}{4} = \dfrac{46}{12} - \dfrac{27}{12} = \dfrac{19}{12} = 1\dfrac{7}{12}$

15. $3\dfrac{1}{8} - 1\dfrac{1}{4} = \dfrac{25}{8} - \dfrac{5}{4} = \dfrac{25}{8} - \dfrac{10}{8} = \dfrac{15}{8} = 1\dfrac{7}{8}$

17. $4\dfrac{5}{6} - 2\dfrac{2}{3} = \dfrac{29}{6} - \dfrac{8}{3} = \dfrac{29}{6} - \dfrac{16}{6} = \dfrac{13}{6} = 2\dfrac{1}{6}$

19. $\dfrac{9}{4} + \dfrac{7}{2} - 2\dfrac{1}{3} = \dfrac{9}{4} + \dfrac{7}{2} - \dfrac{7}{3} = \dfrac{27}{12} + \dfrac{42}{12} - \dfrac{28}{12} = \dfrac{41}{12} = 3\dfrac{5}{12}$

21. $7\dfrac{1}{2} - 2\dfrac{1}{3} + 3\dfrac{1}{4} = \dfrac{15}{2} - \dfrac{7}{3} + \dfrac{13}{4} = \dfrac{90}{12} - \dfrac{28}{12} + \dfrac{39}{12} = \dfrac{101}{12} = 8\dfrac{5}{12}$

23. $2\dfrac{7}{8} + 4\dfrac{3}{4} - 3\dfrac{11}{16} = \dfrac{23}{8} + \dfrac{19}{4} - \dfrac{59}{16} = \dfrac{46}{16} + \dfrac{76}{16} - \dfrac{59}{16} = \dfrac{63}{16} = 3\dfrac{15}{16}$

25. $3\dfrac{7}{16} - \dfrac{15}{32} + 2\dfrac{3}{8} = \dfrac{55}{16} - \dfrac{15}{32} + \dfrac{19}{8} = \dfrac{110}{32} - \dfrac{15}{32} + \dfrac{76}{32} = \dfrac{171}{32} = 5\dfrac{11}{32}$

27. $7\dfrac{2}{3} - 3\dfrac{2}{5} + 2\dfrac{4}{15} = \dfrac{23}{3} - \dfrac{17}{5} + \dfrac{34}{15} = \dfrac{115}{15} - \dfrac{51}{15} + \dfrac{34}{15} = \dfrac{98}{15} = 6\dfrac{8}{15}$

29. $8\dfrac{3}{8} + 4\dfrac{2}{3} - 3\dfrac{1}{12} = \dfrac{67}{8} + \dfrac{14}{3} - \dfrac{37}{12} = \dfrac{201}{24} + \dfrac{112}{24} - \dfrac{74}{24} = \dfrac{239}{24} = 9\dfrac{23}{24}$

End of Chapter Problems 4–11

1. $\dfrac{3}{8} + \dfrac{3}{32} = \dfrac{12}{32} + \dfrac{3}{32} = \dfrac{15}{32} = 0.469$

$\dfrac{3}{8} - \dfrac{3}{32} = \dfrac{12}{32} - \dfrac{3}{32} = \dfrac{9}{32} = 0.281$

$\dfrac{3}{8} \times \dfrac{3}{32} = \dfrac{9}{256} = 0.0352$

$\dfrac{3}{8} \div \dfrac{3}{32} = \dfrac{3}{8} \times \dfrac{32}{3} = 4.00$

3. $\dfrac{7}{16} + \dfrac{2}{7} = \dfrac{49}{112} + \dfrac{32}{112} = \dfrac{81}{112} = 0.723$

$\dfrac{7}{16} - \dfrac{2}{7} = \dfrac{49}{112} - \dfrac{32}{112} = \dfrac{17}{112} = 0.152$

$\dfrac{7}{16} \times \dfrac{2}{7} = \dfrac{14}{112} = 0.125$

$\dfrac{7}{16} \div \dfrac{2}{7} = \dfrac{7}{16} \times \dfrac{7}{2} = \dfrac{49}{32} = 1.53 = 1\dfrac{17}{32}$

5. $\dfrac{5}{8} + \dfrac{37}{64} = \dfrac{40}{64} + \dfrac{37}{64} = \dfrac{77}{64} = 1.20 = 1\dfrac{13}{64}$

$\dfrac{5}{8} - \dfrac{37}{64} = \dfrac{40}{64} - \dfrac{37}{64} = \dfrac{3}{64} = 0.0469$

$\dfrac{5}{8} \times \dfrac{37}{64} = \dfrac{185}{512} = 0.361$

$\dfrac{5}{8} \div \dfrac{37}{64} = \dfrac{5}{8} \times \dfrac{64}{37} = \dfrac{320}{296} = 1.08 = 1\dfrac{24}{296}$ $\qquad$ $\dfrac{5}{16} + \dfrac{13}{64} = 1.54$

7. $\dfrac{3}{5} + \dfrac{3}{10} = \dfrac{6}{10} + \dfrac{3}{10} = \dfrac{9}{10} = 0.900$

$\dfrac{3}{5} - \dfrac{3}{10} = \dfrac{6}{10} - \dfrac{3}{10} = \dfrac{3}{10} = 0.300$

$\dfrac{3}{5} \times \dfrac{3}{10} = \dfrac{9}{50} = 0.180$

$\dfrac{5}{8} \div \dfrac{3}{10} = \dfrac{3}{5} \times \dfrac{10}{3} = \dfrac{30}{15} = 2.00$

9. $3\dfrac{3}{8} + 2\dfrac{1}{3} = \dfrac{27}{8} + \dfrac{7}{3} = \dfrac{81}{24} + \dfrac{56}{24} = \dfrac{137}{24} = 5.71 = 5\dfrac{17}{24}$

$3\dfrac{3}{8} - 2\dfrac{1}{3} = \dfrac{27}{8} - \dfrac{7}{3} = \dfrac{81}{24} - \dfrac{56}{24} = \dfrac{25}{24} = 1.04 = 1\dfrac{1}{24}$

$3\dfrac{3}{8} \times 2\dfrac{1}{3} = \dfrac{27}{8} \times \dfrac{7}{3} = \dfrac{189}{24} = 7.88 = 7\dfrac{21}{24} = 7\dfrac{7}{8}$

$3\dfrac{3}{8} \div 2\dfrac{1}{3} = \dfrac{27}{8} \times \dfrac{3}{7} = \dfrac{81}{56} = 1.45 = 1\dfrac{25}{56}$

11. $4\dfrac{2}{5} + 2\dfrac{15}{64} = \dfrac{22}{5} + \dfrac{143}{64} = \dfrac{1408}{320} + \dfrac{715}{320} = \dfrac{2123}{320} = 6.63 = 6\dfrac{203}{320}$

$4\dfrac{2}{5} - 2\dfrac{15}{64} = \dfrac{1408}{320} - \dfrac{715}{320} = \dfrac{693}{320} = 2.17 = 2\dfrac{53}{320}$

$4\dfrac{2}{5} \times 2\dfrac{15}{64} = \dfrac{22}{5} \times \dfrac{143}{64} = \dfrac{3146}{320} = 9.83 = 9\dfrac{266}{320} = 9\dfrac{133}{160}$

$4\dfrac{2}{5} \div 2\dfrac{15}{64} = \dfrac{22}{5} \times \dfrac{64}{143} = \dfrac{1408}{715} = 1.97 = 1\dfrac{63}{65}$

13. $7\dfrac{1}{2} + 3\dfrac{5}{9} = \dfrac{15}{2} + \dfrac{32}{9} = \dfrac{135}{18} + \dfrac{64}{18} = \dfrac{199}{18} = 11.1 = 11\dfrac{1}{18}$

$7\dfrac{1}{2} + 3\dfrac{5}{9} = \dfrac{135}{18} - \dfrac{64}{18} = \dfrac{71}{18} = 3.94 = 3\dfrac{17}{18}$

$7\dfrac{1}{2} \times 3\dfrac{5}{9} = \dfrac{15}{2} \times \dfrac{32}{9} = \dfrac{480}{18} = 26.7 = 26\dfrac{2}{3}$

$7\dfrac{1}{2} \div 3\dfrac{5}{9} = \dfrac{15}{2} \times \dfrac{9}{32} = \dfrac{135}{64} = 2.11 = 2\dfrac{7}{64}$

15. $4\frac{7}{8}+8\frac{7}{16}=\frac{39}{8}+\frac{135}{16}=\frac{78}{16}+\frac{135}{16}=\frac{213}{16}=13.3=13\frac{5}{16}$

$4\frac{7}{8}-8\frac{7}{16}=\frac{78}{16}-\frac{135}{16}=-\frac{57}{16}=-3.56=-3\frac{9}{16}$

$4\frac{7}{8}\times8\frac{7}{16}=\frac{39}{8}\times\frac{135}{16}=\frac{135}{16}=\frac{5265}{128}=41.1=41\frac{17}{28}$

$4\frac{7}{8}\div8\frac{7}{16}=\frac{39}{8}\times\frac{16}{135}=\frac{624}{1080}=0.578=\frac{156}{270}=\frac{78}{135}$

17. $3\frac{2}{3}+6\frac{2}{3}=\frac{11}{3}+\frac{20}{3}=\frac{31}{3}=10.3=10\frac{1}{3}$

$3\frac{2}{3}-6\frac{2}{3}=\frac{11}{3}-\frac{20}{3}=-\frac{9}{3}=-3.00$

$3\frac{2}{3}\times6\frac{2}{3}=\frac{11}{3}\times\frac{20}{3}=\frac{220}{9}=24.4=24\frac{4}{9}$

$3\frac{2}{3}\div6\frac{2}{3}=\frac{11}{3}\times\frac{3}{20}=\frac{33}{60}=0.550=\frac{11}{20}$

19. $1\frac{7}{12}+3\frac{2}{3}=\frac{19}{12}+\frac{11}{3}=\frac{19}{12}+\frac{44}{12}=\frac{63}{12}=5.25=5\frac{1}{4}$

$1\frac{7}{12}-3\frac{2}{3}=\frac{19}{12}+\frac{44}{12}=-\frac{25}{12}=-2.08=-2\frac{1}{12}$

$1\frac{7}{12}\times3\frac{2}{3}=\frac{19}{12}\times\frac{11}{3}=\frac{209}{36}=5.81=5\frac{29}{36}$

$1\frac{7}{12}\div3\frac{2}{3}=\frac{19}{12}\times\frac{3}{11}=\frac{57}{132}=0.432$

End of Chapter Problems 4–12

	Fraction	Decimal	Percent		Fraction	Decimal	Percent
1.	3/8	.375	37.5%	3.	19/400	.0225	2.25%
5.	7/16	.4375	43.75%	7.	1/15	.0667	6.67%
9.	1/12	.0833	8.33%	11.	1/3	.3333	33.33%
13.	7/10	.700	70.07%	15.	1/20	.050	5.0%
17.	1/5	.200	20.0%	19.	1/25	.004	0.4%
21.	7/40	.175	17.5%	23.	11/16	.6875	68.75%
25.	3/5	.600	60%	27.	3/40	.075	7.5%
29.	3/20	.150	15.0%	31.	1/200	.005	0.50%
33.	5/2	2.50	250%	35.	9/16	.5625	56.25%
37.	5/16	.3125	31.25%				

End of Chapter Problems 4–13

Rewrite the words into numbers and then solve.

1. $\dfrac{64}{128} = \dfrac{1}{2}$

3. $\dfrac{3}{8} \times \dfrac{2}{7} = \dfrac{3}{28}$

5. $\dfrac{3}{4} \Big/ \dfrac{1}{6} = \dfrac{3}{4} \times \dfrac{6}{1} = \dfrac{9}{2} = 4\dfrac{1}{2}$

7. $\dfrac{2}{5} + \dfrac{1}{3} = \dfrac{6}{15} + \dfrac{5}{15} = \dfrac{11}{15}$

9. $\dfrac{9}{22} - \dfrac{4}{11} = \dfrac{9}{22} - \dfrac{8}{22} = \dfrac{1}{22}$

11. $1\dfrac{5}{8} + 3\dfrac{1}{2} = 4\dfrac{5}{8} + \dfrac{1}{8} = 4\dfrac{3}{4}$

13. $\dfrac{9}{10} - 2\dfrac{3}{5} = \dfrac{9}{10} - \dfrac{26}{10} = -\dfrac{17}{10} = -1\dfrac{7}{10}$

15. $3\dfrac{7}{8} \times 6\dfrac{2}{3} = \dfrac{31}{8} \times \dfrac{20}{3} = \dfrac{155}{6} = 25\dfrac{5}{6}$

17. $26\dfrac{5}{6} \Big/ 9\dfrac{3}{4} = \dfrac{161}{6} \Big/ \dfrac{39}{4} = \dfrac{161}{6} \times \dfrac{4}{39} = \dfrac{322}{117} = 2\dfrac{88}{117}$

19. $\dfrac{3}{8} + \dfrac{5}{6} = \dfrac{9}{24} + \dfrac{20}{24} = \dfrac{29}{24} = 1\dfrac{5}{24} = 1.208$ W (thousandths) = 1.21 W (hundredths)

21. efficiency = output power / input power = 100 W / 120 W = 0.8333 = 83.3%

END OF CHAPTER 5 PROBLEMS

End of Chapter Problems 5–1

1. Two terms, binomial expression

3. Three terms, trinomial expression

5. Two terms, binomial expression

7. Two terms, binomial expression

9. Three terms, trinomial expression

11. $3a - 4b + 2c$: The coefficients are 3, 4, and 2. The literal numbers are a, b, and c.

13. $\dfrac{2x}{3} + 7y$: The coefficients are $\dfrac{2}{3}$ and 7. The literal numbers are x and y.

15. $\dfrac{5}{2} - \dfrac{4}{b} = (5/2)a^{-1} - 4b^{-1}$

15. Coefficients are 5/2 and 4. Literal numbers are a and b.

End of Chapter Problems 5–2

1. 5.29	3. 54.8	5. 256	7. 512	9. 46.7
11. 166	13. 16.0	15. 64.0	17. 256	

End of Chapter Problems 5–3

Note To Student: Use your y^x key for powers greater than 2. Write out your calculator sequences for at least a few of these problems. Check and record some of your intermediate answers.

1. $ac = 5 \cdot 6 = 30.0$

3. $a^2c = 5^2 \cdot 6 = 25 \cdot 6 = 150$

5. $(ac)^2 = (5 \cdot 6)^2 = 30^2 = 900$

7. $2(ab)^2 = 2(5 \cdot 3)^2 = 2(15)^2 = 2 \cdot 225 = 450$

9. $a^2b^2 - 3c^2 = 5^2 \cdot 3^2 - 3 \cdot 6^2 = 25 \cdot 9 - 3 \cdot 36 = 225 - 108 = 117$

11. $ac^2 - 2abc = 5 \cdot 6^2 - 2 \cdot 5 \cdot 3 \cdot 6 = 180 - 180 = 0$

13. $(a^2b - 2c^2)^2 = (5^2 \cdot 3 - 2 \cdot 6^2)^2 = (75 - 72)^2 = 3^2 = 9.00$

15. $3a^2b^3c - 2a^3b^2c^2 = 3 \cdot 5^2 \cdot 3^3 \cdot 6 - 2 \cdot 5^3 \cdot 3^2 \cdot 6^2 = 3 \cdot 25 \cdot 27 \cdot 6 - 2 \cdot 125 \cdot 9 \cdot 36$
$= 12{,}150 - 81{,}000 = 68{,}850 = -6.89 \times 10^4$

17. $3ab^3c + 4a^2bc^3 - 2a^4bc^2 = 3 \cdot 5 \cdot 3^3 \cdot 6 + 4 \cdot 5^2 \cdot 3 \cdot 6^3 - 2 \cdot 5^4 \cdot 3 \cdot 6^2$
$= 2.43 \times 10^3 + 6.48 \times 10^4 - 1.35 \times 10^5 = -6.78 \times 10^4$

19. $(3a^2c^4 - 2a^3b^2c)^3 = (3 \cdot 5^2 \cdot 6^4 - 2 \cdot 5^3 \cdot 3^2 \cdot 6)^3 = (9.72 \times 10^4 - 1.35 \times 10^4)^3$
$= (8.37 \times 10^4)^3 = 5.86 \times 10^{14}$

End of Chapter Problems 5–4

Note to Student: When you see a problem like a large expression under a radical sign, rethink it into terms your calculator can understand. Since "everything" under the radical sign goes together, enclose the "everything" inside of a pair of parentheses. This usually gives you the correct calculator sequence.

1. 5.48   3.   6.32   5.   14.1   7.   32.2   9.   44.7

11. $\sqrt{20} = 4.47$ 13. $\sqrt{16} = 4.00$ 15. $\sqrt{450} = 21.2$ 17. $\sqrt{57} = 7.55$

19. $\sqrt{384.6} = 19.6$ 21. $\sqrt{400} + 3 = 23.0$

23. $\sqrt{520} + 10 = 15.2$ 25. $\sqrt{675 + 3888} = \sqrt{4563} = 67.5$

27. $\sqrt{24000 - 16875} = \sqrt{7125} = 84.4$

29. $\sqrt{691200 - 5760} - 5 = \sqrt{685440} - 5 = 828 - 5 = 823$

31. $\sqrt{18144000 - 864000} - 500 = \sqrt{17280000} - 500 = 4157 - 500 = 3657$

End of Chapter Problems 5–5

Note to Student: Remember that slash, / , can be used for division operator. It is helpful to write out calculator sequences using letters, not numbers.
Example: $E = IR$ needs $I \times R$ and $P = I^2R$ needs $I \, X^2 \times R =$

$I = \sqrt{\dfrac{P}{R}}$ needs $\sqrt{} \, (P / R) =$ and $E = \sqrt{PR}$ needs $\sqrt{} \, (P \times R) =$ and $P = \dfrac{E^2}{R}$ needs $E \, X^2 / R =$

1. $E = 660 \ \mu A \cdot 6.8 \ k\Omega = 4.49 \ V$ 3. $E = 3.7 \ mA \cdot 18 \ k\Omega = 66.6 \ V$

5. $E = 50 \ mA \cdot 2.7 \ k\Omega = 135 \ V$ 7. $E = 430 \ mA \cdot 560 \ \Omega = 241 \ V$

9. $P = (7.5 \ mA)^2 \cdot 680 \ \Omega = 38.3 \ mW$ 11. $P = (36.5 \ mA)^2 \cdot 3.3 \ k\Omega = 4.4 \ W$

13. $P = (1.2 \ A)^2 \cdot 5 \ \Omega = 7.20 \ W$ 15. $P = (23.5 \ mA)^2 \cdot 810 \ \Omega = 0.447 \ mW$

17. $I = \sqrt{(65.4 \ mW \ / \ 5.6 \ k\Omega)} = 3.42 \ mA$ 19. $I = \sqrt{(50 \ mW \ / \ 18 \ k\Omega)} = 1.67 \ mA$

21. $I = \sqrt{(4.6 \ W \ / \ 10 \ \Omega)} = 678 \ mA$ 23. $I = \sqrt{(650 \ \mu W \ / \ 56 \ \Omega)} = 3.41 \ mA$

25. $P = \sqrt{(8.3 \ mW \cdot 27 \ k\Omega)} = 15.0 \ V$ 27. $P = \sqrt{(130 \ mW \cdot 750 \ \Omega)} = 9.87 \ V$

29. $P = \sqrt{(18 \ mW \cdot 6.8 \ k\Omega)} = 15.0 \ V$ 31. $P = \sqrt{(100 \ mW \cdot 100 \ \Omega)} = 3.16 \ V$

33. $P = (16 \ V)^2 \ / \ 6.8 \ k\Omega = 37.6 \ mW$ 35. $P = (13.3 \ V)^2 \ / \ 33 \ k\Omega = 5.36 \ mW$

37. $P = (18.2 \ V)^2 \ / \ 10 \ k\Omega = 33.1 \ mW$ 39. $P = (150 \ V)^2 \ / \ 4.7 \ k\Omega = 4.79 \ mW$

End of Chapter Problems 5–6

Note To Student: Write out calculator sequence in letters. Use the pi (π) key instead of numeric 3.1415927

$$X_C = 1 / (2 \times \pi \times f \times C) \quad \text{and} \quad X_L = 2 \times \pi \times f \times L \quad \text{and} \quad f_r = 1 / (2 \times \pi \times \sqrt{(L \times C)})$$
$$Z = \sqrt{(R X^2 + X X^2)} \quad \text{and} \quad R = \sqrt{(Z X^2 - X X^2)}$$

1. $X_C = \dfrac{1}{2\pi \cdot 5 \text{ kHz} \cdot 100 \text{ nF}} = 318 \ \Omega$

3. $X_C = \dfrac{1}{2\pi \cdot 200 \text{ Hz} \cdot 200 \text{ nF}} = 3.98 \text{ k}\Omega$

5. $X_C = \dfrac{1}{2\pi \cdot 6.3 \text{ kHz} \cdot 50 \text{ nF}} = 12.6 \ \Omega$

7. $X_C = \dfrac{1}{2\pi \cdot 65.4 \text{ kHz} \cdot 250 \text{ pF}} = 9.73 \text{ k}\Omega$

9. $X_C = \dfrac{1}{2\pi \cdot 130 \text{ kHz} \cdot 750 \text{ pF}} = 1.63 \text{ k}\Omega$

11. $f_r = \dfrac{1}{6.28\sqrt{80 \text{ mH} \cdot 150 \text{ nF}}} = 1.45 \text{ kHz}$

13. $f_r = \dfrac{1}{6.28\sqrt{150 \mu\text{F} \cdot 50 \text{ nF}}} = 58.1 \text{ kHz}$

15. $f_r = \dfrac{1}{6.28\sqrt{50 \text{ mH} \cdot 250 \text{ nF}}} = 1.42 \text{ kHz}$

17. $f_r = \dfrac{1}{6.28\sqrt{400 \text{ mH} \cdot 5 \text{ nF}}} = 3.56 \text{ kHz}$

19. $f_r = \dfrac{1}{6.28\sqrt{0.25 \text{ mH} \cdot 25 \mu\text{F}}} = 63.7 \text{ Hz}$

21. $Z = \sqrt{(120 \text{ k}\Omega)^2 + (80 \text{ k}\Omega)^2} = 144 \text{ k}\Omega$

23. $Z = \sqrt{(200 \ \Omega)^2 + (100 \ \Omega)^2} = 224 \ \Omega$

25. $Z = \sqrt{(33 \text{ k}\Omega)^2 + (20 \text{ k}\Omega)^2} = 38.6 \text{ k}\Omega$

27. $Z = \sqrt{(4.7 \text{ k}\Omega)^2 + (7.35 \text{ k}\Omega)^2} = 8.72 \text{ k}\Omega$

29. $Z = \sqrt{(2.2 \text{ M}\Omega)^2 + (6.75 \text{ M}\Omega)^2} = 7.10 \text{ M}\Omega$

END OF CHAPTER 6 PROBLEMS

End of Chapter Problems 6–1

1. $2 \cdot 2 \cdot a \cdot a \cdot b \cdot b$

3. $2 \cdot 2 \cdot 2 \cdot 3 \cdot x \cdot x \cdot y$

5. $2 \cdot 3 \cdot 7 \cdot c \cdot c \cdot c$

7. $2 \cdot 2 \cdot 2 \cdot 11 \cdot y \cdot y \cdot z$

9. $3 \cdot 3 \cdot 3 \cdot 5 \cdot a \cdot a \cdot c \cdot c$

End of Chapter Problems 6–2

1. a^3b^3

3. $a^3b^3c^3$

5. $x^2y^3z^4$

7. a^3b^3

9. $a^4b^2c^3$

11. $a^4b^3c^2$

13. $78x^2y^3$

15. $32x^3y^2z^2$

17. $150a^2b^2c$

19. $270x^2y^4z^3$

End of Chapter Problems 6–3

Note To Student: There are several correct ways to write answers. Usually answers are all given on one line, that is $1/X = X^{-1}$. y^0 can be omitted (if multiplying) or included since $y^0 = 1$. z can be written as z or as z^1

1. $21a^4b^3$

3. $20a^{-4}b^{-5}$

5. $20x^6y^3z^4$

7. $6a^3b^{-2}c^{-1}$

9. $60x^5y^{-4}z^4$

End of Chapter Problems 6–4

1. $9a^2$

3. $8ab^2$

5. $5a^{-3}bc^{-1}$

7. $\dfrac{xy}{5}$

9. $11x^{-5}y^{-1}z^{-4}$

End of Chapter Problems 6–5

Note To Student: Remember that final fractions can be proper or improper, but all final fractions must be in lowest terms.

1. $\dfrac{4b}{15} \times \dfrac{3b}{8} = \dfrac{12b^2}{120} = \dfrac{b^2}{10}$

3. $\dfrac{3}{2b} \times \dfrac{5}{7b} = \dfrac{15}{14b^2} = \dfrac{15b^{-2}}{14}$

5. $\dfrac{5a}{9} \times \dfrac{6a^2}{7} = \dfrac{30a^3}{63} = \dfrac{2 \cdot 3 \cdot 5a^3}{3 \cdot 3 \cdot 7} = \dfrac{10a^3}{21}$

7. $\dfrac{3x^2}{10y} \times \dfrac{5x}{8y} = \dfrac{15x^3}{80y^2} = \dfrac{3 \cdot 5x^3}{2 \cdot 2 \cdot 2 \cdot 2 \cdot 5y^2} = \dfrac{3x^3y^{-2}}{16}$

9. $\dfrac{3}{4y^2} \times \dfrac{8xy}{9} = \dfrac{24xy}{36y^2} = \dfrac{2 \cdot 2 \cdot 2 \cdot 3xy}{2 \cdot 2 \cdot 3 \cdot 3y^2} = \dfrac{2xy^{-1}}{3}$

11. $\dfrac{8x^{-1}y}{5} \times \dfrac{10x^2y^{-3}}{3z^{-1}} = \dfrac{80x\,y^{-2}}{15z^{-1}} = \dfrac{2 \cdot 2 \cdot 2 \cdot 2 \cdot 5xy^{-2}}{3 \cdot 5x} = \dfrac{16xy^{-2}z}{31}$

13. $\dfrac{11a^2}{32b^3} \times \dfrac{4a^2b}{33c} = \dfrac{44a^4b}{1060b^3c} = \dfrac{2 \cdot 2 \cdot 11a^4b}{2 \cdot 2 \cdot 2 \cdot 2 \cdot 2 \cdot 3 \cdot 11b^3c} = \dfrac{a^4b^{-2}c^{-1}}{24}$

15. $\dfrac{7x^2}{24y^2} \times \dfrac{4xy^{-2}}{21x} = \dfrac{28x^3y^{-2}}{504xy^2} = \dfrac{2 \cdot 2 \cdot 7x^3y^{-2}}{2 \cdot 2 \cdot 2 \cdot 3 \cdot 3 \cdot 7xyy} = \dfrac{x^2y^{-4}}{18}$

17. $\dfrac{4a^3c^{-2}}{5b^2} \times \dfrac{7b^{-1}c^3}{16a^2} \times \dfrac{20a^3b^{-1}}{21c} = \dfrac{560a^6b^{-2}c}{1680a^2b^2c} = \dfrac{2 \cdot 2 \cdot 2 \cdot 2 \cdot 5 \cdot 7a^6b^{-2}c}{2 \cdot 2 \cdot 2 \cdot 2 \cdot 3 \cdot 5 \cdot 7a^2b^2c} = \dfrac{a^4b^{-4}}{3}$

19. $\dfrac{6xy^{-2}}{15z^2} \times \dfrac{25x^{-3}z^2}{18y} \times \dfrac{12y^2}{5x^{-1}z^{-2}} = \dfrac{1800x^{-2}z^2}{1350x^{-1}y} = \dfrac{2 \cdot 2 \cdot 2 \cdot 3 \cdot 3 \cdot 5 \cdot 5x^{-2}z^2}{2 \cdot 3 \cdot 3 \cdot 3 \cdot 5 \cdot 5x^{-1}y} = \dfrac{4x^{-1}y^{-1}z^2}{3}$

End of Chapter Problems 6–6

Note To Student: When you write down fractions, reduce each fraction individually as you write it down, especially if you have reciprocated the fraction in order to multiply.

1. $\dfrac{3x}{8} \div \dfrac{7x^3}{3} = \dfrac{3x}{8} \times \dfrac{3}{7x^3} = \dfrac{9x}{56x^3} = \dfrac{9x^{-2}}{56}$

3. $\dfrac{7x}{16} \div \dfrac{21x^2}{32} = \dfrac{7x}{16} \times \dfrac{32}{21x^2} = \dfrac{224x}{336x^2} = \dfrac{2 \cdot 2 \cdot 2 \cdot 2 \cdot 2 \cdot 7 \cdot x}{2 \cdot 2 \cdot 2 \cdot 2 \cdot 3 \cdot 7 \cdot x^2} = \dfrac{2x^{-1}}{3}$

5. $\dfrac{16b}{3} \div \dfrac{8b^4}{27} = \dfrac{16b}{3} \times \dfrac{27}{8b^4} = \dfrac{432b}{24b^4} = \dfrac{2 \cdot 2 \cdot 2 \cdot 2 \cdot 3 \cdot 3 \cdot 3b}{2 \cdot 2 \cdot 2 \cdot 3b^4} = 18b^{-3}$

7. $\dfrac{14ab^2}{9c^3} \div \dfrac{35b}{c^2} = \dfrac{14ab^2}{9c^3} \times \dfrac{c^2}{35b} = \dfrac{14ab^2c^2}{315bc^3} = \dfrac{2 \cdot 7ab^2c^2}{3 \cdot 3 \cdot 5 \cdot 7bc^3} = \dfrac{2abc^{-1}}{45}$

9. $\dfrac{3xy^3}{10x^{-1}} \div \dfrac{3xy^3}{10x^{-1}} = \dfrac{3xy^3}{10x^{-1}} \times \dfrac{10x^{-1}}{3xy^3} = \dfrac{30y^3}{30y^3} = 1$

11. $\dfrac{32a}{45b^2} \div \dfrac{16a^2}{25bc} = \dfrac{32a}{45b^2} \times \dfrac{25bc}{16a^2} = \dfrac{800abc}{720a^2b^2} = \dfrac{2 \cdot 2 \cdot 2 \cdot 2 \cdot 2 \cdot 5abc}{2 \cdot 2 \cdot 2 \cdot 2 \cdot 3 \cdot 3 \cdot 5a^2b^2}$

$= \dfrac{10a^{-1}b^{-1}c}{9}$

13. $\dfrac{15a^4b}{64c^3} \div \dfrac{75ab}{32c^2} = \dfrac{15a^4b}{64c^3} \times \dfrac{32c^2}{75ab} = \dfrac{480a^4bc^2}{4800abc^3} = \dfrac{a^3c^{-1}}{10}$

15. $\dfrac{20x^3y^2}{21z^2} \div \dfrac{30xy}{7z^2} = \dfrac{20x^3y^2}{21z^2} \times \dfrac{7z^2}{30xy} = \dfrac{140x^3y^2z^2}{630xyz^2} = \dfrac{2 \cdot 2 \cdot 5 \cdot 7x^3y^2z^2}{2 \cdot 3 \cdot 3 \cdot 5 \cdot 7xyz^2} = \dfrac{2x^2y}{9}$

17. $\dfrac{21a^3b^{-2}}{4c^2} \div \dfrac{14a^{-1}b^2}{3c^{-4}} = \dfrac{21a^3b^{-2}}{4c^2} \times \dfrac{3c^{-4}}{14a-1b^2} = \dfrac{63a^3b^{-2}c^{-4}}{56a^{-1}b^2c^2} = \dfrac{3 \cdot 3 \cdot 7a^3b^{-2}c^{-4}}{2 \cdot 2 \cdot 2 \cdot 7a^{-1}b^2c^2}$

$= \dfrac{9a^4b^{-4}c^{-6}}{8}$

19. $\dfrac{42yz^{-2}}{55x} \div \dfrac{21x^2z^2}{22z} = \dfrac{42yz^{-2}}{55x} \times \dfrac{22z}{21x^2y^2} = \dfrac{924yz^{-1}}{1155x^3y^2} = \dfrac{2 \cdot 2 \cdot 3 \cdot 7 \cdot 11yz^{-1}}{3 \cdot 5 \cdot 7 \cdot x^3y^2}$

$= \dfrac{4x^{-3}y^{-1}z^{-1}}{5}$

End of Chapter Problems 6-7

Note to Student: Remember to reduce each fraction before you look for the Least Common Denominator to add or subtract.

1. $\dfrac{5x^{-1}}{7}$

3. $\dfrac{4x^{-1}}{7}$

5. $\dfrac{9}{12ab} = \dfrac{3a^{-1}b^{-1}}{4}$

7. $\dfrac{7}{14a} = \dfrac{a^{-1}}{2}$

9. $\dfrac{x}{2}$

11. $\dfrac{2x}{5}$

13. $\dfrac{15ab}{25} = \dfrac{3ab}{5}$

15. $\dfrac{15ab}{25} = \dfrac{3ab}{5}$

17. $\dfrac{10x}{9}$

19. $\dfrac{-2x}{7} = -\dfrac{2x}{7}$

21. $\dfrac{-5x}{24} = -\dfrac{5x}{24}$

23. $\dfrac{2ab + 3b}{8}$

25. $\dfrac{7abc - 3ac}{4d}$

27. $-\dfrac{2abc + 3ab}{4x}$

29. $\dfrac{6xy - 4xz + 3yz}{5}$

End of Chapter Problems 6-8

1. $\dfrac{9x}{15} + \dfrac{2x}{15} = \dfrac{11x}{15}$

3. $\dfrac{4a}{6} + \dfrac{9a}{6} = \dfrac{13a}{6}$

5. $\dfrac{3x}{6} - \dfrac{4x}{6} = -\dfrac{x}{6}$

7. $\dfrac{8x}{10} - \dfrac{3x}{10} = -\dfrac{5x}{10} = \dfrac{x}{2}$

9. $\dfrac{y}{2x} + \dfrac{5y}{8} = \dfrac{4y}{8x} + \dfrac{5xy}{8x} = \dfrac{4y + 5xy}{8x}$

11. $\dfrac{3x}{4y} + \dfrac{2y}{3x} = \dfrac{9x^2}{12xy} + \dfrac{8y^2}{12xy} = \dfrac{9x^2 + 8y^2}{12xy}$

13. $\dfrac{2b}{5x} + \dfrac{3}{10y} = \dfrac{4by}{10xy} + \dfrac{3x}{10xy} = \dfrac{4by + 3x}{10xy}$

15. $\dfrac{5ab^2}{16c} - \dfrac{15ab}{32c^2} = \dfrac{10ab^2c}{32c^2} - \dfrac{15ab}{32c^2} = \dfrac{10ab^2c - 15ab}{32c^2}$

17. $\dfrac{3b}{4} + \dfrac{3b}{8} - \dfrac{15b}{16} = \dfrac{12b}{16} + \dfrac{6b}{16} - \dfrac{15b}{16} = \dfrac{3b}{16}$

19. $\dfrac{2a}{7} + \dfrac{7a}{15} - \dfrac{a}{3} = \dfrac{30a}{105} + \dfrac{49a}{105} - \dfrac{35a}{105} = \dfrac{44a}{105}$

21. $\dfrac{x}{10y^2} - \dfrac{2x}{5y^2} + \dfrac{x}{3y^2} = \dfrac{3x}{30y^2} - \dfrac{12x}{30y^2} + \dfrac{10x}{30y^2} = \dfrac{x}{30y^2}$

23. $\dfrac{4x}{3yz} + \dfrac{2y}{5x} - \dfrac{z}{6y} = \dfrac{40x^2}{30xyz} + \dfrac{12y^2z}{30xyz} - \dfrac{5xz^2}{30xyz} = \dfrac{40x^2 + 12y^2z - 5xz^2}{30xyz}$

25. $\dfrac{4a}{33b} + \dfrac{5b}{55c} - \dfrac{3c}{11a} = \dfrac{40a^2c}{330abc} + \dfrac{30ab^2}{330abc} - \dfrac{90bc^2}{330abc} = \dfrac{40a^2c + 30ab^2 - 90bc^2}{330abc}$

$= \dfrac{4a^2c + 3ab - 9bc^2}{33abc}$

27. $\dfrac{5y^2}{6x^2y} + \dfrac{4xy}{15y^2} - \dfrac{2x^2}{9y} = \dfrac{75y^3}{90x^2y^2} + \dfrac{24x^3y}{90x^2y^2} - \dfrac{20x^4y}{90x^2y^2} = \dfrac{75y^3 + 24x^3y - 20x^4y}{90x^2y^2}$

29. $\dfrac{3b}{20a^2} + \dfrac{7c}{10ab} - \dfrac{5a}{12b^3} = \dfrac{9b^4}{60a^2b^3} + \dfrac{42ab^2c}{60a^2b^3} - \dfrac{25a^3}{60a^2b^3} = \dfrac{9b^4 + 42ab^2c - 25a^3}{60a^2b^3}$

END OF CHAPTER 7 PROBLEMS

End of Chapter Problems 7–1

Note To Student: Always prove your answers by inserting answer back into the ORIGINAL equation to be sure both sides are equal.

1. $a - 7 = 3$, $a = 3 + 7$, $a = 10$　　3. $x = 2$　　　　5. $x = 3$

7. $x = 9$　　　　　　　　9. $b = 4$　　　　11. $x = -4$

13. $5y = 20$, $y = 4$　　　15. $b = -9$　　　17. $\dfrac{a}{4} = 3$, $a = 12$

19. $x = -7$　　　　　　　21. $c = 12$　　　23. $a = -10$

25. $x = 16$　　　　　　　27. $x = 12$

29. $\dfrac{3}{5y} = 6$, $\dfrac{5y}{3} = \dfrac{1}{6}$　　　　31. $\dfrac{3x}{4} = 6$, $x = \dfrac{6 \cdot 4}{3}$, $x = 8$

$\quad y = \dfrac{3}{5 \cdot 6} = \dfrac{1}{10}$　　　33. $\dfrac{7}{2y} = 14$, $\dfrac{2y}{7} = \dfrac{1}{14}$

35. $\dfrac{5y}{3} = 10$, $y = \dfrac{-3 \cdot 10}{5} = -6$　　　$y = \dfrac{7}{2 \cdot 14} = \dfrac{1}{4}$

37. $\dfrac{-6}{7y} = 3$, $\dfrac{7y}{-6} = \dfrac{1}{3}$　　　39. $\dfrac{-8}{3b} = 2$, $\dfrac{3b}{-8} = \dfrac{1}{2}$

$\quad y = \dfrac{-6}{7 \cdot 3} = -\dfrac{2}{7}$　　　$b = \dfrac{-8}{3 \cdot 2} = -1\dfrac{1}{3}$

41. $\dfrac{x}{4} = \dfrac{3}{2}$; $x = \dfrac{3 \cdot 4}{2} = 6$　　43. $a = \dfrac{3 \cdot 5}{2 \cdot 7} = \dfrac{15}{14} = 1\dfrac{1}{14}$

45. $\dfrac{3 \cdot 5}{10 \cdot 14} = x = \dfrac{3}{28}$　　47. $\dfrac{2a}{7} = \dfrac{4}{21}$, $a = \dfrac{7 \cdot 4}{2 \cdot 21} = \dfrac{2}{3}$

49. $\dfrac{5x}{3} = \dfrac{9}{4}$, $x = \dfrac{9 \cdot 3}{5 \cdot 4} = 1\dfrac{7}{20}$

End of Chapter Problems 7–2

1. $x^2 = 25$, $x = 5$　　　　　3. $\dfrac{a^2}{4} = 18$, $a^2 = 54$, $a = 7.35$

5. $\dfrac{a^2}{4} = 14$, $a^2 = 56$, $a = 7.48$　　7. $\dfrac{6}{b^2} = 4$, $\dfrac{b^2}{6} = \dfrac{1}{4}$, $b^2 = \dfrac{6}{4}$,

9. $12 = \dfrac{72}{a^2}$, $a^2 = \dfrac{72}{12}$, $a = 2.45$　　　$b = 1.22$

11. $\sqrt{a} = 7$, $a = 49$　　　13. $\dfrac{\sqrt{x}}{3} = 2$, $\sqrt{x} = 6$, $x = 36$

15. $\dfrac{\sqrt{a}}{b} = 2.3$, $\sqrt{a} = 13.8$, $a = 190$　　17. $2 = \dfrac{1}{2\sqrt{x}}$, $\sqrt{x} = \dfrac{1}{4}$, $x = \dfrac{1}{16}$

19. $3 = \dfrac{1}{4\sqrt{x}}$, $\sqrt{x} = \dfrac{1}{12}$, $x = \dfrac{1}{144}$

21. $\dfrac{4}{4\sqrt{a}} = 6$, $\dfrac{4\sqrt{a}}{3} = \dfrac{1}{6}$, $\sqrt{a} = \dfrac{3}{24}$, $a = \dfrac{1}{64}$

23. $\dfrac{2\sqrt{x}}{3} = 6$, $\sqrt{x} = \dfrac{18}{2}$, $x = 81$

25. $2ax = 12$, $ax = 12/2 = 6$, $a = 6/x$, $x = 6/a$

27. $8bc = 14$, $b = 14/8 = 7/4$, $b = 7/4c$, $c = 7/4b$

29. $P = \dfrac{E^2}{R}$, $R = \dfrac{E^2}{P}$, $\dfrac{E^2}{R} = P$, $E^2 = PR$, $\sqrt{E^2} = \sqrt{PR}$, $E = \sqrt{PR}$

31. $B_C = 2\pi fC$; $f = \dfrac{B_C}{2\pi C}$; $C = \dfrac{B_C}{2\pi f}$

33. $3 = \dfrac{1}{2a\sqrt{b}}$, $a = \dfrac{1}{6\sqrt{b}}$, $\sqrt{b} = \dfrac{1}{6a}$, $(\sqrt{b})^2 = \left(\dfrac{1}{6a}\right)^2$, $b = \dfrac{1}{36a^2}$

35. $5 = \dfrac{6}{\sqrt{xy}}$, $\sqrt{xy} = \dfrac{6}{5}$, $(\sqrt{xy})^2 = \left(\dfrac{6}{5}\right)^2$, $xy = \dfrac{36}{25y}$

37. $X_L = 2\pi fL$, $2\pi fL = X_L$, $f = \dfrac{X_L}{2\pi L}$, $L = \dfrac{X_L}{2\pi f}$

39. $f_r = \dfrac{1}{2\pi\sqrt{LC}}$, $\sqrt{LC} = \dfrac{1}{2\pi f_r}$, $LC = \dfrac{1}{(2\pi f_r)^2}$, $L = \dfrac{1}{(2\pi f_r)^2 C}$, $C = \dfrac{1}{(2\pi f_r)^2 L}$

End of Chapter Problems 7-3

1. $R_1 = R_T - R_2 = 12.4\ k\Omega - 5.6\ k\Omega = 6.8\ k\Omega$

3. $G_1 = G_T - G_2 = 54.9\ \mu S - 37\ \mu S = 17.9\ \mu S$

5. $A_V = \dfrac{V_o}{V_{in}}$, $V_o = A_V\ V_{in} = 150 \cdot 55\ mV = 8.25\ V$

7. $R = \dfrac{E^2}{P} = \dfrac{(15\ V)^2}{2W} = 113\ \Omega$

9. $R = \dfrac{E^2}{P} = \dfrac{(450\ mV)^2}{150\ mW} = 1.35\ \Omega$

11. $R = \dfrac{E^2}{P} = \dfrac{(32\ V)^2}{30\ mW} = 34.1\ k\Omega$

13. $E^2 = PR$, $\sqrt{E^2} = \sqrt{PR}$, $E = \sqrt{PR}$, $E = (6.73\ W \cdot 27\ \Omega)^{1/2} = 13.5\ V$

15. $E^2 = PR$, $\sqrt{E^2} = \sqrt{PR}$, $E = \sqrt{PR}$, $E = (10.3\ W \cdot 1.8\ k\Omega)^{1/2} = 136\ V$

17. $E^2 = PR$, $\sqrt{E^2} = \sqrt{PR}$, $E = \sqrt{PR}$, $E = (1.73\ W \cdot 47\ k\Omega)^{1/2} = 285\ V$

19. $I = \left(\dfrac{P}{R}\right)^{1/2}$, $I = \left(\dfrac{600\ mW}{680\ \Omega}\right)^{1/2} = 29.7\ mA$

21. $I = \left(\dfrac{P}{R}\right)^{1/2}$, $I = \left(\dfrac{500\ mW}{2.7\ k\Omega}\right)^{1/2} = 13.6\ mA$

23. $I = \left(\dfrac{P}{R}\right)^{1/2}$, $I = \left(\dfrac{14.7 \text{ W}}{100 \ \Omega}\right)^{1/2} = 383 \text{ mA}$

25. $R = \dfrac{P}{I^2}$, $R = \dfrac{500 \text{ mW}}{(10 \text{ mA})^2} = 5.00 \text{ k}\Omega$

27. $R = \dfrac{P}{I^2}$, $R = \dfrac{600 \text{ mW}}{(47.3 \text{ mA})^2} = 268 \ \Omega$

29. $R = \dfrac{P}{I^2}$, $R = \dfrac{104 \text{ W}}{(3.77 \text{ A})^2} = 7.32 \ \Omega$

31. $N_p = N_s \left(\dfrac{Z_p}{Z_s}\right)^{1/2} = 100 \left(\dfrac{2.5 \text{ k}\Omega}{8 \ \Omega}\right)^{1/2} = 1770$

33. $N_p = N_s \left(\dfrac{Z_p}{Z_s}\right)^{1/2} = 50 \left(\dfrac{40 \ \Omega}{500 \ \Omega}\right)^{1/2} = 14.1$

35. $N_p = N_s \left(\dfrac{Z_p}{Z_s}\right)^{1/2} = 25 \left(\dfrac{750 \ \Omega}{75 \ \Omega}\right)^{1/2} = 79.1$

37. $Z_s = \dfrac{Z_p N_s^2}{N_p^2} = \dfrac{1 \text{ k}\Omega \cdot (100)^2}{(1200)^2} = 6.94 \ \Omega$

39. $Z_s = \dfrac{Z_p N_s^2}{N_p^2} = \dfrac{2.3 \ \Omega \cdot (1800)^2}{(100)^2} = 745 \ \Omega$

41. $Z_s = \dfrac{Z_p N_s^2}{N_p^2} = \dfrac{325 \ \Omega \cdot (60)^2}{(800)^2} = 1.83 \ \Omega$

43. $N_s = N_p \left(\dfrac{Z_s}{Z_p}\right)^{1/2} = 3000 \left(\dfrac{12 \ \Omega}{1.5 \text{ k}\Omega}\right)^{1/2} = 268$

45. $N_s = N_p \left(\dfrac{Z_s}{Z_p}\right)^{1/2} = 2000 \left(\dfrac{4 \ \Omega}{800 \ \Omega}\right)^{1/2} = 141$

47. $Z_p = \dfrac{Z_s N_p^2}{N_s^2} = \dfrac{2 \text{ k}\Omega \cdot (100)^2}{(2500)^2} = 3.20 \ \Omega$

49. $Z_p = \dfrac{Z_s N_p^2}{N_s^2} = \dfrac{40 \ \Omega \cdot (5000)^2}{(1000)^2} = 1.00 \text{ k}\Omega$

51. $C = \dfrac{1}{2\pi f X_C} = \dfrac{1}{2\pi \cdot 2.7 \text{ kHz} \cdot 700 \ \Omega} = 84.2 \text{ nF}$

53. $f = \dfrac{1}{2\pi C X_C} = \dfrac{1}{2\pi \cdot 10 \text{ nF} \cdot 5 \text{ k}\Omega} = 3.18 \text{ kHz}$

55. $L = \dfrac{X_L}{2\pi f} = \dfrac{3.85 \text{ k}\Omega}{2\pi \cdot 4.8 \text{ kHz}} = 128 \text{ mH}$

57. $f = \dfrac{X_L}{2\pi L} = \dfrac{170 \ \Omega}{2\pi \cdot 54.1 \text{ mH}} = 500 \text{ Hz}$

59. $L = \dfrac{1}{C(2\pi f_r)^2} = \dfrac{1}{100 \text{ pF } (2\pi \cdot 30 \text{ kHz})^2} = 281 \text{ mH}$

61. $C = \dfrac{1}{L(2\pi f_r)^2} = \dfrac{1}{100 \text{ mH } (2\pi \cdot 100 \text{ Hz})^2} = 25.3 \ \mu\text{F}$

63. With word problems, remember to simply write down in equation form (and on a diagram when possible) whatever the word problem gives you as information.
Since $E = I \times R_{eq}$, then $R_{eq} = E / I = 5 \text{ V} / 0.8 \text{ A} = 6.25 \ \Omega$

65. Since $E = I \times R_{eq}$, then $R_{eq} = E / I = 12 \text{ V} / 0.3 \text{ A} = 40 \ \Omega$

67. Since $P = E^2 / R_{eq}$, then $E^2 = PR_{eq}$, so $E = \sqrt{(PR_{eq})} = \sqrt{(5 \text{ W } (5 \ \Omega))} = 5 \text{ V}$

69. Since $P = E^2 / R_{eq}$, then $PR_{eq} = E^2$, so $R_{eq} = E^2 / P = (5 \text{ V})^2 / (3 \text{ W}) = 8.33 \ \Omega$

END OF CHAPTER 8 PROBLEMS

End of Chapter Problems 8–1

1. $3(a + 3) = 3a + 9$

3. $4(a - 1) = 4a - 4$

5. $7(4 - b) = 28 - 7b$

7. $3a - 2(3a - 1) = 3a - 6a + 2 = -3a + 2$

9. $6a - 3(4a + 2) = 6a - 12a - 6 = -6a - 6$

11. $4(2x - 3) - 2x = 8x - 12 - 2x = 6x - 12$

13. $3x(2 + 2y) = 6x + 6xy$

15. $3a(2a + 3b) = 6a^2 + 9ab$

17. $3(3x^2 + 6x - 12) = 9x^2 + 18x - 36$

19. $2(4a^2 - 3a + 2) = 8a^2 - 6a + 4$

21. $4a(a + b) - 3a(a + 5b) = 4a^2 + 4ab - 3a^2 - 15ab = a^2 - 11ab$

23. $a(2ab + 2b) - 3(a^2b - 2ab) = 2a^2b + 2ab - 3a^2b + 6ab = -a^2b + 8ab$

25. $2x(4xy - 3y) - 3(x^2y + xy) = 8x^2y - 6xy - 3x^2y - 3xy = 5x^2y - 9xy$

27. $2x(3xy - 4y) - 4(x^2y + 3xy) = 6x^2y - 8xy - 4x^2y - 12xy = 2x^2y - 20xy$

29. $x(x^2 + 8x + 15) + 2x(x^2 - x - 6) = x^3 + 8x^2 + 15x + 2x^3 - 2x^2 - 12x = 3x^3 + 6x^2 + 3x$

31. $4a(a^2 - 3a + 6) - 3a(a^2 + 5a - 6) = 4a^3 - 12a^2 + 24a - 3a^3 - 15a^2 + 18a = a^3 - 27a^2 + 42a$

33. $3a^2 + 2a(a - b + 2) - 2a(2a + b) = 3a^2 + 2a^2 - 2ab + 4a - 4a^2 - 2ab = a^2 - 4ab + 4a$

35. $4x(2x - 3y + 2) - 2x^2 - 3x(x + 2y - 3) = 8x^2 - 12xy + 8x - 2x^2 - 3x^2 - 6xy + 9x = 3x^2 - 18xy + 17x$

End of Chapter Problems 8–2

1. $\dfrac{44x^2}{3}$

3. $5y^2$

5. $8a^2 + 9a$

7. $5b^2 - 6b$

9. $6a^2 - 16a + 8$

11. $2a - 6a + \dfrac{9}{2}$

13. $-2x^2 + 7x$

15. $8x^2 - 15$

17. $5b^2 - 6b$

19. $\dfrac{6x^2}{5} + \dfrac{21b}{4}$

of Chapter Problems 8–3

$+ 6a + 9$

3. $a^2 - 12a + 36$

5. $4x^2 - 16x + 16$

$24x + 9$

9. $4a^2 + 12ab + 9b^2$

11. $x^6 - 8x^3y + 16y^2$

$+ 9y^2$

15. $a^2 + 4a + 3$

17. $y^2 - 3y - 18$

21. $x^2 - 5x + 4$

25. $4x^2 - 9$

27. $x^2 + 4xy + 3y^2$

31. $4a^2 + 5ab - 6b^2$

33. $2a^2 - 10ab + 8b^2$

37. $6x^2 + 23xy + 20y^2$

39. $4x^2 - 16xy + 15y^2$

End of Chapter Problems 8–4

Note To Student: Always prove a division problem by multiplying.

1. $x^2 + 3x + 2$
3. $3x^2 + x + 2$
5. $(9 / 5)x - 1$
7. $x + 3y$
9. $x - 3$
11. $x - 7$
13. $3x - 2$
15. $a - 5$
17. $2x + 3y$
19. $3a - 4b$
21. $x - 9y$
23. $8 + 4x$

25. $4x - 4 + \dfrac{3}{3x + 2}$

27. $2x + 3y - \dfrac{2xy}{4x + 5y}$

29. $4a - 2 + \dfrac{4}{a + 1}$

31. $6a + 3 + \dfrac{1}{a - 1}$

33. $a + b + \dfrac{2ab}{a + b}$

35. $6x^2 - 3x + 7 - \dfrac{3}{x + 1}$

End of Chapter Problems 8–5

1. $3(a + 3)$
3. $7(b - 3)$
5. $2xy(2x + 3)$
7. $2a(8a + 1)$
9. $8abc^2(3ac - 2b)$
11. $3a^2b^2(4a + 3b^2 - 2a^2b^2)$
13. $5xy^2(2x^2 - 4x^3y^2 + 3y)$
15. $3b^2c(5a^3c^3 - a^2bc^3 - 4)$
17. $5x^2y^2z^2(7x^2z \setminus + 5y^2z^2 - 6)$
19. $6x^2yz^2(4xyz^2 - 7y^2 - 12)$

21. $\dfrac{7x^2z^2}{3}\left(\dfrac{z}{4} - \dfrac{2xy^2}{3} \right)$

23. $\dfrac{6x^2y^2z}{5}\left(\dfrac{2x^2}{7} + \dfrac{4yz^2}{11} - \dfrac{3xyz^3}{5} \right)$

25. $\dfrac{7a^2c^2}{11b^2}\left(\dfrac{3a}{2} - \dfrac{4}{3b} - \dfrac{6ac}{4} \right)$

End of Chapter Problems 8–6

1. $(x + 2)(x + 3)$
3. $(x + 8)(x - 4)$
5. $(a + 3)(a + 3)$
7. $(a + 4)(a - 4)$
9. $(x + 7)(x - 7)$
11. $(x - 3)(x - 5)$
13. $(a - 5)(a - 7)$
15. $(a - 4)(a - 7)$
17. $(y - 4)(y + 9)$
19. $(x - 7)(x + 5)$
21. $(x + 4)(x - 6)$
23. $(2x + 3)(3x - 2)$
25. $8a^2 - 20a + 8 = 4(2a^2 - 5a + 2) = 4(2a - 1)(a - 2)$
27. $9x^2 + 6x - 8 = (3x + 4)(3x - 2)$
29. $6b^2 - 18b + 12 = 6(b^2 - 3b + 2) = 6(b - 2)(b - 1)$
31. $10a^2 + 31a + 15 = (5a + 3)(2a + 5)$
33. $2x^2 + 7xy + 6y^2 = (2x + 3y)(x + 2y)$
35. $20a^2 - 7ab - 6b^2 = (4a - 3b)(5a + 2b)$
37. $8x^2 + 20xy - 12y^2 = 4(2x^2 + 5xy - 3y^2) = 4(2x - y)(x + 3y)$
39. $12x^2 + 18xy + 6y^2 = 6(2x^2 + 3xy + y^2) = 6(2x + y)(x + y)$

END OF CHAPTER 9 PROBLEMS

End of Chapter Problems 9–1

Note To Student: Always prove your answers by inserting the answer values into the ORIGINAL equation to be sure both sides of the equation are equal. Often you can simply store the answer in memory on your calculator and recall the answer from memory in place of the unknown in the equation.

1. $\dfrac{5x}{2} + 3 = 6$

   $5x + 6 = 12; x = \dfrac{6}{5} = 1\dfrac{1}{5}$

3. $\dfrac{4a}{3} - 5 = 2$

   $4a - 15 = 6; a = 5\dfrac{1}{4}$

5. $\dfrac{2I}{4} + \dfrac{I}{6} = 2$

   $6I + 2I = 24; I = 3$

7. $\dfrac{2x}{3} - \dfrac{3x}{4} = 8$

   $8x - 9x = 23; x = -12$

9. $\dfrac{4R}{2} = 3 + \dfrac{R}{3}$

   $12R = 18 + 2R; R = 1\dfrac{4}{5}$

11. $\dfrac{R + 3}{4} - 2 = \dfrac{3R + 1}{2} + 4$

    $R + 3 - 2(4) = 2(3R + 1) + 4(4)$

    $R + 3 - 8 = 6R + 2 + 16; R = -4\dfrac{3}{5}$

13. $\dfrac{R - 2}{5} + 3 = \dfrac{2R + 2}{3} + 4$

    $3(R - 2) + 3(15) = 5(2R + 2) + 4(15)$

    $3R - 6 + 45 = 10R + 10 + 60; R = -4\dfrac{3}{7}$

15. $\dfrac{c - 3}{4} - \dfrac{c + 1}{3} = 2 + 3c$

    $3(c - 3) + 4(c + 1) = 12(2 + 3c)$

    $c = -1$

17. $\dfrac{3}{I - 3} + 3 = 4$

    $3 + 3(I - 3) = 4(I - 3)$

    $3 + 3I - 9 = 4I - 12; I = 6$

19. $\dfrac{4}{R - 2} + 2 = 3$

    $4 + 2(R - 2) = 3(R - 2)$

    $4 + 2R - 4 = 3R - 6; R = 6$

21. $\dfrac{5x}{2} + \dfrac{x - 2}{6} = \dfrac{3x - 6}{4}$

    $6(5x) + 2(x - 2) = 3(3x - 6)$

    $30x + 2x - 4 = 9x - 18; x = -\dfrac{14}{23}$

23. $\dfrac{4a}{3} + \dfrac{a + 2}{5} = \dfrac{2a - 3}{5}$

    $5(4a) + 3(a + 2) = 3(2a - 3)$

    $20a + 3a + 6 = 6a - 9; a = -\dfrac{15}{17}$

25. $\dfrac{4-x}{2x} - \dfrac{3}{x} = \dfrac{1}{x}$

$4 - x - 3(2) = 1(2);\ 4 - x - 6 = 2$

$x = -4$

27. $\dfrac{3-y}{2y} - \dfrac{2}{y} = \dfrac{3}{y}$

$3 - y - 4 = 6;\ y = -7$

29. $\dfrac{3}{G-3} - \dfrac{1}{4} = 5$

$3(4) - 1(G-3) = 5(4)(G-3)$

$12 - 6 + 3 = 20G - 60$

$G = 3\dfrac{4}{7}$

31. $\dfrac{2}{R+3} - \dfrac{1}{3} = 4$

$2(3) - 1(R+3) = 4(3)(R+3)$

$6 - R - 3 = 12R + 36$

$R = -2\dfrac{7}{13}$

33. $\dfrac{1}{a} + \dfrac{1}{b} = 2$

$b + a = 2ab$

solve for a: $2ab - a\ = b$

$a(2b-1)\ = b$

$a\ = b\,/\,(2b-1)$

solve for b: $2ab - b\ = a$

$b(2a-1)\ = a;\ b = a\,/\,(2a-1)$

35. $\dfrac{2}{a} - 3 = \dfrac{1}{b} = 2$

$2b - 3a = a$

solve for a: $a + 3ab\ = 2b$

$a(1 + 3b)\ = 2b$

$a = 2b\,/\,(1+3b)$

solve for b: $b(2-3a)\ = a$

$b = 3a\,/\,(2-3a)$

37. $\dfrac{x}{2a} + \dfrac{x}{3b} = 2$

$3bx + 2ax = 12ab$

solve for a: $12ab - 2ax\ = 3bx$

$a(12b - 2x)\ = 3bx$

$a\ = 3bx\,/\,(12b-2x)$

solve for b: $12ab - 3bx\ = 2ax$

$b(12a - 3x)\ = 2ax)$

$b\ = 2ax\,/\,(12a - 3x)$

solve for x: $x(3b + 2a)\ = 12ab$

$x\ = 12ab\,/\,(2a + 3b)$

39. $\dfrac{3x}{2a} - \dfrac{x}{3b} = 4$

$9bx - 2ax = 24ab$

solve for a: $24ab + 2ax\ = 9bx$

$a(24b + 2x)\ = 9bx$

$a\ = 9bx\,/\,(24b + 2x)$

solve for b: $9bx - 24ab\ = 2ax$

$b(9x - 24a)\ = 2ax$

$b\ = 2ax\,/\,(9x - 24a)$

solve for x: $x(9b - 2a)\ = 23ab$

$x\ = 24ab\,/\,(9b - 2a)$

41. $\dfrac{3}{a-2} + \dfrac{2}{a+2} = \dfrac{b}{a+2}$

$3(A+2) + 2(a-2) = b(a-2)$

$3a + 6 + 2a - 4 = ab - 2b$

$5a + 2 = ab - 2b$

solve for a: $\quad ab - 5a \;=\; 2b + 2$

$\qquad\qquad\qquad a(b-5) \;=\; 2b + 2$

$\qquad\qquad\qquad\quad a \;=\; (2b+2)\,/\,(b-5)$

solve for b: $\quad ab - 5a \;=\; 5a + 2$

$\qquad\qquad\qquad a(b-5) \;=\; 5a + 2$

$\qquad\qquad\qquad\quad b \;=\; (5a+2)\,/\,(a-2)$

43. $\dfrac{2}{2a-1} + \dfrac{3}{3a+2} = \dfrac{2b}{2a-1}$

$2(3a+2) + 3(2a-1) = 2b(3a+2)$

$6a + 4 + 6a - 3 = 6ab + 4b$

$12a + 1 = 6ab + 4b$

solve for a: $\quad 12a - 6ab \;=\; 4b - 1$

$\qquad\qquad\qquad a(12-6b) \;=\; 4b - 1$

$\qquad\qquad\qquad\quad a \;=\; (4b-1)/(12-6b)$

solve for b: $\quad b(a+4) \;=\; 12a + 1$

$\qquad\qquad\qquad\quad b \;=\; (12a+1)/(6a+4)$

45. $\dfrac{5}{3b-2} - \dfrac{4}{3b-1} = \dfrac{3}{3b-1}$

$5(3b-1) - 4(3b-2) = 3(3b-2)$

$15b - 5 - 12b + 8 \;=\; 9b - 6; \; b = 1\dfrac{1}{2}$

End of Chapter Problems 9–2

1. $V_L = \dfrac{V_{OC} R_L}{R_{TH} + R_L}$

$V_L R_{TH} + V_L R_L = V_{OC} R_L$

$V_{OC} = \dfrac{V_L R_{TH} + V_L R_L}{R_L}$

$R_{TH} = \dfrac{V_{OC} R_L - V_L R_L}{V_L}$

$R_L = \dfrac{V_L R_{TH}}{V_{OC} - V_L}$

3. $I_L = \dfrac{I_{SC} G_L}{G_L + G_N}$

$I_L G_L + I_L G_N = I_{SC} G_L$

$I_{SC} = \dfrac{I_L G_L + I_L G_N}{G_L}$

$G_L = \dfrac{I_L G_N}{I_{SC} - I_L}$

$G_N = \dfrac{I_{SC} G_L - I_L G_L}{I_L}$

5. $R_s = \dfrac{R_i R_o}{R_i + R_o}$

$R_s R_i + R_s R_o = R_i R_o$

$R_o = \dfrac{R_s R_i}{R_i - R_s}$

$R_i = \dfrac{R_s R_o}{R_o - R_s}$

β = beta = lower case Greek letter;

α = alpha = lower case Greek letter

7. $r_i = \beta\left(r_o + \dfrac{r_b}{\beta} \right)$

$r_i = \beta r_o + r_b$

$r_o = \dfrac{r_i - r_b}{\beta}$

$r_b = r_i - \beta r_o$

9. $R_T = \dfrac{R_1 R_2}{R_1 + R_2}$

$R_T R_1 + R_T R_2 = R_1 R_2$

$R_1 = \dfrac{R_T R_2}{R_2 - R_T}$

$R_2 = \dfrac{R_T R_1}{R_1 - R_T}$

11. $\alpha \left(1 + \dfrac{1}{\alpha}\right) = B$

$\alpha + 1 = B; \ \alpha = B - 1$

13. $2\pi f C(R_1 + R_2) = 1$

$2\pi f C R_1 + 2\pi f C R_2 = 1$

$R_1 = \dfrac{1 - 2\pi f C R_2}{2\pi f C}$

15. $I_B(R_I + R_2) = V_{CC} - V_B$

$V_B = V_{CC} - I_B(R_I + R_2)$

$I_B R_I + I_B R_2 = V_{CC} - V_B$

$R_I = \dfrac{V_{CC} - I_B R_2 - V_B}{I_B}$

End of Chapter Problems 9–3

1. $V_2 = R_i + R_2$

$V_2 R_1 + V_2 R_2 = E R_2$

a. $R_2 = \dfrac{V_2 R_1}{E - V_2} = 4.8 \ \text{k}\Omega$

b. $R_1 = \dfrac{E R_2 - V_2 R_2}{V_2}$

$R_1 = 773 \ \Omega$

3. $I_1 = \dfrac{I_T G_1}{G_1 + G_2}$

$I_1 G_1 + I_1 G_2 = I_T G_1$

a. $I_T = \dfrac{I_1 G_1 + I_1 G_1}{G_1} = 12 \ \text{mA}$

b. $G_2 = \dfrac{I_T G_1 - I_1 G_1}{I_1} = 1.79 \ \text{mS}$

5. $A_i + A_i A_{oe} A L_i = h_{fe}$

a. $h_{oe} = \dfrac{h_{fe} - A_i}{A_i R_L} = 74.3 \ \mu\text{S}$

b. $R_L = \dfrac{h_{fe} - A_i}{A_i h_{oe}} = 20.8 \ \text{k}\Omega$

7. $R_T = \dfrac{R_1 R_2}{R_1 + R_2}$

$R_1 = \dfrac{R_2 R_T}{R_2 - R_T} = 3 \ \text{k}\Omega$

9. $Z_T = \dfrac{Z_1 Z_2}{Z_1 + Z_L}$

$Z_2 = \dfrac{Z_1 Z_T}{Z_1 - Z_2} = 220 \ \text{k}\Omega$

11. $I_B R_1 + I_B R_2 = V_{CC} - V_B$

$R_2 = \dfrac{V_{CC} - V_B - I_B R_1}{I_B} = 3.94 \ \text{k}\Omega$

13. $I_C = \dfrac{\beta V_{CC}}{\beta R_E + R_B}$

$\beta I_C R_E + I_C R_B = \beta V_{CC}$

$R_B = \dfrac{\beta V_{CC} - \beta I_C R_E}{I_C} = 550 \ \text{k}\Omega$

15. $2\pi f C R_1 + 2\pi f C R_2$

$R_1 = \dfrac{1 - 2\pi f C R_2}{2\pi f C} = 9.34 \ \text{k}\Omega$

End of Chapter Problems 9–4

1. $(x - 4)(x + 4) = 0$
    $x - 4 = 0 \qquad x + 4 = 0$
    $x = 4 \qquad\quad x = -4$

3. $x^2 + 6x + 8 = 0$
    $(x + 2)(x + 4) = 0$
    $x = -2 \qquad x = 2$

5. $x^2 + 3x - 18 = 0$
    $(x + 6)(x - 3) = 0$
    $x + 6 = 0 \qquad x - 3 = 0$
    $x = -6 \qquad\quad x = 3$

7. $x^2 - 6x + 8 = 0$
    $(x - 4)(x - 2) = 0$
    $x - 4 = 0 \qquad x - 2 = 0$
    $x = 4 \qquad\quad x = 2$

9. $x^2 - x - 56 = 0$
    $(x + 7)(x - 8) = 0$
    $x + 7 = 0 \qquad x - 8 = 0$
    $x = -7 \qquad\quad x = 8$

11. $x^2 - 3x - 40 = 0$
    $(x + 5)(x - 8) = 0$
    $x + 5 = 0 \qquad x - 8 = 0$
    $x = -5 \qquad\quad x = 8$

13. $x^2 - 13x + 36 = 0$
    $(x - 9)(x - 4) = 0$
    $x - 9 = 0 \qquad x - 4 = 0$
    $x = +9 \qquad\quad x = 4$

15. $x^2 - 3x - 18 = 0$
    $(x + 3)(x - 6) = 0$
    $x + 3 = 0 \qquad x - 6 = 0$
    $x = -3 \qquad\quad x = 6$

17. $x^2 + 10x + 21 = 0$
    $(x + 3)(x + 7) = 0$
    $x + 3 = 0 \qquad x + 7 = 0$
    $x = -3 \qquad\quad x = -7$

19. $x^2 - 3x + 2 = 0$
    $(x - 2)(x - 1) = 0$
    $x - 2 = 0 \qquad x - 1 = 0$
    $x = -2 \qquad\quad x = 1$

21. $x^2 + 8x + 12 = 0 = (x + 2)(x + 6) = 0$
    $x + 2 = 0 \qquad x + 6 = 0$
    $x = -2 \qquad\quad x = -6$

23. $a = 1, b = 6, c = 6$

$$x = \frac{-6 \pm [6^2 - 4(1)(6)]^{1/2}}{2(1)} = \frac{-6 \pm 3.46}{2} \quad x = -4.73, x = -1.27$$

25. $a = 1, b = 2, c = -14$

$$x = \frac{-2 \pm [2^2 - 4(1)(-14)]^{1/2}}{2(1)} = \frac{-2 \pm 7.75}{2}; x = -4.87, x = 2.87$$

27. $a = 1, b = 15, c = -15$

$$x = \frac{-(15) \pm [-15^2 - 4(1)(-15)]^{1/2}}{2(1)} = \frac{15 \pm 16.9}{2} \quad x = 15.9, x = -0.941$$

29. $a = 1, b = -7, c = -4$

$$x = \frac{-(-7) \pm [-7^2 - 4(1)(-4)]^{1/2}}{2(1)} = \frac{7 \pm 8.06}{2}; x = 7.53, x = -0.531$$

31. $a = 3, b = 2, c = -1$

$$x = \frac{-2 \pm [2^2 - 4(3)(-1)]^{1/2}}{2(3)} = \frac{-2 \pm 4}{6}; x = -1, x = 0.333$$

33. $a = 2, b = -5, c = -5$

$$x = \frac{-(-5) \pm [-5^2 - 4(2)(-5)]^{1/2}}{2(2)} = \frac{5 \pm 8.06}{4} \quad x = 3.27, x = -0.766$$

35. $a = 4, b = 12, c = 8$

$$x = \frac{-12 \pm [12^2 - 4(4)(8)]^{1/2}}{2(4)} = \frac{-12 \pm 4}{8} \quad x = -2, x = -1$$

37. $3x^2 + 7x + 3 = 0 \quad$ So $a = 3, b = 7, c = 3$

$$x = \frac{-7 \pm [7^2 - 4(3)(3)]^{1/2}}{2(3)} = \frac{-7 \pm 3.61}{6} \quad x = -1.77, x = -0.566$$

39. $3x^2 - 14x - 20 = 0 \quad$ So $a = 3, b = -14, c = -20$

$$x = \frac{-(-14) \pm [-14^2 - 4(3)(-20)]^{1/2}}{2(3)} = \frac{14 \pm 20.9}{6} \quad x = 5.81, x = -1.15$$

END OF CHAPTER 10 PROBLEMS

End of Chapter Problems 10–1

In problems 1–8: $I_T = I_1 + I_2 + I_3$

1. $I_T = I_1 + I_2 + I_3 = 3\text{ A} + 2\text{ A} + 4\text{ A} = 9\text{ A}$

3. $I_3 = I_T - (I_1 + I_2) = 20\text{ mA} - (6\text{ mA} + 11\text{ mA}) = 3\text{ mA}$

5. $I_2 = I_T - (I_1 + I_3) = 65\ \mu\text{A} - (10\ \mu\text{A} + 10\ \mu\text{A}) = 45\ \mu\text{A}$

7. $I_1 = I_T - (I_2 + I_3) = 1.3\text{ A} - (300\text{ mA} + 40\text{ mA}) = 960\text{ mA}$

In problems 9–14: $I_2 = I_3$ $I_T = I_1 + I_2 = I_1 + I_3$

9. $I_T = I_1 + I_2 = 10\text{ mA} + 15\text{ mA} = 25\text{ mA}$; $I_3 = I_2 = 15\text{ mA}$

11. $I_1 = I_T - I_3 = 1.6\text{ mA} - 800\text{ mA} = 800\text{ mA}$; $I_2 = I_3 = 800\text{ mA}$

13. $I_2 = I_T - I1_2 = 600\ \mu\text{A} - 400\ \mu\text{A} = 200\ \mu\text{A}$; $I_3 = I_2 = 200\ \mu$

In problems 15–18: $I_T = I_1 = I_4 + I_2 = I_4 + I_3$

15. $I_T = I_1 = 1.4\text{ A}$; $I_4 = I_1 - I_2 = 1.4\text{ A} - 800\text{ mA} = 600\text{ mA}$; $I_3 = I_2 = 600\text{ mA}$

17. $I_2 = I_3 = 500\ \mu\text{A}$; $I_T = I_1 = I_3 + I_4 = 500\ \mu\text{A} + 2.7\text{ mA} = 3.2\text{ mA}$

In problems 19–22: $I_T = I_1 + I_2 + I_3 = I_1 + I_4; I_2 + I_3 = I_4$

19. $I_1 = I_T - I_4 = 6.7\text{ mA} - 5\text{ mA} = 1.7\text{ mA}$; $I_3 = I_4 - I_2 = 5\text{ mA} - 1.2\text{ mA} = 3.8\text{ mA}$

21. $I_T = I_1 + I_4 = 6\text{ mA} + 8.2\text{ mA} = 14.2\text{ mA}$; $I_2 = I_4 - I_3 = 8.2\text{ mA} - 3.4\text{ mA} = 4.8\text{ mA}$

23. $I_T = I_6 + I_1 = I_6 + I_5 = I_6 + I_2 + I_3 = I_6 + I_2 + I_4$; $I_1 = I_5 = 305\text{ mA}$;

   $I_6 = I_T - I_5 = 100\text{ mA} - 30\text{ mA} = 70\text{ mA}$; $I_3 = I_4 = I_1 - I_2 = 30\text{ mA} - 20\text{ mA} = 10\text{ mA}$

End of Chapter Problems 10–2

In problems 1–4: $E = V_1 + V_2$

1. $V_2 = E - V_1 = 30\text{ V} - 12\text{ V} = 18\text{ V}$

3. $E = V_1 + V_2 = 7\text{ V} + 6\text{ V} = 13\text{ V}$

In problems 5–10: $E = V_1 + V_2 + V_3$

5. $V_3 = E - (V_1 + V_2) = 70\text{ V} - (22\text{ V} + 37\text{ V}) = 11\text{ V}$

7. $E - V_1 + V_2 + V_3 = 3\text{ V} + 8\text{ V} + 7\text{ V} = 18\text{ V}$

9. $V_1 = E - (V_2 + V_3) = 37\text{ V} - (20\text{ V} + 3\text{ V}) = 14\text{ V}$

In problems 11–16: $E = V_1 + V_2 = V_1 + V_3; V_2 = V_3$

11. $V_2 = V_3 = 8\text{ V}; V_1 = E - V_3 = 20\text{ V} - 8\text{ V} = 12\text{ V}$

13. $V_2 = V_3 = E - V_1 = 18\text{ V} - 5\text{ V} = 13\text{ V}$

15. $E = V_1 + V_3 = 12\text{ V} + 5\text{ V} = 17\text{ V}; V_2 = V_3 = 5\text{ V}$

In problems 17–22: $E = V_1 + V_4 = V_1 + V_2 + V_3$; $V_4 = V_2 + V_3$

17. $V_4 = V_2 + V_3 = 3\text{ V} + 6\text{ V} = 9\text{ V}$; $V_1 = E - V_4 = 12\text{ V} - 9\text{ V} = 3\text{ V}$

19. $V_3 = V_4 - V_2 = 1.3\text{ V} - 500\text{ mV} = 800\text{ mV}$; $V_1 = E - V_4 = 3\text{ V} - 1.3\text{ V} = 1.7\text{ V}$

21. $E = V_1 + V_4 = 20\text{ V} + 40\text{ V} = 60\text{ V}$; $V_3 = V_4 - V_2 = 40\text{ V} - 30\text{ V} = 10\text{ V}$

In problems 23–26: $E = V_6$; $E = V_1 + V_2 + V_5 = V_1 + V_5 + V_3 + V_4$; $V_2 = V_3 + V_4$

23. $V_2 = E - (V_1 + V_5) = 50\text{ V} - (10\text{ V} + 15\text{ V}) = 25\text{ V}$;

   $V_4 = V_2 - V_3 = 25\text{ V} - 8\text{ V} = 17\text{ V}$; $V_6 = E = 50\text{ V}$

25. $E = V_6 = 25\text{ V}$; $V_2 = E - (V_1 + V_5) = 25\text{ V} - (9\text{ V} + 4\text{ V}) = 12\text{ V}$;

   $V_3 = V_2 - V_4 = 12\text{ V} - 6.5\text{ V} = 5.5\text{ V}$

End of Chapter Problems 10–3

1. a) $V_2 = V_3 - V_1 = 25\text{ V} - 15\text{ V} = 10\text{ V}$

   b) $V_4 = E - V_3 = 30\text{ V} - 25\text{ V} = 5\text{ V}$

   c) 25 V positive

   d) 30 V positive

   e) 5 V negative

5. a) $V_3 = E_1 - (V_1 + V_2)$

   $= 25\text{ V} - (6\text{ V} + 8\text{ V}) = 11\text{ V}$

   b) $V_4 = V_3 - E_2 = 11\text{ V} - 6\text{ V} = 5\text{ V}$

   c) 19 V positive

   d) 13 V negative

3. a) $V_1 = E_1 - V_2 = 20\text{ V} - 8\text{ V} = 12\text{ V}$

   b) $V_3 = E_2 + V_2 = 35\text{ V} + 8\text{ V} = 43\text{ V}$

   c) 43 V negative

   d) 35 V negative

   e) 8 V negative

7. a) $V_1 = E_1 - V_3 = 40\text{ V} - 6\text{ V} = 34\text{ V}$

   b) $V_2 = E_2 + V_3 = 10\text{ V} + 6\text{ V} = 16\text{ V}$

   c) 6 V positive

   d) 50 V negative

END OF CHAPTER 11 PROBLEMS

End of Chapter Problems 11–1

In the following problems: $R_T = R_1 + R_2$

1. a) $R_T = 45\ k\Omega$

    b) $R_T = 1.95\ k\Omega$

    c) $R_T = 16.8\ k\Omega$

    d) $R_T = 300\ k\Omega$

3. a) $R_2 = 1.8\ k\Omega$

    b) $R_2 = 39\ k\Omega$

In the following problems: $R_T = R_1 + R_2 + R_3$

5. a) $R_T = 2.29\ k\Omega$

    b) $R_T = 130\ k\Omega$

    c) $R_T = 297\ \Omega$

    d) $R_T = 1.36\ k\Omega$

7. a) $R_3 = 5.6\ k\Omega$

    b) $R_3 = 82\ k\Omega$

In the following problem: $G_T = G_1 + G_2$

9. a) $G_T = 150\ \mu S;\ R_T = 6.67\ k\Omega$

    b) $G_T = 1.20\ mS;\ R_T = 831\ \Omega$

    c) $G_T = 76.8\ \mu S;\ R_T = 13.0\ k\Omega$

    d) $G_T = 20\ \mu S;\ R_T = 50.0\ k\Omega$

In the following problems: $G_T = G_1 + G_2 + G_3$ $R_T = 1/G_T$

11. a) $G_T = 685\ \mu S;\ R_T = 1.46\ k\Omega$

    b) $G_T = 31.9\ mS;\ R_T = 31.3\ \Omega$

    c) $G_T = 2.39\ mS;\ R_T = 419\ \Omega$

    d) $G_T = 26.7\ \mu S;\ R_T = 37.4\ k\Omega$

13. a) $G_2 = G_T - (G_1 + G_3) = 261\ \mu S - (48.2\ \mu S) = 213\ \mu S;\ R_2 = \dfrac{1}{G_2} = \dfrac{1}{213\ \mu S} = 4.7\ k\Omega$

    b) $G_2 = G_T - (G_1 + G_3) = 18.4\ mS - (13.3\ mS) = 5.02\ mS;\ R_2 = \dfrac{1}{G_2} = \dfrac{1}{5.02\ mS} = 199\ \Omega$

End of Chapter Problems 11–2

In the following problem: $R_T = R_1 + R_2 \| R_3 = R_1 + (G_2 + G_3)^{-1}$

1. a) $R_T = 560 \text{ k}\Omega + \dfrac{1}{2.22 \text{ mS}} = 1.01 \text{ k}\Omega$

   b) $R_T = 7.5 \text{ k}\Omega + \dfrac{1}{92.6 \text{ } \mu S} = 18.3 \text{ k}\Omega$

   c) $R_T = 27 \text{ k}\Omega + \dfrac{1}{105 \text{ } \mu S} = 36.6 \text{ k}\Omega$

   d) $R_T = 330 \text{ k}\Omega + \dfrac{1}{2.47 \text{ } \mu S} = 735 \text{ k}\Omega$

In the following problem: $G_X = \dfrac{1}{R_1 + R_2}$; $R_T = (R_1 + R_2) \| R_3 = 1/(G_X + G_3)$

3. a) $R_T = \dfrac{1}{87 \text{ } \mu S + 110 \text{ } \mu S} = 5.08 \text{ k}\Omega$

   b) $R_T = \dfrac{1}{303 \text{ } \mu S + 1.22 \text{ mS}} = 657 \text{ } \Omega$

   c) $R_T = 27 \text{ k}\Omega + \dfrac{1}{22.2 \text{ } \mu S + 17.9 \text{ } \mu S}$

   $= 25.0 \text{ k}\Omega$

   d) $R_T = \dfrac{1}{870 \text{ } \mu S + 455 \text{ } \mu S} = 755 \text{ } \Omega$

In the following problems: $G_X = G_2 + G_3 + G_4$ and $R_T = R_1 + 1/G_X$

5. a) $R_T = 12 \text{ k}\Omega + \dfrac{1}{88.6 \text{ } \mu S} = 23.3 \text{ k}\Omega$

   b) $R_T = 120 \text{ } \Omega + \dfrac{1}{4.91 \text{ mS}} = 324 \text{ } \Omega$

   c) $R_T = 390 \text{ k}\Omega + \dfrac{1}{3.39 \text{ } \mu S} = 685 \text{ k}\Omega$

   d) $R_T = 5.1 \text{ k}\Omega + \dfrac{1}{347 \text{ } \mu S} = 7.98 \text{ k}\Omega$

7. a) $R_X = R_2 \| R_3 = 6 \text{ k}\Omega$; $R_Y = R_5 \| R_6 = 2.56 \text{ k}\Omega$

   b) $R_Z = R_X + R_Y + R_4 = 6 \text{ k}\Omega + 2.56 \text{ k}\Omega = 6.8 \text{ k}\Omega = 15.4 \text{ k}\Omega$; $R_T = R_1 \| R_Z = 1.11 \text{ k}\Omega$

9. $R_X = R_1 \| R_2 + R_3 = 83.1 \text{ k}\Omega + 91 \text{ k}\Omega = 174 \text{ k}\Omega$

   $R_Y = R_5 \| R_6 \| R_7 + R_8 \| R_9 = 204 \text{ k}\Omega + 372 \text{ k}\Omega = 575 \text{ k}\Omega$

   $R_T = R_X \| R_Y \| R_4 = 174 \text{ k}\Omega \| 575 \text{ k}\Omega \| 330 \text{ k}\Omega = 95.1 \text{ k}\Omega$

End of Chapter Problems 11–3

1. a) $R_T = R_1 + R_2 = 950\ \Omega$, $I = \dfrac{E}{R_T} = \dfrac{9\ V}{950\ \Omega} = 9.47\ mA$

   $V_1 = IR_1 = 2.56\ V$, $V_2 = IR_2 = 6.44\ V$

   b) $R_T = R_1 + R_2 = 4.5\ k\Omega$, $I = \dfrac{E}{R_T} = \dfrac{12\ V}{4.5\ k\Omega} = 2.67\ mA$

   $V_1 = IR_1 = 3.2\ V$, $V_2 = IR_2 = 8.80\ V$

   c) $R_T = R_1 + R_2 = 340\ k\Omega$, $I = \dfrac{E}{R_T} = \dfrac{40\ V}{340\ k\Omega} = 118\ \mu A$

   $V_1 = IR_1 = 14.1\ V$, $V_2 = IR_2 = 25.9\ V$

   d) $R_T = R_1 + R_2 = 13.3\ k\Omega$, $I = \dfrac{E}{R_T} = \dfrac{10\ V}{13.3\ k\Omega} = 752\ \mu A$

   $V_1 = IR_1 = 7.52\ V$, $V_2 = IR_2 = 2.48\ V$

3. a) $V_1 = E - V_2 = 10\ V - 3\ V = 7\ V$, $I = \dfrac{V_1}{R_1} = \dfrac{7\ V}{1\ k\Omega} = 7\ mA$

   $R_T = \dfrac{E}{I} = \dfrac{10\ V}{7\ mA} = 1.43\ k\Omega$, $R_2 = R_T - R_1 = 429\ \Omega$

   b) $V_1 = E - V_2 = 40\ V - 23.5\ V = 16.5\ V$, $I = \dfrac{V_1}{R_1} = \dfrac{16.5\ V}{6.8\ k\Omega} = 2.43\ mA$

   $R_T = \dfrac{E}{I} = \dfrac{40\ V}{2.43\ mA} = 16.5\ k\Omega$, $R_2 = R_T - R_1 = 9.68\ k\Omega$

   c) $V_1 = E - V_2 = 15\ V - 12\ V = 3\ V$, $I = \dfrac{V_1}{R_1} = \dfrac{3\ V}{8.2\ k\Omega} = 366\ \mu A$

   $R_T = \dfrac{E}{I} = \dfrac{15\ V}{366\ \mu A} = 41\ k\Omega$, $R_2 = R_T - R_1 = 32.8\ k\Omega$

   d) $V_1 = E - V_2 = 100\ V - 29.3\ V = 70.7\ V$, $I = \dfrac{V_1}{R_1} = \dfrac{70.7\ V}{220\ k\Omega} = 321\ \mu A$

   $R_T = \dfrac{E}{I} = \dfrac{100\ V}{320\ \mu A} = 311\ k\Omega$, $R_2 = R_T - R_1 = 91.2\ k\Omega$

5.   a) $V_2 = IR_2 = $ 213 μA $\times$ 33 kΩ = 7.03 V, $V_1 = E - V_2 = $ 13 V

$$R_1 = \frac{V_1}{I} = \frac{13 \text{ V}}{213 \text{ }\mu\text{A}} = 60.9 \text{ k}\Omega, R_T = R_1 + R_2 = 93.9 \text{ k}\Omega$$

   b) $V_2 = IR_2 = $ 1 mA $\times$ 10 kΩ = 10 V, $V_1 = E - V_2 = $ 15 V

$$R_1 = \frac{V_1}{I} = \frac{15 \text{ V}}{1 \text{ mA}} = 15 \text{ k}\Omega, R_T = R_1 + R_2 = 25 \text{ k}\Omega$$

   c) $V_2 = IR_2 = $ 7.69 mA $\times$ 1 kΩ = 7.69 V, $V_1 = E - V_2 = $ 4.31 V

$$R_1 = \frac{V_1}{I} = \frac{4.31 \text{ V}}{7.69 \text{ mA}} = 560 \text{ }\Omega, R_T = R_1 + R_2 = 1.56 \text{ k}\Omega$$

   d) $V_2 = IR_2 = $ 20 μA $\times$ 180 kΩ = 3.60 V, $V_1 = E - V_2 = $ 5.4 V

$$R_1 = \frac{V_1}{I} = \frac{5.4 \text{ V}}{20 \text{ }\mu\text{A}} = 270 \text{ k}\Omega, R_T = R_1 + R_2 = 450 \text{ k}\Omega$$

7.   a) $V_2 = IR_2 = $ 75 μA $\times$ 3 kΩ = 225 mV, $E = V_1 + V_2 = $ 231 mV

$$R_T = \frac{E}{I} = \frac{231 \text{ mV}}{75 \text{ }\mu\text{A}} = 3.08 \text{ k}\Omega, R_1 = R_T - R_2 = 82.7 \text{ }\Omega$$

   b) $V_2 = IR_2 = $ 2 mA $\times$ 12 kΩ = 24 V, $E = V_1 + V_2 = $ 38.3 V

$$R_T = \frac{E}{I} = \frac{38.3 \text{ mV}}{2 \text{ mA}} = 19.2 \text{ k}\Omega, R_1 = R_T - R_2 = 7.15 \text{ k}\Omega$$

   c) $V_2 = IR_2 = $ 167 μA $\times$ 33 kΩ = 5.50 V, $E = V_1 + V_2 = $ 10 V

$$R_T = \frac{E}{I} = \frac{4.56 \text{ V}}{167 \text{ }\mu\text{A}} = 60 \text{ k}\Omega, R_1 = R_T - R_2 = 27 \text{ k}\Omega$$

   d) $V_2 = IR_2 = $ 14.9 mA $\times$ 82 Ω = 1.22 V, $E = V_1 + V_2 = $ 3 V

$$R_T = \frac{E}{I} = \frac{3 \text{ V}}{14.9 \text{ mA}} = 202 \text{ k}\Omega, R_1 = R_T - R_2 = 120 \text{ }\Omega$$

9. a) $R_T = R_1 + R_2 + R_3 = 61 \text{ k}\Omega$; $I = \dfrac{E}{R_T} = \dfrac{9 \text{ V}}{61 \text{ k}\Omega} = 148 \, \mu\text{A}$

$V_1 = IR_1 = 4.87 \text{ V}, V_2 = IR_2 = 1.48 \text{ V}, V_3 = IR_3 = 2.66 \text{ V}$

b) $R_T = R_1 + R_2 + R_3 = 388 \text{ k}\Omega$; $I = \dfrac{E}{R_T} = \dfrac{40 \text{ V}}{388 \text{ k}\Omega} = 103 \, \mu\text{A}$

$V_1 = IR_1 = 22.7 \text{ V}, V_2 = IR_2 = 10.3 \text{ V}, V_3 = IR_3 = 7.01 \text{ V}$

c) $R_T = R_1 + R_2 + R_3 = 2.58 \text{ k}\Omega$; $I = \dfrac{E}{R_T} = \dfrac{25 \text{ V}}{2.58 \text{ k}\Omega} = 9.69 \text{ mA}$

$V_1 = IR_1 = 7.95 \text{ V}, V_2 = IR_2 = 11.6 \text{ V}, V_3 = IR_3 = 5.43 \text{ V}$

d) $R_T = R_1 + R_2 + R_3 = 8.6 \text{ k}\Omega$; $I = \dfrac{E}{R_T} = \dfrac{15 \text{ V}}{8.6 \text{ k}\Omega} = 1.74 \text{ mA}$

$V_1 = IR_1 = 3.14 \text{ V}, V_2 = IR_2 = 7.5 \text{ V}, V_3 = IR_3 = 4.36 \text{ V}$

11. a) $V_2 = IR_2 = 1 \text{ mA} \times 10 \text{ k}\Omega = 10 \text{ V}, V_3 = E - (V_1 + V_2) = 10 \text{ V}$

$R_1 = \dfrac{V_1}{I} = \dfrac{5 \text{ V}}{1 \text{ mA}} = 5 \text{ k}\Omega, R_3 = \dfrac{V_3}{I} = 10 \text{ k}\Omega, R_T = R_1 + R_2 + R_3 = 25 \text{ k}\Omega$

b) $V_2 = IR_2 = 150 \, \mu\text{A} \times 47 \text{ k}\Omega = 7.05 \text{ V}, V_3 = E - (V_1 + V_2) = 6.25 \text{ V}$

$R_1 = \dfrac{V_1}{I} = 44.7 \text{ k}\Omega, R_3 = \dfrac{V_3}{I} = 41.7 \text{ k}\Omega, R_T = R_1 + R_2 + R_3 = 133 \text{ k}\Omega$

c) $V_2 = IR_2 = 1.66 \text{ mA} \times 8.2 \text{ k}\Omega = 13.6 \text{ V}, V_3 = E - (V_1 + V_2) = 36.5 \text{ V}$

$R_1 = \dfrac{V_1}{I} = 187 \text{ k}\Omega, R_3 = \dfrac{V_3}{I} = 22 \text{ k}\Omega, R_T = R_1 + R_2 + R_3 = 48.2 \text{ k}\Omega$

d) $V_2 = IR_2 = 15.5 \text{ mA} \times 91 \, \Omega = 1.41 \text{ V}, V_3 = E - (V_1 + V_2) = 1.16 \text{ V}$

$R_1 = \dfrac{V_1}{I} = 27.9 \, \Omega, R_3 = \dfrac{V_3}{I} = 74.6 \, \Omega, R_T = R_1 + R_2 + R_3 = 194 \, \Omega$

13. a) $E = IR_T = 3 \text{ mA} \times 12 \text{ k}\Omega = 36 \text{ V}, V_1 = IR_1 = 14.1 \text{ V}$

$V_3 = E - (V_1 + V_2) = 14.6 \text{ V}, R_2 = \dfrac{V_2}{I} = 2.43 \text{ k}\Omega, R_3 = \dfrac{V_3}{I} = 4.87 \text{ k}\Omega$

b) $E = IR_T = 270 \, \mu\text{A} \times 43.2 \text{ k}\Omega = 11.7 \text{ V}, V_1 = IR_1 = 4.05 \text{ V}$

$V_3 = E - (V_1 + V_2) = 3.95 \text{ V}, R_2 = \dfrac{V_2}{I} = 13.7 \text{ k}\Omega, R_3 = \dfrac{V_3}{I} = 14.6 \text{ k}\Omega$

c) $E = IR_T = 66.7 \, \mu\text{A} \times 450 \text{ k}\Omega = 30 \text{ V}, V_1 = IR_1 = 13.3 \text{ V}$

$V_3 = E - (V_1 + V_2) = 10 \text{ V}, R_2 = \dfrac{V_2}{I} = 100 \text{ k}\Omega, R_3 = \dfrac{V_3}{I} = 150 \text{ k}\Omega$

d) $E = IR_T = 2.3 \text{ mA} \times 870 \, \Omega = 2 \text{ V}, V_1 = IR_1 = 1.08 \text{ V}$

$V_3 = E - (V_1 + V_2) = 229 \text{ mV}, R_2 = \dfrac{V_2}{I} = 300 \, \Omega, R_3 = \dfrac{V_3}{I} = 100 \, \Omega$

End of Chapter Problems 11–4

1. a) $G_T = G_1 + G_2 = 3.7 \text{ mS} + 1.79 \text{ mS} = 5.49 \text{ mS}, R_T = \dfrac{1}{G_T} = 182 \ \Omega$

$V = \dfrac{I_T}{G_T} = \dfrac{3 \text{ mA}}{5.49 \text{ mS}} = 547 \text{ mV}, I_1 = VG_1 = 2.02 \text{ mA}, I_2 = VG_2 = 977 \ \mu A$

   b) $G_T = G_1 + G_2 = 14.7 \ \mu S + 25.6 \ \mu S = 40.3 \ \mu S, R_T = \dfrac{1}{G_T} = 24.8 \text{ k}\Omega$

$V = \dfrac{I_T}{G_T} = \dfrac{700 \ \mu A}{40.3 \ \mu S} = 17.3 \text{ V}, I_1 = VG_1 = 255 \ \mu A, I_2 = VG_2 = 444 \ \mu A$

   c) $G_T = G_1 + G_2 = 4.55 \text{ mS} + 3.7 \text{ mS} = 8.25 \text{ mS}, R_T = \dfrac{1}{G_T} = 121 \ \Omega$

$V = \dfrac{I_T}{G_T} = \dfrac{37.6 \text{ mA}}{8.25 \text{ mS}} = 4.56 \text{ V}, I_1 = VG_1 = 20.7 \text{ mA}, I_2 = VG_2 = 16.9 \text{ mA}$

   d) $G_T = G_1 + G_2 = 17.9 \ \mu S + 30.3 \ \mu S = 48.2 \ \mu S, R_T = \dfrac{1}{G_T} = 20.8 \text{ k}\Omega$

$V = \dfrac{I_T}{G_T} = \dfrac{100 \ \mu A}{48.2 \ \mu S} = 2.08 \text{ V}, I_1 = VG_1 = 37.1 \ \mu A, I_2 = VG_2 = 62.9 \ \mu A$

3. a) $I_1 = I_1 - I_2 = 10 \text{ mA}, V = I_1 R_1 = 6.8 \text{ V}, R_2 = \dfrac{V}{I_2} = 453 \ \Omega$

$G_T = \dfrac{I_T}{V} = \dfrac{25 \text{ mA}}{6.8 \text{ V}} = 3.68 \text{ mS}, R_T = \dfrac{1}{G_T} = 272 \ \Omega$

   b) $I_1 = I_1 - I_2 = 4 \text{ mA}, V = I_1 R_1 = 7.2 \text{ V}, R_2 = \dfrac{V}{I_2} = 7.2 \text{ k}\Omega$

$G_T = \dfrac{I_T}{V} = \dfrac{5 \text{ mA}}{7.2 \text{ V}} = 694 \ \mu S, R_T = \dfrac{1}{G_T} = 1.44 \text{ k}\Omega$

   c) $I_1 = I_1 - I_2 = 1.25 \text{ mA}, V = I_1 R_1 = 5.88 \text{ V}, R_2 = \dfrac{V}{I_2} = \dfrac{5.88 \text{ V}}{1.05 \text{ mA}} = 5.6 \text{ k}\Omega$

$G_T = \dfrac{I_T}{V} = \dfrac{2.3 \text{ mA}}{5.88 \text{ V}} = 391 \ \mu S, R_T = \dfrac{1}{G_T} = 256 \text{ k}\Omega$

   d) $I_1 = I_1 - I_2 = 17.7 \text{ mA}, V = I_1 R_1 = 83.4 \text{ V}, R_2 = \dfrac{V}{I_2} = 6.8 \text{ k}\Omega$

$G_T = \dfrac{I_T}{V} = \dfrac{30 \text{ mA}}{83.2 \text{ V}} = 360 \ \mu S, R_T = \dfrac{1}{G_T} = 2.78 \text{ k}\Omega$

5. a) $G_T = \dfrac{I_T}{V} = \dfrac{10 \text{ mA}}{20 \text{ V}} = 500 \ \mu S, R_T = \dfrac{1}{G_T} = 2 \text{ k}\Omega$

$I_1 = \dfrac{V}{R_1} = 4.26 \text{ mA}, I_2 = I_T - I_1 = 5.74 \text{ mA}, R_2 = \dfrac{V}{I_2} = 3.48 \text{ k}\Omega$

   b) $G_T = \dfrac{I_T}{V} = \dfrac{350 \ \mu A}{25 \text{ V}} = 14.0 \ \mu S, R_T = \dfrac{1}{G_T} = 71.4 \text{ k}\Omega$

$I_1 = \dfrac{V}{R_1} = 139 \ \mu A, I_2 = I_T - I_1 = 211 \ \mu A, R_2 = \dfrac{V}{I_2} = 118 \text{ k}\Omega$

c) $G_T = \dfrac{I_T}{V} = \dfrac{20\text{ mA}}{9.74\text{ V}} = 2.05\text{ mS}$, $R_T = \dfrac{1}{G_T} = 488\ \Omega$

$I_1 = \dfrac{V}{R_1} = \dfrac{9.74\text{ V}}{820\ \Omega} = 11.9\text{ mA}$, $I_2 = I_T - I_1 = 8.12\text{ mA}$, $R_2 = \dfrac{V}{I_2} = 1.2\text{ k}\Omega$

d) $G_T = \dfrac{I_T}{V} = \dfrac{2\text{ mA}}{48.6\text{ V}} = 41.2\ \mu S$, $R_T = \dfrac{1}{G_T} = 24.3\text{ k}\Omega$

$I_1 = \dfrac{V}{R_1} = \dfrac{48.6\text{ V}}{43\text{ k}\Omega} = 1.13\text{ mA}$, $I_2 = I_T - I_1 = 870\ \mu A$, $R_2 = \dfrac{V}{I_2} = 55.9\text{ k}\Omega$

7. a) $I_2 = \dfrac{V}{R_2} = \dfrac{12\text{ V}}{20\text{ k}\Omega} = 600\ \mu A$, $I_T = I_1 + I_2 = 1.13\text{ mA}$

$G_T = \dfrac{I_T}{V} = \dfrac{1.13\text{ mA}}{12\text{ V}} = 94.2\ \mu S$, $R_T = \dfrac{I}{G_T} = 10.6\text{ k}\Omega$, $R_1 = \dfrac{V}{I_1} = 22.6\text{ k}\Omega$

b) $I_2 = \dfrac{V}{R_2} = \dfrac{5\text{ V}}{15\text{ k}\Omega} = 333\ \mu A$, $I_T = I_1 + I_2 = 1.33\text{ mA}$

$G_T = \dfrac{I_T}{V} = \dfrac{1.33\text{ mA}}{5\text{ V}} = 267\ \mu S$, $R_T = \dfrac{I}{G_T} = 3.75\text{ k}\Omega$, $R_1 = \dfrac{V}{I_1} = 5\text{ k}\Omega$

c) $I_2 = \dfrac{V}{R_2} = \dfrac{30.9\text{ V}}{10\text{ k}\Omega} = 3.09\text{ mA}$, $I_T = I_1 + I_2 = 4.80\text{ mA}$

$G_T = \dfrac{I_T}{V} = \dfrac{4.80\text{ mA}}{30.9\text{ V}} = 155\ \mu S$, $R_T = \dfrac{I}{G_T} = 6.44\text{ k}\Omega$, $R_1 = \dfrac{V}{I_1} = 18.1\text{ k}\Omega$

d) $I_2 = \dfrac{V}{R_2} = \dfrac{2.16\text{ V}}{91\text{ k}\Omega} = 23.7\ \mu A$, $I_T = I_1 + I_2 = 287\ \mu A$

$G_T = \dfrac{I_T}{V} = \dfrac{287\ \mu A}{21.6\text{ V}} = 133\ \mu S$, $R_T = \dfrac{I}{G_T} = 7.53\text{ k}\Omega$, $R_1 = \dfrac{V}{I_1} = 8.21\text{ k}\Omega$

9. a) $G_T = G_1 + G_2 + G_3 = 370\ \mu S + 813\ \mu S + 1\text{ mS} = 2.2\text{ mS}$, $R_T = \dfrac{1}{G_T} = 454\ \Omega$

$V = \dfrac{I_T}{G_T} = \dfrac{1.73\text{ mA}}{2.2\text{ mS}} = 785\text{ mV}$, $I_1 = VG_1 = 291\ \mu A$, $I_2 = VG_2 = 654\ \mu A$, $I_3 = VG_3 = 785\ \mu A$

b) $G_T = G_1 + G_2 + G_3 = 123\ \mu S + 133\ \mu S + 213\ \mu S = 469\ \mu S$, $R_T = \dfrac{1}{G_T} = 2.13\text{ k}\Omega$

$V = \dfrac{I_T}{G_T} = \dfrac{500\ \mu A}{470\ \mu S} = 1.07\text{ V}$, $I_1 = VG_1 = 131\ \mu A$, $I_2 = VG_2 = 142\ \mu A$, $I_3 = VG_3 = 227\ \mu A$

c) $G_T = G_1 + G_2 + G_3 = 45.4\ \mu S + 25.6\ \mu S + 17.9\ \mu S = 89\ \mu S$, $R_T = \dfrac{1}{G_T} = 11.2\text{ k}\Omega$

$V = \dfrac{I_T}{G_T} = \dfrac{500\ \mu A}{89\ \mu S} = 5.62\text{ V}$, $I_1 = VG_1 = 255\ \mu A$, $I_2 = VG_2 = 144\ \mu A$, $I_3 = VG_3 = 101\ \mu A$

d) $G_T = G_1 + G_2 + G_3 = 370\ \mu S + 256\ \mu S + 556\ \mu S = 1.18\text{ mS}$, $R_T = \dfrac{1}{G_T} = 846\ \Omega$

$V = \dfrac{I_T}{G_T} = \dfrac{2\text{ mA}}{1.18\text{ mS}} = 1.69\text{ V}$, $I_1 = VG_1 = 627\ \mu A$, $I_2 = VG_2 = 434\ \mu A$, $I_3 = VG_3 = 942\ \mu A$

11. a) $I_2 = \dfrac{V}{R_2} = \dfrac{12.6\ V}{12\ k\Omega} = 1.05\ mA$, $I_3 = I_T - (I_1 + I_2) = 2.25\ mA$

$G_T = \dfrac{I_T}{V} = \dfrac{4\ mA}{12.6\ V} = 317\ \mu S$, $R_T = \dfrac{I}{G_T} = 3.15\ k\Omega$, $R_1 = \dfrac{V}{I_1} = 18\ k\Omega$, $R_3 = \dfrac{V}{I_3} = 5.6\ k\Omega$

b) $I_2 = \dfrac{V}{R_2} = \dfrac{20\ V}{270\ k\Omega} = 74.1\ \mu A$, $I_3 = I_T - (I_1 + I_2) = 151\ \mu A$

$G_T = \dfrac{I_T}{V} = \dfrac{300\ mA}{20\ V} = 15\ \mu S$, $R_T = \dfrac{I}{G_T} = 66.7\ k\Omega$, $R_1 = \dfrac{V}{I_1} = 267\ k\Omega$, $R_3 = \dfrac{V}{I_3} = 133\ k\Omega$

c) $I_2 = \dfrac{V}{R_2} = \dfrac{23.4\ V}{750\ k\Omega} = 31.2\ \mu A$, $I_3 = I_T - (I_1 + I_2) = 234\ \mu A$

$G_T = \dfrac{I_T}{V} = \dfrac{300\ \mu A}{23.4\ V} = 12.85\ \mu S$, $R_T = \dfrac{I}{G_T} = 78.0\ k\Omega$

$R_1 = \dfrac{V}{I_1} = 678\ k\Omega$, $R_3 = \dfrac{V}{I_3} = 99.9\ k\Omega$

d) $I_2 = \dfrac{V}{R_2} = \dfrac{13.8\ V}{680\ k\Omega} = 20.3\ mA$, $I_3 = I_T - (I_1 + I_2) = 24.6\ mA$

$G_T = \dfrac{I_T}{V} = \dfrac{60\ mA}{13.8\ V} = 4.35\ mS$, $R_T = \dfrac{I}{G_T} = 230\ \Omega$, $R_1 = \dfrac{V}{I_1} = 910\ \Omega$, $R_3 = \dfrac{V}{I_3} = 560\ \Omega$

13. a) $I_T = VG_T = 15\ V \times 1\ mS = 15\ mA$; $I_1 = VG_1 = 3.2\ mA$; $I_3 = I_T - (I_1 + I_2) = 8.81\ mA$

$R_T = \dfrac{1}{G_T} = 1\ k\Omega$; $R_1 = \dfrac{V}{I_1} = 4.70\ k\Omega$; $R_2 = \dfrac{V}{I_2} = 5.00\ k\Omega$; $R_3 = \dfrac{V}{I_3} = 1.70\ k\Omega$

b) $I_T = VG_T = 30\ V \times 8\ mS = 240\ mA$; $I_1 = VG_1 = 60\ mA$; $I_3 = I_T - (I_1 + I_2) = 120\ mA$

$R_T = \dfrac{1}{G_T} = 125\ \Omega$; $R_1 = \dfrac{V}{I_1} = 500\ \Omega$; $R_2 = \dfrac{V}{I_2} = 500\ \Omega$; $R_3 = \dfrac{V}{I_3} = 250\ \Omega$

c) $I_T = VG_T = 6.09\ V \times 3.29\ mS = 20\ mA$; $I_1 = VG_1 = 6.09\ mA$; $I_3 = I_T - (I_1 + I_2) = 3.04\ mA$

$R_T = \dfrac{1}{G_T} = 3045\ \Omega$, $R_1 = \dfrac{V}{I_1} = 1\ k\Omega$; $R_2 = \dfrac{V}{I_2} = 560\ \Omega$; $R_3 = \dfrac{V}{I_3} = 2\ k\Omega$

d) $I_T = VG_T = 5.29\ V \times 28.3\ \mu S = 150\ \mu A$, $I_1 = VG_1 = 70.6\ \mu A$; $I_3 = I_T - (I_1 + I_2) = 26.5\ \mu A$

$R_T = \dfrac{1}{G_T} = 35.3\ k\Omega$; $R_1 = \dfrac{V}{I_1} = 75\ k\Omega$; $R_2 = \dfrac{V}{I_2} = 100\ k\Omega$; $R_3 = \dfrac{V}{I_3} = 200\ k\Omega$

End of Chapter Problems 11–5

1. a) $R_T = R_1 + R_2 \| R_3 = 10\ k\Omega + 19.4\ k\Omega = 29.4\ k\Omega$

$$I_T = \frac{E}{R_T} = \frac{15\ V}{29.4\ k\Omega} = 510\ \mu A,\ I_1 = I_T = 510\ \mu A$$

$$V_1 = I_1 R_1 = 510\ \mu A \times 10\ k\Omega = 5.1\ V,\ V_2 = V_3 = E - V_1 = 9.9\ V$$

$$I_2 = \frac{V_2}{R_2} = \frac{9.9\ V}{33\ k\Omega} = 300\ \mu A,\ I_3 = \frac{V_3}{R_3} = \frac{9.9\ V}{47\ k\Omega} = 211\ \mu A$$

   b) $R_T = R_1 + R_2 \| R_3 = 180\ k\Omega + 307\ \Omega = 487\ \Omega$

$$I_T = \frac{E}{R_T} = \frac{9\ V}{487\ \Omega} = 18.5\ mA,\ I_1 = I_T = 18.5\ mA$$

$$V_1 = I_1 R_1 = 18.5\ mA \times 180\ \Omega = 3.33\ V,\ V_2 = V_3 = E - V_1 = 5.67\ V$$

$$I_2 = \frac{V_2}{R_2} = \frac{5.67\ V}{560\ \Omega} = 10.1\ mA,\ I_3 = \frac{V_3}{R_3} = \frac{5.67\ V}{680\ \Omega} = 8.34\ mA$$

3. a) $V_1 = I_1 R_1 = 500\ \mu A \times 12\ k\Omega = 6\ V,\ V_2 = V_3 = E - V_1 = 4\ V$

$$I_2 = \frac{V_2}{R_2} = \frac{4\ V}{47\ k\Omega} = 85.1\ \mu A,\ I_3 = I_T - I_2 = 415\ \mu A$$

$$R_3 = \frac{V_3}{I_3} = \frac{4\ V}{415\ \mu A} = 9.64\ k\Omega,\ R_T = \frac{E}{I_T} = \frac{10\ V}{500\ \mu A} = 20\ k\Omega,$$

   b) $R_T = \frac{E}{I_T} = \frac{12\ V}{600\ \mu A} = 20\ k\Omega,\ R_1 = R_T - R_2 \| R_3 = 20\ k - 16\ k = 4.05\ k\Omega$

$$V_1 = I_1 R_1 = 600\ \mu A \times 4.05\ k\Omega = 2.43\ V,\ V_2 = V_3 = E - V_1 = 9.57\ V$$

$$I_2 = \frac{V_2}{R_2} = \frac{9.57\ V}{39\ k\Omega} = 245\ \mu A,\ I_3 = \frac{V_2}{R_2} = \frac{9.57\ V}{27\ k\Omega} = 355\ \mu A$$

5. a) $R_T = R_3 \| (R_1 + R_2) = 18\ k\Omega \| 34\ k\Omega = 11.8\ k\Omega,\ I_T = \frac{E}{R_T} = 5.10\ mA$

$$V_3 = E = 60\ V,\ I_3 = \frac{V_3}{R_3} = \frac{60\ V}{18\ k\Omega} = 3.33\ mA,\ I_1 = I_2 = I_T - I_3 = 1.77\ mA$$

$$V_2 = I_2 R_2 = 1.77\ mA \times 22\ k\Omega = 38.9\ V,\ V_1 = E - V_2 = 21.2\ V$$

   b) $R_T = R_3 \| (R_1 + R_2) = 47\ k\Omega \| 34.5\ k\Omega = 19.9\ k\Omega,\ I_T = \frac{E}{R_T} = 151\ \mu A$

$$V_3 = E = 3\ V,\ I_3 = \frac{V_3}{R_3} = \frac{3\ V}{47\ k\Omega} = 63.8\ \mu A,\ I_1 = I_2 = I_T - I_3 = 87.2\ \mu A$$

$$V_2 = I_2 R_2 = 87.2\ \mu A \times 27\ k\Omega = 2.35\ V,\ V_1 = E - V_2 = 652\ mV$$

7. a) $R_X = R_2 \| R_3 = 964 \ \Omega$, $R_y = R_y = R_1 + R_x = 1.64 \ k\Omega$, $R_T = R_y \| R_4 = 1.22 \ k\Omega$

$I_T = \dfrac{E}{R_T} = 32.8 \ mA$, $V_4 = E = 40 \ V$, $I_4 = \dfrac{V_4}{R_4} = \dfrac{40 \ V}{4.7 \ k\Omega} = 8.51 \ mA$

$I_1 = I_T - I_4 = 24.3 \ mA$, $V_1 = I_1 R_1 = 16.5 \ V$, $V_2 = V_3 = E - V_1 = 23.5 \ V$

$I_2 = \dfrac{V_2}{R_2} = \dfrac{23.5 \ V}{1.5 \ k\Omega} = 15.6 \ mA$, $I_3 = \dfrac{V_3}{R_3} = \dfrac{23.5 \ V}{2.7 \ k\Omega} = 8.69 \ mA$

b) $R_X = R_2 \| R_3 = 278 \ \Omega$, $R_y = R_y = R_1 + R_x = 428 \ k\Omega$, $R_T = R_y \| R_4 = 263 \ k\Omega$

$I_T = \dfrac{E}{R_T} = \dfrac{30 \ V}{263 \ k\Omega} = 114 \ \mu A$, $V_4 = E = 30 \ V$, $I_4 = \dfrac{V_4}{R_4} = \dfrac{30 \ V}{680 \ k\Omega} = 44.1 \ \mu A$

$I_1 = I_T - I_4 = 69.9 \ \mu A$, $V_1 = I_1 R_1 = 10.5 \ V$, $V_2 = V_3 = E - V_1 = 19.5 \ V$

$I_2 = \dfrac{V_2}{R_2} = \dfrac{19.5 \ V}{470 \ k\Omega} = 41.5 \ \mu A$, $I_3 = \dfrac{V_3}{R_3} = \dfrac{19.5 \ V}{680 \ k\Omega} = 28.7 \ \mu A$

9. a) $R_T = R_1 + R_2 \| R_3 \| R_4 = 3 \ k\Omega + 5.96 \ k\Omega = 8.96 \ k\Omega$

$I_T = \dfrac{E}{R_T} = \dfrac{25 \ V}{8.96 \ k\Omega} = 2.79 \ mA$, $I_1 = I_T = 2.79 \ mA$

$V_1 = I_1 R_1 = 8.37 \ V$, $V_2 = V_3 = V_4 = E - V_1 = 16.6 \ V$

$I_2 = \dfrac{V_2}{R_2} = 1.11 \ mA$, $I_3 = \dfrac{V_3}{R_3} = 756 \ \mu A$, $I_4 = \dfrac{V_4}{R_4} = 924 \ \mu A$

b) $R_T = \dfrac{E}{I_T} = \dfrac{25 \ V}{250 \ \mu A} = 100 \ k\Omega$, $V_3 = V_4 = V_2 = 10 \ V$, $V_1 = E - V_2 = 15 \ V$

$I_1 = I_T = 250 \ \mu A$, $R_1 = \dfrac{V_1}{I_1} = \dfrac{15 \ V}{250 \ \mu A} = 60 \ k\Omega$

$I_3 = \dfrac{V_3}{R_3} = \dfrac{10 \ V}{150 \ k\Omega} = 66.7 \ \mu A$, $I_4 = \dfrac{V_4}{R_4} = \dfrac{10 \ V}{200 \ k\Omega} = 50 \ \mu A$

$I_2 = I_T - (I_3 + I_4) = 133 \ \mu A$, $R_2 = \dfrac{V_2}{I_2} = \dfrac{10 \ V}{133 \ \mu A} = 75 \ k\Omega$

11.   a) $R_T = R_1 + R_2 \| R_3 \| R_4 = 10 \text{ k}\Omega + 33 \text{ k}\Omega + 18.2 \text{ k}\Omega = 61.2 \text{ k}\Omega$

$$I_T = \frac{E}{R_T} = \frac{40 \text{ V}}{61.2 \text{ k}\Omega} = 653 \text{ } \mu\text{A}, \; I_1 = I_4 = I_T = 653 \text{ } \mu\text{A}$$

$V_1 = I_1 R_1 = 6.53 \text{ V}, \; V_4 = I_4 R_4 = 21.6 \text{ V}, \; V_2 = V_3 = E - (V_1 + V_4) = 11.9 \text{ V}$

$$I_2 = \frac{V_2}{R_2} = 441 \text{ } \mu\text{A}, \; I_3 = \frac{V_3}{R_3} = 213 \text{ } \mu\text{A}$$

b) $R_T = R_1 + R_2 \| R_3 \| R_4 = 150 \text{ k}\Omega + 150 \text{ k}\Omega + 278 \text{ k}\Omega = 578 \text{ k}\Omega$

$$I_T = \frac{E}{R_T} = \frac{15 \text{ V}}{578 \text{ k}\Omega} = 26 \text{ } \mu\text{A}, \; I_1 = I_4 = I_T = 26 \text{ } \mu\text{A}$$

$V_1 = I_1 R_1 = 3.89 \text{ V}, \; V_4 = I_4 R_4 = 3.89 \text{ V}, \; V_2 = V_3 = E - (V_1 + V_4) = 7.21 \text{ V}$

$$I_2 = \frac{V_2}{R_2} = \frac{7.21 \text{ V}}{470 \text{ k}\Omega} = 15.3 \text{ } \mu\text{A}, \; I_3 = \frac{V_3}{R_3} = \frac{7.21 \text{ V}}{680 \text{ k}\Omega} = 10.6 \text{ } \mu\text{A}$$

End of Chapter Problems 11–6

Write down all of the facts as you figure them out. Draw a diagram to be sure you understand the words in the problem. Most of the problems you will face in the real world will be word problems rather than conveniently laid-out diagrams.

1.   The total resistance is 6 kΩ because the two resistors are in series.
The total voltage is 3 V, so the total current is 3 V / 6 kΩ = 500 μA.
The current through each resistor is also 500 μA.
The voltage drop across the 5-kΩ resistor is (5/6) of total voltage or (5/6)(3) = 2.5 V.
The voltage drop across the 1-kΩ resistor is (1/6) of total voltage or (1/6)(3) = 0.5 V.

3.   We know that 3 mA flows through the 2-kΩ resistor giving 6 V for voltage drop across the 2-kΩ resistor. Because the resistors are in parallel, the voltage drop across the other resistor will be 6 V, and the battery voltage will also be 6 V. Since we know that the voltage drop across the other resistor is 6 V, and we know that 2 mA flows through that resistor, then the value of that resistor is 6 V / 2 mA = 3 kΩ.

5.   The total current is 3 mA, so the total resistance is 9-V / 3 mA = 3 kΩ. Since the 9-V battery voltage is divided equally among the 3 resistors, then the resistors are of equal value. Therefore each resistor has a resistance of 1 kΩ, a voltage drop of 3 V, and a current of 3 mA.

7.   180 mA of current flows and then splits through 3 parallel branches, each of which has one resistor. 50% goes through the first branch (so 90 mA), 30% through the second branch (so 54 mA), and the remainder, which is 100% − 50% − 30% = 20% (so 36 mA), goes through the third branch.

   The first branch has a resistance of 100 Ω, and a current of 90 mA, so voltage drop is (90 mA)(100 Ω) = 9 V.

   The second branch has a current of 54 mA, a voltage drop of 9 V, so resistance is (9 V / 54 mA) = 167 Ω.

   The third branch has current of 36 mA, a voltage drop of 9 V, so resistance is (9 V / 36 mA) = 250 Ω.

   Is this correct? The total circuit has a total resistance of 9 V / 180 mA = 50 Ω. 1 / (1/100 + 1/167 + 1/250) = 50 Ω. Yes, that was the correct set of answers.

9.   The 5-kΩ and 6-kΩ resistors are connected in parallel so the combined resistance is 2727 Ω. They are in series with the 2-kΩ resistor, so the total resistance is 4727 Ω.
   The battery has 9 V, thus the total current is 9 V / 4727 Ω = 1.90 mA for the battery current.
   The 2-kΩ resistor also has 1.90-mA current, so the voltage drop is 3.8 V.
   The voltage drop across the 5-kΩ resistor is (9 V − 3.8 V = 5.2 V).
   The current through the 5-kΩ resistor is (5.2 V / 5 kΩ = 1.04 mA).
   The voltage drop across the 6-kΩ resistor (which is parallel to 5 kΩ) is also 5.2 V.
   The current through the 6-kΩ resistor is (5.2 V / 6 kΩ = 0.86 mA).
   As a partial proof, 1.04 mA + 0.86 mA = 1.90 mA.

11.   The first branch has two 6-kΩ resistors in series for total branch resistance for that branch of 12 kΩ. The second branch has a 4-kΩ resistor in series with 2-kΩ resistor for a total branch resistance of 6 kΩ. Since the two branches are in parallel, the total resistance is 4 kΩ. The 6-V battery with 4-kΩ resistance has current of 1.5 mA.

   The first branch has a total voltage drop of 6 V, and since the two resistors are equal in size, each of the two 6-kΩ resistors has a voltage drop of 3 V and current of 500 μA.

   The second branch has a total voltage drop of 6 V, and current of 1 mA (since 1 mA + 500 μA = 1.5 mA).
   The current will be 1 mA across the 4-kΩ resistor and across the 2-kΩ resistor.
   The voltage drop across the 4-kΩ resistor is (1 mA × 4 kΩ = 4 V).
   The voltage drop across the 2-kΩ resistor is (1 mA × 2 kΩ = 2 V).
   As a partial proof, 2 V + 4 V = 6 V.

END OF CHAPTER 12 PROBLEMS

End of Chapter Problems 12–1

1. I_2 (with E_2 shorted) = 3.42 mA I_2 (with E_1 shorted) = 12.6 mA

    The currents are opposing and the resultant current is: I_2 = 12.6 mA − 3.42 mA = 9.13 mA,

    V_1 = 41.4 V, V_2 = 16.4 V, V_3 = 33.6 V, I_1 = 18.8 mA, I_2 = 9.13 mA, I_3 = 28 mA

3. I_3 (with E_2 shorted) = 12.1 mA I_3 (with E_1 shorted) = 6.17 mA

    The currents are aiding and the resultant current is: I_3 = 12.1 mA + 6.17 mA = 18.2 mA,

    V_1 = 36.8 V, V_2 = 45 V, V_3 = 18.2 V, V_4 = 21.8 V, I_1 = 13.6 mA, I_2 = 13.6 mA, I_3 = 18.2 mA,

    I_4 = 4.64 mA

5. I_3 (with E_2 shorted) = 1.01 mA I_3 (with E_1 shorted) = 1.42 mA

    The currents are aiding and the resultant current is:

    I_3 = 1.01 mA + 1.42 mA = 2.43 mA, V_1 = 1 V, V_2 = 10 V, V_3 = 8 V, I_1 = 0.303 mA, I_2 = 2.13 mA,

    I_3 = 2.43 mA

7. I_2 (with E_2 shorted) = 17 mA I_2 (with E_1 shorted) = 4.63 mA

    The currents are aiding and the resultant current is:

    I_2 = 17 mA + 4.63 mA = 21.6 mA, V_1 = 14.8 V, V_2 = 10.2 V, V_3 = 0.2 V, I_1 = 21.8 mA,

    I_2 = 21.6 mA, I_3 = 0.2 mA

9. I_2 (with E_2 shorted) = 3.96 mA I_2 (with E_1 shorted) = 1.53 mA

    The currents are aiding and the resultant current is:

    I_3 = 3.96 mA + 1.53 mA = 5.49 mA, V_1 = 14.2 V, V_2 = 7.73 V, V_3 = 18.1 V, V_4 = 3.12 V,

    I_1 = 6.44 mA, I_2 = 6.44 mA, I_3 = 5.49 mA, I_4 = 945 μA

End of Chapter Problems 12–2

1. $V_{OC} = \dfrac{ER_2}{R_1 + R_2} = \dfrac{30\ V \times 47\ k\Omega}{22\ k\Omega + 47\ k\Omega} = 20.4\ V,\ R_{TH} = R_1 \| R_2 = 15\ k\Omega$

    $I_L = \dfrac{V_{OC}}{R_{TH} + R_L} = \dfrac{20.4\ V}{25\ k\Omega} = 8.16\ \mu A;\ V_L = I_L R_L = 816\ \mu A \times 10\ k\Omega = 8.16\ V$

3. $V_{OC} = E = 12\ V,\ R_{TH} = R_1 + R_2 \| R_3 = 680\ \Omega + 320\ \Omega = 1\ k\Omega$

    $I_L = \dfrac{V_{OC}}{R_{TH} + R_L} = \dfrac{12\ V}{1\ k\Omega + 750\ \Omega} = 6.86\ mA;\ V_L = I_L R_L = 6.86\ mA \times 750\ \Omega = 5.14\ V$

5. $V_{OC} = \dfrac{ER_3}{R_1 + R_2 + R_3} = \dfrac{50\ V \times 33\ k\Omega}{65\ k\Omega} = 25\ V,\ R_{TH} = R_3 \| (R_1 + R_2) = 16.2\ k\Omega$

    $I_L = \dfrac{V_{OC}}{R_{TH} + R_L} = \dfrac{25.4\ V}{31.2\ k\Omega} = 814\ \mu A;\ V_L = I_L R_L = 814\ \mu A \times 15\ k\Omega = 12.2\ V$

End of Chapter Problems 12–3

1. $R_{TH} = 776 \ \Omega$; $V_{TH} = 23.5$ V; $V_L = 18.0$ V; $I_L = 7.18$ mA

3. $R_{TH} = 2.64 \ \Omega$; $V_{TH} = 66.4$ V; $V_L = 28.6$ V; $I_L = 14.3$ mA

5. With R_L open, $V_1 = 8.17$ V, $V_2 = 11.8$ V, $V_3 = 6.67$ V and $V_4 = 13.3$ V.

    Then $V_{OC} = 1.5$ V. $R_{TH} = R_1 \| R_2 + R_3 \| R_4$ 3.78 kΩ

    $$I_L = \frac{V_{OC}}{R_{TH} + R_L} = \frac{1.5 \text{ V}}{3.78 \text{ k}\Omega + 1 \text{ k}\Omega} = 314 \ \mu A; \ V_L = I_L R_L = 314 \ \mu A \times 1 \text{ k}\Omega = 314 \text{ mV}$$

7. $V_{OC} = \dfrac{V_{CC} R_2}{R_1 + R_2} = 2.53$ V, $R_{TH} = R_1 \| R_2 = 5.94$ kΩ

    $R_L = R_4 (H_{FE} + 1) = 470 \ \Omega \times 81 = 38.1$ kΩ

    $$I_B = \frac{V_{OC} - V_{BE}}{R_{TH} + R_L} = 43.9 \ \mu A, \ I_C = H_{FE} I_B = 80 \times 43.9 \ \mu A = 3.51 \text{ mA}$$

    $V_C = V_{CC} - V_3 = 20$ V $- 3.51$ mA $\times 2$ k$\Omega = 13$ V

End of Chapter Problems 12–4

1. a) $I_{SC} = \dfrac{E}{R_1} = \dfrac{30 \text{ V}}{22 \text{ k}\Omega} = 1.36$ mA, $G_N = G_1 + G_2 = 66.7 \ \mu S$

    $$V_L = \frac{I_{SC}}{G_N + G_L} = \frac{1.36 \text{ mA}}{66.7 \ \mu S + 100 \ \mu S} = 8.16 \text{ V}; \ I_L = V_L G_L = 8.16 \text{ V} \times 100 \ \mu S = 816 \ \mu A$$

    b) $I_{SC} = \dfrac{E}{R_1} = \dfrac{50 \text{ V}}{18 \text{ k}\Omega} = 2.78$ mA, $G_N = G_1 + G_2 = 85.9 \ \mu S$

    $$V_L = \frac{I_{SC}}{G_N + G_L} = \frac{2.78 \text{ mA}}{85.9 \ \mu S + 25.6 \ \mu S} = 24.9 \text{ V}; \ I_L = V_L G_L = 24.9 \text{ V} \times 25.6 \ \mu S = 639 \ \mu A$$

3. a) $I_{SC} = \dfrac{E}{R_1 + R_2 \| R_3} = \dfrac{12 \text{ V}}{680 \ \Omega + 320 \ \Omega} = 12$ mA, $R_{TH} = R_1 + R_2 \| R_3 = 1$ kΩ

    $G_N = \dfrac{I}{1 \text{ k}\Omega} = 1$ mS; $V_L = \dfrac{I_{SC}}{G_N + G_L} = \dfrac{12 \text{ mA}}{2.33 \text{ mS}} = 5.15$ V

    $I_L = V_L G_L = 5.15$ V $\times 1.33$ mS $= 6.85$ mA

    b) $I_{SC} = \dfrac{E}{R_1 + R_2 \| R_3} = \dfrac{10 \text{ V}}{12 \text{ k}\Omega + 8.18 \text{ k}\Omega} = 496 \ \mu A$

    $R_{TH} = R_1 + R_2 \| R_3 = 20.2$ kΩ; $\dfrac{I}{1 \text{ k}\Omega} = 1$ mS; $G_N = \dfrac{I}{20.2 \text{ k}\Omega} = 49.6 \ \mu S$

    $$V_L = \frac{I_{SC}}{G_N + G_L} = \frac{496 \ \mu A}{49.6 \ \mu S + 100 \ \mu S} = 3.31 \text{ V}; \ I_L = V_L G_L = 331 \ \mu A$$

5. a) $I_{SC} = \dfrac{E}{R_1 + R_2 \| R_3} = 1.56 \text{ mA}, \; G_N = R_3 \|(R_1 + R_2) = 61.6 \, \mu S$

   $V_L = \dfrac{I_{SC}}{G_N + G_L} = \dfrac{1.56 \text{ mA}}{61.6 \, \mu S + 66.7 \, \mu S} = 12.2 \text{ V}; \; I_L = V_L G_L = 812 \, \mu A$

   b) $I_{SC} = \dfrac{E}{R_1 + R_2} = 1.52 \text{ mA}, \; G_N = R_3 \|(R_1 + R_2) = 299 \, \mu S$

   $V_L = \dfrac{I_{SC}}{G_N + G_L} = \dfrac{1.52 \text{ mA}}{299 \, \mu S + 500 \, \mu S} = 1.90 \text{ V}; \; I_L = V_L G_L = 1.9 \text{ V} \times 500 \, \mu S = 951 \, \mu A$

END OF CHAPTER 13 PROBLEMS

End of Chapter Problems 13–1

1.

3.

End of Chapter Problems 13–2

First rearrange each equation into y = mx + b format.
Then calculate 6 points for each line, both for the practice and for accuracy.
To find 5 of those 6 points, let x = –2, –1, 0, +1, +2. The middle point is the y-intercept.
To find the 6th point, solve for x when y = 0. This point is the x-intercept.

1.   y = –x + 4; (–2, 6) (–1, 5) (0, 4) (1, 3) (2, 2) (4, 0)

3.   y = 2x – 6; (–2, –10) (–1, –8) (0, –6) (1, –4) (2, –2) (3, 0)

5.   y = –x/3 + 1; (–2, 1.67) (–1, 1.33) (0, 1) (1, .667) (2, .333) (3, 0)

7.   y = –2x/3 + 8/3; (–2, 4) (–1, 3.33) (0, 2.67) (1, 2) (2, 1.33) (4, 0)

9.   y = –x/4 + 3/2; (–2, 2) (–1, 1.75) (0, 1.5) (1, 1.25) (2, 1) (6, 0)

11.   y = –4x/3 – 8; (–2, –5.33) (–1, –6.67) (0, –8) (1, –9.33) (2, –10.67) (–6, 0)

13.   y = x/2 – 3.5; (–2, –4.5) (–1, –4) (0, –3.5) (1, –3) (2, –2.5) (7, 0)

15.   y = 3x/2 + 3; (–2, 0) (–1, 1.5) (0, 3) (1, 4.5) (2, 6) (–2, 0)

17.   5 + 2y = 7x; 2y = 7x – 5; y = 3.5x – 2.5 = 7x/2 – 5/2; (–2, –9.5) (–1, –6) (0, –2.5)
      (1, 1) (2, 4.5) (.714, 0)

19.   21 – 7y = 36x; 21 – 36x = 7y; y = 36x/7 + 3; (–2, –7.29) (–1, –2.14) (0, 3) (1, 8.14)
      (2, 13.3) (–.583, 0)

End of Chapter Problems 13–3

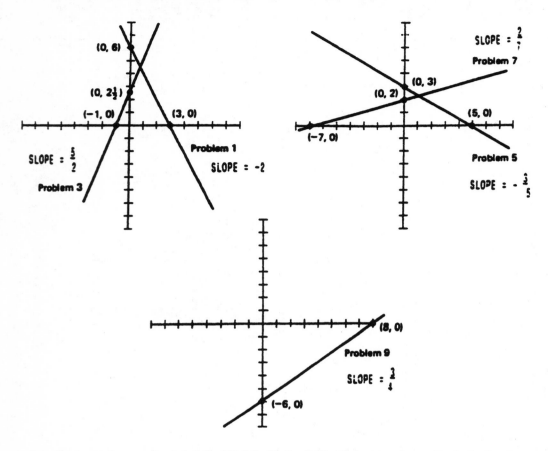

1. $2x + y = 6$; $y = -2x + 6$; $(-2, 10)$ $(-1, 8)$ $(1, 4)$ $(2, 2)$; intercepts are $(0, 6)$ $(3, 0)$; slope $= -2$

3. $2y = 5x + 5$; $y = 5x/2 + 5/2$; $(-2, -2.5)$ $(1, 5)$ $(2, 7.5)$; intercepts are $(-1,0)$ $(0, 2.5)$; slope $= 5/2$

5. $3x + 5y = 15$; $5y = -3x + 15$; $y = -3x/5 + 3$; $(-2, 4.2)$ $(-1, 3.6)$ $(1, 2.4)$ $(2, 1.8)$

    intercepts are $(0, 3)$ $(5, 0)$; slope $= -3/5$

7. $2x - 7y = -14$; $7y = 2x + 14$; $y = 2x/7 + 2$; $(-2, 1.43)$ $(-1, 1.71)$ $(1, 2.29)$ $(2, 2.59)$

    intercepts are $(0, 2)$ $(-7, 0)$; slope is $2/7$

9. $-3x + 4y = -24$; $4y = 3x - 24$; $y - 3x/4 - 6$; $(-2, -7.5)$ $(-1, -6.75)$ $(1, -5.25)$ $(2, -4.5)$

    intercepts are $(0, -6)$ $(8, 0)$

11. $x - 2 = y/5$; $5x - 10 = y$; $y = 5x - 10$; $(-2, 20)$ $(-1, -15)$ $(1, -5)$

    intercepts are $(0, -10)$ $(2, 0)$; slope is 5

13. $y + 3 = -2x$; $y = -2x - 3$; $(-2, 1)$ $(-1, -1)$ $(1, -5)$ $(2, -7)$; intercepts are $(0, -3)$ $(-1.5, 0)$; slope is -2

End of Chapter Problems 13–4

1. $x + 3y = 3$; $3y = -x + 3$; $y = -x/3 + 1$; $(-2, 1.67)$ $(-1, 1.33)$ $(1, .667)$ $(2, .333)$

    intercepts are $(0, 1)$ $(3, 0)$; slope is $-1/3$

3. $3x + 4y = 12$; $4y = -3x + 12$; $y = (-3/4)x + (12/4)$; $y = (-3/4)x + 3$;

    $(-2, 9/2)$ $(-1, 15/4)$ $(0, 3)$ $(1, 9/4)$ $(2, 3/2)$ $(4, 0)$; intercepts are $(0, 3)$ $(4, 0)$; slope is $-3/4$

5. $x - 4y = 12$; $4y = x - 12$; $y = x/4 - 3$; $(-2, -3.5)$ $(-1, -3.25)$ $(1, -2.75)$ $(2, -2.5)$

    intercepts are $(0, -3)$ $(12, 0)$; slope is $1/4$

7. $5y - 2x = 10$; $5y = 2x + 10$; $y = 2x/5 + 2$; $(-2, 1.2)$ $(-1, 1.6)$ $(1, 2.4)$ $(2, 2.8)$

    intercepts are $(0, 2)$ $(-5, 0)$; slope is $2/5$

9. $3x - 7y = 21$; $7y = 3x - 21$; $y = 3x/7 - 3$; $(-2, -3.86)$ $(-1, -3.43)$ $(1, -2.57)$ $(2, -2.14)$

    intercepts are $(0, -3)$ $(7, 0)$; slope $= 3/7$

11. $x + 3y = 6$; $3y = -x + 6$; $y = -x/3 + 2$; $(-2, 2.67)$ $(-1, 2.33)$ $(1, 1.67)$ $(2, 1.33)$;

    intercepts are $(0, 2)$ $(6, 0)$; slope is $-1/3$

13. $2x - 3y = 8$; $3y = 2x - 8$; $y = 2x/3 - 8/3$; $(-2, -4)$ $(-1, -3.33)$ $(1, -2)$ $(2, -1.33)$

    intercepts are $(0, -8/3)$ $(4, 0)$; slope is $2/3$

15. $2y - x = 6$; $2y = x + 6$; $y = x/2 + 3$; $(-2, 2)$ $(-1, 2.5)$ $(1, 3.5)$ $(2, 4)$

    intercepts are $(0, 3)$ $(-6, 0)$; slope is $1/2$

17. $3x - 8 = 2y$; $y = 3x/2 - 4$; $(-2, 7)$ $(-1, 5.5)$ $(1, 2.5)$ $(2, -1)$

    intersections are $(0, 4)$ $(2.67, 0)$; slope is $3/2$

19. $3x + y = -9$; $y = -3x - 9$; $(-2, -3)$ $(-1, -6)$ $(1, -12)$ $(2, -15)$

    intercepts are $(0, -9)$ $(-3, 0)$; slope is 3

End of Chapter Problems 13–5

1. $\Delta V = 3$ V; $\Delta I = 2$ mA; $R_{DC} = \Delta V/\Delta I = 1500$ Ω; $G_{DC} = 667$ μS; $\Delta v = 6$ V; $\Delta i = 8$ mA;

    $r_{dc} = \Delta v/\Delta i = 1333$ V; $g_{dc} = 750$ μS

3. $\Delta V = 0.5$ V; $\Delta I = 6$ mA; $R_D = \Delta V/\Delta I = 83.3$ Ω; $G_D = 12$ mS; $\Delta v = .2$ V; $\Delta i = 6$ mA;

    $r_d = 33.3$ Ω; $g_d = 30$ mS

5. a) $V_R = 60$ V; $V_C = 40$ V   b) $V_R = 5$ V; $V_C = 95$ V

7. a) $V_R = 4.5$ V; $V_C = 15.5$ V   b) $V_R = .4$ V; $V_C = 19.6$ V

9. a) $TC = 1.6$ b) $TC = .51$

11. slope = rise/run = 6.5 mA/50 V = 130 μS = G; R = 7692 Ω

End of Chapter Problems 13–6

1.

#1

3.

#3

5.

#5

7.

#7

END OF CHAPTER 14 PROBLEMS

End of Chapter Problems 14–1

#1
Intersect is (3,2)

#3
Intersect is (2,–4)

#5
Intersect is (2,1)

#7
Intersect is (–2,–1)

#9
Intersect is (4.6,1.7)

#11
Intersect is (1,0.15)

#13
Intersect is (4,3)

End of Chapter Problems 14–2

1.   original   rearrange   mult b by –2   mult a by –2

    a) $2x - y = 4$ $2x - y = 4$ $2x - y = 4$ $-4x + 2y = -8$

    b) $2y = x + 1$ $x - 2y = -1$ $\underline{-2x + 4y = 2}$ $\underline{x - 2y = -1}$

                                          $3y = 6$ $-3x = -9$

                                             $y = 2$ $x = 3$

3.   original   mult b by 2   mult a by 3 and b by –5

    a) $5x + 2y = 2$ $5x + 2y = 2$ $15x + 6y = 6$

    b) $3x - y = 10$ $\underline{6x - 2y = 20}$ $\underline{-15x + 5y = -50}$

                                 $11x = 22$ $11y = -44$

                                  $x = 2$ $y = -4$

5.   original   mult b by –8   mult b by 2

    a) $8x - 4y = 12$ $8x - 4y = 12$ $8x - 4y = 12$

    b) $x + 2y = 4$ $\underline{-8x - 16y = -32}$ $\underline{2x + 4y = 8}$

                                 $-20y = -20$ $10x = 20$

                                     $y = 1$ $x = 2$

7.   original   mult a by –3, b by 2   mult a by –8, b by –5

    a) $2x - 5y = 1$ $-6x + 15y = -3$ $16x - 40y = 8$

    b) $3x - 8y = 2$ $\underline{6x - 16y = 4}$ $\underline{-15x + 40y = -10}$

                                     $-y = 1$ $x = -2$

                                     $y = -1$

9.   original   mult by 6   mult b by –1

    a) $x/2 + y/3 = 1$ $3x + 2y = 6$ $3x + 2y = 6$

    b) $x/2 - y/3 = 1$ $\underline{3x - 2y = 6}$ $\underline{-3x + 2y = -6}$

                                 $6x = 12$ $4y = 0$

                                 $x = 2$ $y = 0$

11.   original   mult b by –2   mult a by 2, b by 3

    a) $2x - 3y = 4$ $2x - 3y = 4$ $4x - 6y = 8$

    b) $x + 2y = 8$ $\underline{-2x - 4y = -16}$ $\underline{3x + 6y = 24}$

                                 $-7y = -12$ $7x = 32$

                                 $y = 12/7 = 1.71$ $x = 32/7 = 4.57$

13.　　　original　　　　　　mult a by 12, b by 24　　　mult aa by 3, bb by −2

a)　$x/3 + y/2 = 5/12$　　(aa) $4x + 6y = 5$　　　$12x + 18y = 15$

b)　$x/4 − y/3 = 5/24$　　(bb) $6x − 8y = 5$　　　$\underline{−12x + 16y = −10}$

　　　　　　　　　　　　　　　　　　　　　　$34y = 5$

mult aa by 4, bb by 3　　　　　　　　　　　　$y = 5/34 = .1471$

$16x + 24y = 20$

$\underline{18x − 24y = 15}$

$34x \qquad = 35$

　$x = 35/34 = 1.029$

End of Chapter Problems 14–3

1.　$x + 2y = 4$　　(1)　　solve for x in (1) gives $x = 4 − 2y$

　　$2x − y = 2$　　(2)　　substitute for x in (2):　$2(4 − 2y) − y = 2$

　　　　　　　　　　　　　　　　　　　　　　　　$8 − 4y − y = 2$

　　　　　　　　　　　　　　　　　　　　　　　　　　$y = 6/5 = 1.2$

　　$x + 2(1.2) = 4; x = 1.6$

3.　$4x − 2y = 3$　　(1)　solve for x in (1) $x = \dfrac{3 + 2y}{4}$

　　$3x + 2y = 5$　　(2)　substitute for x in (2): $\dfrac{3(3 + 2y)}{4} + 2y = 5; y = 0.786$

　　$4x − 2(0.786) = 3; 4x = 3 + 2(0.786); x = 1.14$

　　$23y/2 = 2; 23y = 4; y = 4/23 = .17391; x = 2 + 5(4/23)/2 = 2 + 10/23 = 2.43 = 56 / 23$

5.　$5x + 3y = 5$　　(1)　solve for y in (1) $y = \dfrac{5 − 5x}{3}$

　　$3x − 4y = 6$　　(2)　substitute for y in (2): $3x − \dfrac{4(5 − 5x)}{3} = 6; x = 1.31$

　　$5(1.31) + 3y = 5; 3y = 5 − 5(1.31); y = −0.517$

7.　$x + y = 10$　　(1)　solve for x in (1)　$x = 10 − y$

　　$4x − 4y = 0$　　(2)　substitute for x in (2): $4(10 − y) − 4y = 0; y = 5$ $x + 5 = 10; x = 5$

9.　$3x − 3y = −5$　　(1)　solve for x in (1)　$x = \dfrac{3y − 5}{3}$

　　$−x − y = 4$　　(2)　substitute for x in (2):　$\dfrac{−(3y − 5)}{3} − y = 4; y = −7 / 6 = −1.17$

　　$3x − 3(−1.17) = −5; 3x = −5 + 3(−1.17); x = −2.83 = −17 / 6$

End of Chapter Problems 14–4

1. $x + 2y = 4$
    $2x - y = 2$

$$x = \frac{\begin{vmatrix} 4 & 2 \\ 2 & -1 \end{vmatrix}}{\begin{vmatrix} 1 & 2 \\ 2 & -1 \end{vmatrix}} = \frac{4(-1) - 2(2)}{1(-1) - 2(2)} = 1.6$$

$$y = \frac{\begin{vmatrix} 1 & 4 \\ 2 & 2 \end{vmatrix}}{\begin{vmatrix} 1 & 2 \\ 2 & -1 \end{vmatrix}} = \frac{1(2) - 2(4)}{1(-1) - 2(2)} = 1.2$$

3. $4x - 2y = 3$
    $3x + 2y = 5$

$$x = \frac{\begin{vmatrix} 3 & -2 \\ 5 & 2 \end{vmatrix}}{\begin{vmatrix} 4 & -2 \\ 3 & 2 \end{vmatrix}} = \frac{3(2) - 5(-2)}{4(2) - 3(-2)} = 1.14$$

$$y = \frac{\begin{vmatrix} 4 & 3 \\ 3 & 5 \end{vmatrix}}{\begin{vmatrix} 4 & -2 \\ 3 & 2 \end{vmatrix}} = \frac{4(5) - 3(3)}{4(2) - 3(-2)} = 0.786$$

5. $5x + 3y = 5$
    $3x - 4y = 6$

$$x = \frac{\begin{vmatrix} 5 & 3 \\ 6 & -4 \end{vmatrix}}{\begin{vmatrix} 5 & 3 \\ 3 & -4 \end{vmatrix}} = \frac{5(-4) - 6(3)}{5(-4) - 3(3)} = 1.31$$

$$y = \frac{\begin{vmatrix} 5 & 5 \\ 3 & 6 \end{vmatrix}}{\begin{vmatrix} 5 & 3 \\ 3 & -4 \end{vmatrix}} = \frac{5(6) - 3(5)}{5(-4) - 3(3)} = -0.517$$

7. $x + y = 10$
    $4x - 4y = 0$

$$x = \frac{\begin{vmatrix} 10 & 1 \\ 0 & -4 \end{vmatrix}}{\begin{vmatrix} 1 & 1 \\ 4 & -4 \end{vmatrix}} = \frac{10(-4) - 0(1)}{1(-4) - 1(4)} = 5$$

$$y = \frac{\begin{vmatrix} 1 & 10 \\ 4 & 0 \end{vmatrix}}{\begin{vmatrix} 1 & 1 \\ 4 & -4 \end{vmatrix}} = \frac{1(0) - 4(10)}{1(-4) - 1(4)} = 5$$

9. $3x - 3y = -5$
    $-x - y = 4$

$$x = \frac{\begin{vmatrix} -5 & -3 \\ 4 & -1 \end{vmatrix}}{\begin{vmatrix} 3 & -3 \\ -1 & -1 \end{vmatrix}} = \frac{-5(-1) - 4(-3)}{3(-1) - (-1)(-3)} = -2.83$$

$$y = \frac{\begin{vmatrix} 3 & -5 \\ -1 & 4 \end{vmatrix}}{\begin{vmatrix} 3 & -3 \\ -1 & -1 \end{vmatrix}} = \frac{3(4) - (-1)(-5)}{3(-1) - (-1)(-3)} = -1.17$$

End of Chapter Problems 14–5

1. $x + 2y + 3z = 14$
    $2x + y + 2z = 10$
    $3x + 4y - 3z = 2$

$$x = \frac{\begin{vmatrix} 14 & 2 & 3 \\ 10 & 1 & 2 \\ 2 & 4 & -3 \end{vmatrix}}{\begin{vmatrix} 1 & 2 & 3 \\ 2 & 1 & 2 \\ 3 & 4 & -3 \end{vmatrix}} = \frac{28}{28} = 1$$

$$y = \frac{\begin{vmatrix} 1 & 14 & 3 \\ 2 & 10 & 2 \\ 3 & 2 & -3 \end{vmatrix}}{\begin{vmatrix} 1 & 2 & 3 \\ 2 & 1 & 2 \\ 3 & 4 & -3 \end{vmatrix}} = \frac{56}{28} = 2 \qquad z = \frac{\begin{vmatrix} 1 & 2 & 14 \\ 2 & 1 & 10 \\ 3 & 4 & 2 \end{vmatrix}}{\begin{vmatrix} 1 & 2 & 3 \\ 2 & 1 & 2 \\ 3 & 4 & -3 \end{vmatrix}} = \frac{84}{28} = 3$$

3. $x - 2y + 4z = 4$
    $x + 3y - 2z = 6$
    $3x + y + 3z = 5$

$$x = \frac{\begin{vmatrix} 4 & -2 & 4 \\ 6 & 3 & -2 \\ 5 & 1 & 3 \end{vmatrix}}{\begin{vmatrix} 1 & -2 & 4 \\ 1 & 3 & -2 \\ 3 & 1 & 3 \end{vmatrix}} = \frac{64}{-3} = -21.3$$

$$y = \frac{\begin{vmatrix} 1 & 4 & 4 \\ 1 & 6 & -2 \\ 3 & 5 & 3 \end{vmatrix}}{\begin{vmatrix} 1 & -2 & 4 \\ 1 & 3 & -2 \\ 3 & 1 & 3 \end{vmatrix}} = \frac{-60}{-3} = 20 \qquad z = \frac{\begin{vmatrix} 1 & -2 & 4 \\ 1 & 3 & 6 \\ 3 & 1 & 5 \end{vmatrix}}{\begin{vmatrix} 1 & -2 & 4 \\ 1 & 3 & -2 \\ 3 & 1 & 3 \end{vmatrix}} = \frac{-49}{-3} = 16.3$$

5. $\begin{aligned} x + y + z &= 12 \\ 2x - 3y - 4z &= 8 \\ -3x + 2y + 2z &= 5 \end{aligned}$

$$x = \frac{\begin{vmatrix} 12 & 1 & 1 \\ 8 & -3 & -4 \\ 5 & 2 & 2 \end{vmatrix}}{\begin{vmatrix} 1 & 1 & 1 \\ 2 & -3 & -4 \\ -3 & 2 & 2 \end{vmatrix}} = \frac{19}{5} = 3.8$$

$$y = \frac{\begin{vmatrix} 1 & 12 & 1 \\ 2 & 8 & -4 \\ -3 & 5 & 2 \end{vmatrix}}{\begin{vmatrix} 1 & 1 & 1 \\ 2 & -3 & -4 \\ -3 & 2 & 2 \end{vmatrix}} = \frac{166}{5} = 33.2; \quad z = \frac{\begin{vmatrix} 1 & 1 & 12 \\ 2 & -3 & 8 \\ -3 & 2 & 5 \end{vmatrix}}{\begin{vmatrix} 1 & 1 & 1 \\ 2 & -3 & -4 \\ -3 & 2 & 2 \end{vmatrix}} = \frac{-125}{5} = -25$$

End of Chapter Problems 14–6

1. $20 - I_1R_1 + I_2R_2 = R_1(I_2 + I_3) + R_2R_2 = 4.7\text{ k } I_2 + 4.7\text{ k } I_3 + 10\text{ k } I_2$

    $20 - I_1R_1 + I_3R_3 = R_1(I_2 + I_3) + R_3R_3 = 4.7\text{ k } I_2 + 4.7\text{ k } I_3 + 20\text{ k } I_3$

    (1) $20 = 14.7\text{ k } I_2 + 4.7\text{ k } I_3$

    (2) $20 = 4.7\text{ k } I_2 + 24.7\text{ k } I_3$

    $I_1 = 1.76$ mA, $I_2 = 1.17$ mA, $I_3 = 587\ \mu\text{A}$, $V_1 = 8.27$ V, $V_2 = V_3 = 11.7$ V

End of Chapter Problems 14–7

1. *Starting from the positive side of E_1 and moving clockwise:*

    (1) $I_1R_1 + I_2R_2 - 20\text{ V} = 0$; $20 = I_1R_1 + I_2R_2$; $20 = R_1(I_2 + I_3) + I_2R_2$; $20 = 3\text{ k } I_2 + 3\text{ k } I_3 + 2\text{ k } I_2$;
         $20 = 5\text{ k } I_2 + 3\text{ k } I_3$

    (2) $I_1R_1 - 40\text{ V} + I_3R_3 - 20\text{ V} = 0$; $60 = I_1R_1 + I_3R_3$; $60 = R_1(I_2 + I_3) + I_3R_3$;
         $60 = 3\text{ k } I_2 + 3\text{ k } I_3 + 1\text{ k}$; I_2; $60 = 3\text{ k } I_2 + 4\text{ k } I_3$

    $I_1 = 12.7$ mA, $I_2 = 9.08$ mA, $I_3 = 21.8$ mA, $V_1 = 38.2$ V, $V_2 = 18.2$ V, $V_3 = 21.8$ V

3. *Starting from the positive side of E_1 and moving clockwise:*

    (1) $I_1R_1 + I_2R_2 + 40\text{ V} - 100\text{ V} = 0$; $60 = I_1R_1 + I_2R_2$; $60 = R_1(I_2 + I_3) + I_2R_2$;
         $60 = 12\text{ k } I_2 + 12\text{ k } I_3 + 20\text{ k } I_2$; $60 = 32\text{ k } I_2 + 12\text{ k } I_3$

    (2) $I_1R_1 + I_3R_3 - 100\text{ V} = 0$; $100 = I_1R_1 + I_3R_3$; $100 = R_1(I_2 + I_3) + I_3R_3$;
         $100 = 12\text{ k } I_2 + 12\text{ k } I_3 + 10\text{ k } I_2$; $100 = 12\text{ k } I_2 + 22\text{ k } I_3$

    $I_1 = 4.63$ mA, $I_2 = 220\ \mu\text{A}$, $I_3 = 4.44$ mA, $V_1 = 55.6$ V, $V_2 = 4.44$ V, $V_3 = 44.4$ V

    (3) $I_1R_1 + I_3R_3 - 25\text{ V} = 0$; $25 = I_1R_1 + I_3R_3$; $25 = R_1(I_2 + I_3) + I_3R_3$;
         $25 = 470\text{ k } I_2 + 470\text{ k } I_3 + 330\text{ k } I_2$; $25 = 470\text{ k } I_2 + 800\text{ k } I_3$

    $I_1 = 11.1$ mA, $I_2 = 49$ mA, $I_3 = 60$ mA, $V_1 = 5.2$ V, $V_2 = 40.2$ V, $V_3 = 19.8$ V

5. *Starting from the positive side of E_1 and moving counterclockwise:*

  (1) $I_3R_3 + 30\ V + I_1R_1 - 40\ V = 0$; $10 = I_1R_1 + I_3R_3$; $10 = R_1(I_2 + I_3) + R_3I_3$;

  $10 = 100\ I_2 + 100\ I_3 + 220\ I_2$; $10 = 100\ I_2 + 330\ I_3$

  (2) $I_2R_2 + I_1R_1 - 40\ V = 0$; $40 = I_1R_1 + I_2R_2$; $40 = R_1(I_2 + I_3) + R_2I_2$;

  $40 = 100\ I_2 + 100\ I_3 + 330\ I_2$; $40 = 430\ I_2 + 100\ I_3$

  $I_1 = 251\ mA$, $I_2 = 45.3\ mA$, $I_3 = 204\ mA$, $V_1 = 25.1\ V$, $V_2 = 14.9\ V$, $V_3 = 44.9\ V$

7. *Starting from the positive side of E_1 and moving counterclockwise:*

  (1) $I_2R_2 - 8\ V + I_1R_1 - 12\ V = 0$; $20 = I_1R_1 + I_2R_2$; $20 = R_1(I_2 + I_3) + I_2R_2$;

  $20 = 2.7\ k\ I_2 + 2.7\ k\ I_3 + 3.3\ k\ I_2$; $20 = 6\ k\ I_2 + 2.7\ k\ I_3$

  (2) $I_3R_3 + I_1R_1 - 12\ V = 0$; $12 = I_1R_1 + I_3R_3$; $12 = R_1(I_2 + I_3) + I_3R_3$;

  $120 = 2.7\ k\ I_2 + 2.7\ k\ I_3 + 1\ k\ I_3$; $12 = 2.7\ k\ I_2 + 3.7\ k\ I_3$

  $I_1 = 4\ mA$, $I_2 = 2.79\ mA$, $I_3 = 1.2\ mA$, $V_1 = 10.8\ V$, $V_2 = 9.2\ V$, $V_3 = 1.2\ V$

END OF CHAPTER 15 PROBLEMS

End of Chapter Problems 15–1

1.	j13	3.	j	5.	−25	7.	18
9.	j35	11.	j6.60	13.	−j18	15.	12
17.	j3	19.	−j2	21.	7	23.	−j20

End of Chapter Problems 15–2

1.	−4 − j4	3.	4 − j8	5.	3.1 − j4.5	7.	11 + j7
9.	1.9 − j4.2	11.	−1 − j7	13.	−10 − j6	15.	0 + j0
17.	6 + j0	19.	0 − j6				

Note To Student: When making a graph using rectangular numbers, be sure to draw the rectangle since a rectangular or j number is two dimensional and is not just a single point.

21, 22, 23, 24

25, 26, 27, 28, 29, 30

31, 32, 33, 34   37, 38

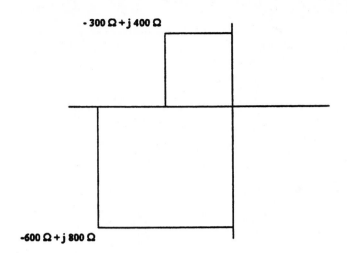

End of Chapter Problems 15–3

1. $15 + j27$ 3. $25 + j25$ 5. $-27 - j8$ 7. $30 + j10$

9. $20 + j2$ 11. $20 - j8$ 13. $10 - j6$ 15. $17 - j10$

17. $-10 - j12$ 19. $-21 - j20$ 21. $5 + j3$ 23. $-1 - j5$

25. $1 + j20$ 27. $20 + j50$ 29. $12 - j10$ 31. $4 - j24$

33. $-2 + j0$ 35. $3 - j2$ 37. $2 + j2$ 39. $-9 + j0$

End of Chapter Problems 15–4

1. $(5 - j2)(3 - j2) = 15 + j6 - j10 - j^2 4 = 19 - j4$

3. $(2 + j3)(2 - j3) = 4 + j6 - j6 - j^2 9 = 13$

5. $(4 - j3)(4 - j3) = 16 - j12 - j12 + j^2 9 = 7 - j24$

7. $(1 - j5)(3 - j3) = 3 - j15 - j3 + j^2 15 = -12 - j18$

9. $(4 + j5)(6 + j2) = 24 + j30 + j8 + j^2 10 = 14 + j38$

11. $(5 - j3)(6 + j1) = 30 - j18 + j5 - j^2 3 = 33 - j13$

13. $\dfrac{5 + j3}{1 + j4} \times \dfrac{1 - j4}{1 - j4} = \dfrac{5 + j3 - j20 - j^2 12}{1 + j4 - j4 - j^2 16} = \dfrac{17 - j17}{17} = 1 - j1$

15. $\dfrac{4 + j4}{3 - j} \times \dfrac{3 + j}{3 + j} = \dfrac{12 + j4 + j12 + j^2 4}{9 - j3 + j3 - j^2} = \dfrac{8 + j16}{10} = 0.8 + j1.6$

17. $\dfrac{1 + j2}{5 + j2} \times \dfrac{5 - j2}{5 - j2} = \dfrac{5 + j10 - j2 - j^2 4}{25 + j10 - j10 - j^2 4} = \dfrac{9 + j8}{29} = 0.31 + j0.276$

19. $\dfrac{2 - j5}{-3 + j4} \times \dfrac{3 + j4}{3 + j4} = \dfrac{6 - j15 + j8 - j^2 20}{-9 + j12 - j12 + j^2 16} = \dfrac{26 - j7}{-25} = -1.04 + j0.280$

21. $\dfrac{-8 - j2}{-4 - j5} \times \dfrac{-4 + j5}{-4 + j5} = \dfrac{32 - j40 + j8 - j^2 10}{16 - j^2 25} = \dfrac{42}{41} - j\dfrac{32}{41} = 1.02 - j.780$

23. $\dfrac{3 + j4}{4 + j5} \times \dfrac{4 - j5}{4 - j5} = \dfrac{12 + j16 - j15 - j^2 20}{16 - j^2 25} = \dfrac{32}{41} + j\dfrac{1}{41} = 0.780 + j0.0244$

END OF CHAPTER 16 PROBLEMS

End of Chapter Problems 16–1

1. a) $\emptyset = 55°$

    b) side R is the greater side

    c) side R lies opposite $\underline{/\emptyset}$

    d) side R lies adjacent $\underline{/\theta}$

5. a) $Y = [G^2 + B^2]^{1/2} = 2.99$ mS

    b) $G = [Y^2 - B^2]^{1/2} = 800\ \mu S$

    c) $B = [Y^2 - G^2]^{1/2} = 425\ \mu S$

3. a) $Z = [R^2 + X^2]^{1/2} = 4.83$ kΩ

    b) $R = [Z^2 - X^2]^{1/2} = 487\ \Omega$

    c) $X = [Z^2 - R^2]^{1/2} = 98.9$ kΩ

End of Chapter Problems 16–2

1. $c = [a^2 + b^2]^{1/2} = 26.1$ and $\emptyset > \theta$

5. $a = [c^2 - b^2]^{1/2} = 68.1$ and $\emptyset. > \theta$

3. $b = [c^2 - a^2]^{1/2} = 245$ and $\theta > \emptyset$

For the following problems: $Z = [R^2 + X^2]^{1/2}$

7. $Z = 976\ \Omega$. Angle θ is greater.

11. $Z = 84.5$ kΩ. Angle $\emptyset$ is greater.

9. $Z = 731$ kΩ. Angle θ is greater.

For the following problems: $X = [Z^2 - R_2]^{1/2}$

13. $X = 6.8$ kΩ. Angle θ is greater.

15. $X = 150$ kΩ. Angle θ is greater.

For the following problems: $R = [Z^2 - X^2]^{1/2}$

17. $R = 27$ kΩ. Angle θ is greater.

19. $R = 90.5\ \Omega$. Angle $\emptyset$ is greater.

For the following problems: $Y = [G^2 + B^2]^{1/2}$

21. $Y = 832\ \mu S$. Angle θ is greater.

23. $Y = 4.37$ mS. Angle $\emptyset$ is greater.

For the following problems: $B = [Y^2 - G^2]^{1/2}$

25. $B = 21.3\ \mu S$. Angle $\emptyset$ is greater.

27. $B = 4.54$ mS. Angle $\emptyset$ is greater.

For the following problems: $G = [Y^2 - B^2]^{1/2}$

29. $G = 556\ \mu S$. Angle $\emptyset$ is greater.

31. $G = 13.3$ mS. Angle θ is greater.

End of Chapter Problems 16–3

1. a) $\sin \theta = X/Z$; $\cos \theta = R/Z$; $\tan \theta = X/R$

    b) $\sin \emptyset = R/Z$; $\cos \emptyset = X/Z$; $\tan \emptyset = R/X$

    b) $\sin \theta = B/Y$; $\cos \theta = G/Y$; $\tan \theta = B/G$

    b) $\sin \emptyset = G/Y$; $\cos \emptyset = B/Y$; $\tan \emptyset = G/B$

End of Chapter Problems 16–4

1. sin 27.3° = 0.4586   3. sin 63.6° = −.8957   5. cos 78.3° = 0.2028   7. cos 23.7° = .9157

9. tan 67.3° = 2.391   11. tan 40.3° = .8481

End of Chapter Problems 16–5

Note To Student: Notice that "$\sin^{-1}$" is always read as "arcsin" and it always means the inverse of sine, not the reciprocal.
  Notice that $\sin^{-1}$ .39715 = arcsin .39715 = angle whose sine is .39715 = 23.4°

1. $\sin^{-1}$ .39715 = 23.4°   3. $\sin^{-1}$ 0.87036 = 60.5°   5. $\cos^{-1}$ .55630 = 56.2°

7. $\cos^{-1}$ 0.78043 = 38.7°   9. $\tan^{-1}$ 1.47146 = 55.8°

End of Chapter Problems 16–6

Note To Student: Be sure to draw a separate triangle for EVERY problem Fill in all numbers and letters and units right on each triangle.

1. θ = $\tan^{-1}$ a/b = $\tan^{-1}$ 25/40 = 32°. ø = 90° − θ = 58°; c = a/sin θ = 25/sin 32° = **47.2**

3. θ = 90° − ø = 55°. b - a/tan θ = 200/tan 55° = 140. c = a/sin θ = 200/sin 55° = **244**

5. a = c sin θ = 17.3 × sin 40° = 11.1, b = c cos θ = 17.3 × cos 40° = 13.3

7. R = X/tan θ = 17.6 kΩ/tan 22.3° = 42.9 kΩ, Z = X/sin θ = 17.6 kΩ/sin 22.3° = **46.4 kΩ**

9. R = X/tan θ = 650 Ω/tan 22.3° = 1.58 kΩ, Z = X/sin θ = 650 Ω/sin 22.3° = **171 kΩ**

11. θ = $\tan^{-1}$ X/R = $\tan^{-1}$ 10 kΩ/5.6 kΩ = 60.8°, Z = X/sin θ = 10 kΩ/sin 60.8° = **11.5 kΩ**

13. θ = $\tan^{-1}$ X/R = $\tan^{-1}$ 19.7 kΩ/27 kΩ = 36.1°, Z = X/sin θ = 19.7 kΩ/sin 36.1° = **33.4 kΩ**

15. X = R tan θ = 20 kΩ × tan 30° = 11.5 kΩ, Z = R/cos θ = 20 kΩ/cos 30° = **23.1 kΩ**

17. X = R tan θ = 270 kΩ × tan 37.5° = 207 kΩ, Z = R/cos θ = 270 kΩ/cos 37.5° = **340 kΩ**

19. R = Z cos θ = 40 kΩ × cos 67.5° = 15.3 kΩ, X = Z sin θ = 40 kΩ × sin 67.5° = **37 kΩ**

21. R = Z cos θ = 785 Ω × cos 40.3° = 599 Ω, X = Z sin θ = 785 kΩ × sin 40.3° = **508 Ω**

23. θ = $\cos^{-1}$ (R/Z) = $\cos^{-1}$ 12 kΩ/22 kΩ = 56.9°, X = Z sin θ = 22 kΩ × sin 56.9° = **18.4 kΩ**

25. θ = $\cos^{-1}$ (R/Z) = $\cos^{-1}$ 1.8 kΩ/2.55 kΩ = 45.1°, X = Z sin θ = 2.55 kΩ × sin 45.1° = **1.81 kΩ**

27. θ = $\sin^{-1}$ (X/Z) = $\sin^{-1}$ 17.5 kΩ/38 kΩ = 27.4°, R = Z cos θ = 38 kΩ × cos 27.4° = **33.7 kΩ**

29. θ = $\sin^{-1}$ (X/Z) = $\sin^{-1}$ 15.3 kΩ/26.8 kΩ = 34.8°, R = Z cos θ = 26.8 kΩ × cos 34.8° = **22.0 kΩ**

31. B = G tan θ = 60 μS × tan 25° = 28 μS, Y = G/cos θ = 60 μS/cos 25° = **66.2 μS**

33. B = G tan θ = 135 μS × tan 65° = 290 μS, Y = G/cos θ = 135 μS/cos 65° = **319 μS**

35. θ = $\tan^{-1}$ B/G = $\tan^{-1}$ 8.73 mS/12.5 mS = 34.9°, Y = B/sin θ = 8.73 mS/sin 34.9° = **15.3 mS**

37. θ = $\tan^{-1}$ B/G = $\tan^{-1}$ 17.3 μS/12.7 μS = 53.7°, Y = B/sin θ = 17.3 μS/sin 53.7° = **21.5 μS**

39. G = B/tan θ = 35 mS/tan 10.7° = 185 mS, Y = B/sin θ = 35 mS/sin 10.7° = **189 mS**

41. G = B/tan θ = 3.32 mS/tan 27.4° = 6.40 mS, Y = B/sin θ = 3.32 mS/sin 27.5° = **7.20 mS**

43. $\cos^{-1}$ G/Y = $\cos^{-1}$ 6.35 mS/9.35 mS = 47.2°, B = Y sin θ = 9.35 mS × sin 47.2° = **6.86 mS**

45. $\cos^{-1}$ G/Y = $\cos^{-1}$ 2.33 mS/3.30 mS = 45.1°, B = Y sin θ = 3.3 mS × sin 45.1° = **2.34 mS**

47. G = Y cos θ = 70 μS × cos 32° = 59.4 μS, B = Y sin θ = 70 μS × sin 32° = **37.1 μS**

49. $G = Y \cos \theta = 6.57 \text{ mS} \times \cos 55° = 3.77 \text{ mS}$, $B = Y \sin \theta = 6.57 \text{ mS} \times \sin 55° = 5.38 \text{ mS}$

51. $\theta = \sin^{-1} B/Y = \sin^{-1} 7.5 \text{ mS}/11.5 \text{ mS} = 40.7°$, $G = Y \cos \theta = 11.5 \text{ mS} \times \cos 40.7° = 8.72 \text{ mS}$

53. $\theta = \sin^{-1} B/Y = \sin^{-1} 170 \mu\text{S}/320 \mu\text{S} = 32.1°$, $G = Y \cos \theta = 320 \mu\text{S} \times \cos 32.1° = 271 \mu\text{S}$

END OF CHAPTER 17 PROBLEMS

End of Chapter Problems 17–1

Note To Student: Be sure to draw a separate triangle for every problem. Label all sides and angles with numbers as well as letters and units.

1. $B = 180° − (A + C) = 180° − 120° = 60°$

    $a = \dfrac{c \sin A}{\sin C} = \dfrac{35 \times \sin 50°}{\sin 70°} = 28.5$; $b = \dfrac{c \sin B}{\sin C} = \dfrac{35 \times \sin 60°}{\sin 70°} = 32.3$

3. $\sin B = \dfrac{b \sin C}{C} = \dfrac{60 \times \sin 35°}{100} = 0.344$, $B = \sin^{-1} 0.344 = 20.1°$

    $A = 180° − (B + C) = 180° − 55.1° = 125°$; $a = \dfrac{c \sin A}{\sin C} = \dfrac{100 \times \sin 125°}{\sin 35°} = 143$

5. $\sin B = \dfrac{b \sin A}{a} = \dfrac{22 \times \sin 28°}{15} = 0.689$, $B = \sin^{-1} 0.689 = 43.5°$

    $C = 180° − (A + B) = 180° − 71.5° = 109°$; $c = \dfrac{a \sin C}{\sin A} = \dfrac{15 \times \sin 35°}{\sin 28°} = 30.3$

    Second solution: $B = 180° − 43.5° = 137°$

    $C = 180° − (A + B) = 180° − 165° = 15.5°$; $c = \dfrac{a \sin C}{\sin A} = \dfrac{15 \times \sin 15.5°}{\sin 28°} = 8.55$

7. $C = 180° − (A + B) = 180° − 100° = 80°$

    $b = \dfrac{a \sin B}{\sin A} = \dfrac{10 \times \sin 70°}{\sin 30°} = 18.8$; $c = \dfrac{a \sin C}{\sin A} = \dfrac{10 \times \sin 80°}{\sin 30°} = 19.7$

9. $\sin B = \dfrac{b \sin C}{c} = \dfrac{160 \times \sin 22°}{100} = 0.599$, $B = \sin^{-1} 0.599 = 36.8°$

    $A = 180° − (B + C) = 180° − 58.8° = 121°$; $a = \dfrac{a \sin A}{\sin C} = \dfrac{100 \times \sin 121°}{\sin 22°} = 228$

    Second solution: $B = 180° − 36.8° = 143°$

    $A = 180° − (B + C) = 180° − 165° = 14.8°$; $a = \dfrac{c \sin A}{\sin C} = \dfrac{100 \times \sin 14.8°}{\sin 22°} = 68.3$

11. $\sin B = \dfrac{b \sin A}{a} = \dfrac{20 \times \sin 25°}{10} = 0.845, \ B = \sin^{-1} 0.845 = 57.7°$

$C = 180° - (A + B) = 180° - 82.7° = 97.3°; \ c = \dfrac{a \sin C}{\sin A} = \dfrac{10 \times \sin 97.3°}{\sin 25°} = 23.5$

Second solution: $B = 180° - 57.7° = 122°; \ C = 180° - (A + B) = 147° = 32.7°$

$c = \dfrac{a \sin C}{\sin A} = \dfrac{10 \times \sin 32.7°}{\sin 25°} = 12.8$

13. $A = 180° - (B + C) = 180° - 155° = 25°$

$a = \dfrac{b \sin A}{\sin B} = \dfrac{55 \times \sin 25°}{50°} = 30.3; \ c = \dfrac{c \sin C}{\sin B} = \dfrac{55 \times \sin 105°}{\sin 50°} = 69.4$

15. $\sin B = \dfrac{b \sin A}{a} = \dfrac{65 \times \sin 95°}{120} = 0.540, \ B = \sin^{-1} 0.540 = 32.7°$

$C = 180° - (A + B) = 180° - 128° = 52.3°; \ c = \dfrac{a \sin C}{\sin A} = \dfrac{120 \times \sin 52.3°}{\sin 95°} = 95.4$

17. $\sin B = \dfrac{b \sin C}{c} = \dfrac{6 \times \sin 34°}{4.7} = 0.714, \ B = \sin^{-1} 0.714 = 45.6°$

$A = 180° - (B + C) = 180° - 79.6° = 100°; \ a = \dfrac{c \sin A}{\sin C} = \dfrac{4.7 \times \sin 100°}{\sin 34°} = 8.27$

Second solution: $B = 180° - 45.6° = 135°$

$A = 180° - (B + C) = 180° - 168° = 11.5°; \ a = \dfrac{c \sin A}{\sin c} = \dfrac{4.7 \times \sin 11.6°}{\sin 34°} = 1.68$

19. $B = 180° - (A + C) = 180° - 170° = 10°$

$a = \dfrac{a \sin A}{\sin C} = \dfrac{14 \times \sin 125°}{\sin 45°} = 16.2; \ b = \dfrac{c \sin B}{\sin C} = \dfrac{14 \times \sin 10°}{\sin 45°} = 3.44$

21. $B = 180° - (A + C) = 180° - 140° = 40°$

$a = \dfrac{c \sin A}{\sin C} = \dfrac{350 \times \sin 30°}{\sin 110°} = 186; \ b = \dfrac{c \sin B}{\sin C} = \dfrac{350 \times \sin 40°}{\sin 110°} = 239$

23. $\sin C = \dfrac{c \sin B}{b} = \dfrac{65 \times \sin 28°}{40} = 0.763, \ C = \sin^{-1} 0.763 = 49.7°$

$A = 180° - (B + C) = 180° - 77.7° = 102°; \ a = \dfrac{b \sin A}{\sin B} = \dfrac{40 \times \sin 102°}{\sin 28°} = 83.3$

Second solution: $C = 180° - 49.7° = 130°$

$A = 180° - (B + C) = 180° - 158° = 21.7°; \ a = \dfrac{b \sin A}{\sin B} = \dfrac{40 \times \sin 21.7°}{\sin 28°} = 31.5$

25. $\sin C = \dfrac{c \sin B}{b} = \dfrac{275 \times \sin 100°}{350} = 0.774$, $C = \sin^{-1} 0.774 = 50.7°$

   $A = 180° - (B + C) = 180° - 151° = 29.3°$; $a = \dfrac{b \sin A}{\sin B} = \dfrac{350 \times \sin 29.3°}{\sin 100°} = 174$

27. $A = 180° - (B + C) = 180° - 117° = 63°$

   $a = \dfrac{b \sin A}{\sin B} = \dfrac{17 \times \sin 63°}{\sin 95°} = 15.2$; $c = \dfrac{b \sin C}{\sin B} = \dfrac{17 \times \sin 22°}{\sin 95°} = 6.39$

29. $A = 180° - (B + C) = 180° - 40° = 140°$

   $a = \dfrac{b \sin A}{\sin B} = \dfrac{95 \times \sin 140°}{\sin 20°} = 179$; $c = \dfrac{b \sin C}{\sin B} = \dfrac{95 \times \sin 20°}{\sin 20°} = 95$

31. $\sin C = \dfrac{c \sin B}{b} = \dfrac{200 \times \sin 70°}{250} = 0.752$, $C = \sin^{-1} 0.752 = 48.7°$

   $A = 180° - (B + C) = 180° - 119° = 61.3°$; $a = \dfrac{b \sin A}{\sin B} = \dfrac{250 \times \sin 61.3°}{\sin 70°} = 233$

33. $\sin C = \dfrac{c \sin B}{b} = \dfrac{100 \times \sin 120°}{150} = 0.577$, $C = \sin^{-1} 0.577 = 35.3°$

   $A = 180° - (B + C) = 180° - 155° = 24.7°$; $a = \dfrac{b \sin A}{\sin B} = \dfrac{150 \times \sin 24.7°}{\sin 120°} = 72.5$

35. $\sin C = \dfrac{c \sin B}{b} = \dfrac{33 \times \sin 33°}{20} = 0.899$, $C = \sin^{-1} 0.899 = 64.0°$

   $A = 180° - (B + C) = 180° - 97° = 83°$; $a = \dfrac{b \sin A}{\sin B} = \dfrac{20 \times \sin 83°}{\sin 33°} = 36.4$

   Second solution: $C = 180° - 64° = 116°$

   $A = 180° - (B + C) = 180° - 149° = 31°$; $a = \dfrac{b \sin A}{\sin B} = \dfrac{20 \times \sin 31°}{\sin 33°} = 18.9$

37. $B = 180° - (A + C) = 180° - 142° = 38°$

   $a = \dfrac{c \sin A}{\sin C} = \dfrac{110 \times \sin 47°}{\sin 95°} = 80.8$; $b = \dfrac{c \sin B}{\sin C} = \dfrac{110 \times \sin 38°}{\sin 95°} = 68$

39. $B = 180° - (A + C) = 180° - 120° = 60°$

   $a = \dfrac{c \sin A}{\sin C} = \dfrac{4.3 \times \sin 75°}{\sin 45°} = 5.87$; $b = \dfrac{c \sin B}{\sin C} = \dfrac{4.3 \times \sin 60°}{\sin 45°} = 5.27$

End of Chapter Problems 17–2

1. $\cos A = \dfrac{a^2 - b^2 - c^2}{-2b} = \dfrac{b^2 + c^2 - a^2}{2bc} = \dfrac{130^2 + 90^2 - 70^2}{2 \times 130 \times 90} = 0.859$

   $\cos B = \dfrac{a^2 + c^2 - b^2}{2ac} = \dfrac{70^2 + 90^2 - 130^2}{2 \times 70 \times 90} = 0.310$

   $A = \cos^{-1} 0.859 = 30.8°, \ B = \cos^{-1} -0.310 = 108°$

   $C = 189° - (A + B) = 180° - 139° = 41.2°$

3. $\cos A = \dfrac{b^2 + c^2 - a^2}{2bc} = \dfrac{100^2 + 200^2 - 250^2}{2 \times 100 \times 200} = 0.313, \ \cos^{-1} -0.313 = 108° = A$

   $\cos B = \dfrac{a^2 + c^2 - b^2}{2ac} = \dfrac{250^2 + 200^2 - 100^2}{2 \times 250 \times 200} = 0.925, \ \cos^{-1} 0.925 = 22.3° = B$

   $C = 180° - (A + B) = 180° - 130° = 49.7°$

5. $a = [b^2 + c^2 - 2bc \cos A]^{1/2} = [60^2 + 80^2 - 2 \times 60 \times 80 \times \cos 95°]^{1/2} = 104$

   $\sin B = \dfrac{b \sin A}{a} = \dfrac{60 \times \sin 95°}{104} = 0.575, \ \sin^{-1} 0.575 = 35.1° = B$

   $C = 180° - (A + B) = 180° - 130° = 49.9°$

7. $a = [b^2 + c^2 - 2bc \cos A]^{1/2} = [12^2 + 36^2 - 2 \times 12 \times 36 \times \cos 80°]^{1/2} = 35.9$

   $\sin B = \dfrac{b \sin A}{a} = \dfrac{12 \times \sin 80°}{35.9} = 0.329, \ \sin^{-1} 0.329 = 19.2° = B$

   $C = 180° - (A + B) = 180° - 99.2° = 80.8°$

9. $b = [a^2 + c^2 - 2ac \cos B]^{1/2} = [500^2 + 400^2 - 2 \times 500 \times 400 \times \cos 100°]^{1/2} = 692$

   $\sin A = \dfrac{a \sin B}{b} = \dfrac{500 \times \sin 100°}{692} = 0.712, \ \sin^{-1} 0.712 = 45.3° = A$

   $C = 180° - (A + B) = 180° - 145° = 34.7°$

11. $\cos A = \dfrac{b^2 + c^2 - a^2}{2bc} = \dfrac{300^2 + 150^2 - 400^2}{2 \times 300 \times 150} = -528, \ \cos^{-1} -0.528 = 122° = A$

   $\cos B = \dfrac{a^2 + c^2 - b^2}{2ac} = \dfrac{400^2 + 150^2 - 300^2}{2 \times 400 \times 150} = 0.771, \ \cos^{-1} 0.771 = 39.6° = B$

   $C = 180° - (A + B) = 180° - 162° = 18.6°$

13. $\cos A = \dfrac{b^2 + c^2 - a^2}{2bc} = \dfrac{40^2 + 25^2 - 35^2}{2 \times 40 \times 25} = 0.500,\ \cos^{-1}\ -0.500 = 60° = A$

$\cos B = \dfrac{a^2 + c^2 - b^2}{2ac} = \dfrac{35^2 + 25^2 - 40^2}{2 \times 35 \times 25} = 0.143,\ \cos^{-1}\ 0.143 = 81.8° = B$

$C = 180° - (A + B) = 180° - 142° = 38.2°$

15. $b = [a^2 + c^2 - 2ac \cos B]^{1/2} = [8.4^2 + 10^2 - 2 \times 8.4 \times 10 \times \cos 30°]^{1/2} = 5.01$

$\sin A = \dfrac{a \sin B}{b} = \dfrac{8.4 \times \sin 30°}{5.01} = 0.839,\ \sin^{-1}\ 0.839 = 57.0° = A$

$C = 180° - (A + B) = 180° - 87° = 93°$

17. $b = [a^2 + c^2 - 2ac \cos B]^{1/2} = [40^2 + 62^2 - 2 \times 40 \times 62 \times \cos 105°]^{1/2} = 82$

$\sin A = \dfrac{a \sin B}{b} = \dfrac{40 \times \sin 105°}{82} = 0.471,\ \sin^{-1}\ 0.471 = 28.1° = A$

$C = 180° - (A + B) = 180° - 133° = 46.9°$

19. $a = [b^2 + c^2 - 2bc \cos A]^{1/2} = [600^2 + 400^2 - 2 \times 600 \times 400 \times \cos 95°]^{1/2} = 750$

$\sin B = \dfrac{b \sin A}{a} = \dfrac{600 \times \sin 95°}{750} = 0.797,\ \sin^{-1}\ 0.797 = 52.9° = B$

$C = 180° - (A + B) = 180° - 148° = 32.1°$

21. $a = [b^2 + c^2 - 2bc \cos A]^{1/2} = [10^2 + 15^2 - 2 \times 10 \times 15 \times \cos 120°]^{1/2} = 21.8$

$\sin B = \dfrac{b \sin A}{a} = \dfrac{10 \times \sin 120°}{21.8} = 0.397,\ \sin^{-1}\ 0.397 = 23.4° = B$

$C = 180° - (A + B) = 180° - 143° = 36.6°$

23. $\cos A = \dfrac{b^2 + c^2 - a^2}{2bc} = \dfrac{45^2 + 60^2 - 45^2}{2 \times 45 \times 60} = 0.667,\ \cos^{-1}\ 0.667 = 48.2° = A$

$\cos B = \dfrac{a^2 + c^2 - b^2}{2ac} = \dfrac{45^2 - 60^2 - 45^2}{2 \times 45 \times 60} = 0.667,\ \cos^{-1}\ 0.667 = 48.2° = B$

$C = 180° - (A + B) = 180° - 96.4° = 83.6°$

25. $\cos A = \dfrac{b^2 + c^2 - a^2}{2bc} = \dfrac{140^2 + 190^2 - 170^2}{2 \times 140 \times 190} = 0.504,\ \cos^{-1}\ 0.504 = 59.8° = A$

$\cos B = \dfrac{a^2 + c^2 - b^2}{2ac} = \dfrac{170^2 + 190^2 - 140^2}{2 \times 170 \times 190} = 0.703,\ \cos^{-1}\ 0.703 = 45.4° = B$

$C = 180° - (A + B) = 180° - 105° = 74.9°$

27. $\cos A = \dfrac{b^2 + c^2 - a^2}{2bc} = \dfrac{525^2 + 300^2 - 425^2}{2 \times 525 \times 300} = 0.587,\ \cos^{-1}\ 0.587 = 54° = A$

$\cos B = \dfrac{a^2 + c^2 - b^2}{2ac} = \dfrac{425^2 + 300^2 - 525^2}{2 \times 425 \times 300} = -0.0196,\ \cos^{-1}\ 0.0196 = 91.1° = B$

$C = 180° - (A + B) = 180° - 145° = 34.8°$

29. $\cos A = \dfrac{b^2 + c^2 - a^2}{2bc} = \dfrac{8.5^2 + 8.5^2 - 5.35^2}{2 \times 8.5 \times 8.5} = 0.802,\ \cos^{-1}\ 0.802 = 36.7° = A$

$\cos B = \dfrac{a^2 + c^2 - b^2}{2ac} = \dfrac{5.35^2 + 8.5^2 - 8.5^2}{2 \times 5.35 \times 8.5} = 0.315,\ \cos^{-1}\ 0.315 = 71.7° = B$

$C = 180° - (A + B) = 180° - 108° = 71.7°$

END OF CHAPTER 18 PROBLEMS

End of Chapter Problems 18–1

Note To Student: $T = 1/f = 1 / (cycles/sec) = sec/cycle$ and $f = 1/T$
   D degrees $\times \pi$ radians/180° = R radians and R rad $\times$ 180°/π rad = D deg
   Be sure to be in radian mode if your angle value is in radians.
   Be sure to be in degrees mode if your angle value is in degrees.

1.   T = 1/600 Hz = 1.67 msec

3.   T = 1/1.2 kHz = 833 μ sec

5.   T = 1/1.76 Mhz = 568 nsec

7.   f = 1/400 μ sec = 2.50 kHz

9.   f = 1/1.33 m Sec = 752 kHz

11.   f = 1/25 μ sec = 40.0 kHz

13.   25° $\times \pi$ radians/180° = .436 rad

15.   90° $\times \pi$ radians/180° = .1.57 rad

17.   180° $\times \pi$ radians/180° = π rad

19.   75° $\times$ radians/180° = .1.31 rad

21.   600° $\times \pi$ radians/180° = 10.5 rad
      also 600° = 600° − 360° = 240° = 10.5 rad

23.   0.146 rad $\times$ 180° / π rad = 8.37°

25.   0.5 rad $\times$ 180° / π rad = 28.6°

27.   (π / 2) rad $\times$ 180° / π rad = 90°

29.   1.75 rad $\times$ 180° / π rad = 100°

31.   10 rad $\times$ 180° / π rad = 573°

End of Chapter Problems 18–2

Note To Student: If you want answer in degrees, use ω = 360° f.
   If you want answer in radians, use ω = 2 π f.
   Usually you don't round your value for ω.
   $f = \omega / (2 \pi)$ only if ω is in rad/sec. $f = \omega / 360°$ only if X is in degrees/sec.
   The angle ω t [for both formulas for ω] is different from θ [phase angle].

1.   (a) ω = 21600°/sec = 377 rad/sec

   (b) ω = 54000°/sec = 942 rad/sec

   (c) ω = 72000°/sec = 1257 rad/sec

   (d) ω = 1.26 M°/sec = 21991 rad/sec

   (e) ω = 4.32 M°/sec = 75398 rad/sec

   (f) ω = 28.8 M°/sec = 502655 rad/sec

   (g) ω = 45 M°/sec = 785398 rad/sec

   (h) ω = 144 M°/sec = 2513274 rad/sec

3.   (a) f = 12 rad/sec / (2π) = 1.91 Hz;   (b)   7.96 Hz;   (c)   63.7 Hz;   (d)   143 Hz
      (e)   398 Hz;   (f)   796 Hz;   (g)   1.11 Hz

5.   (a) f = ω / 360° = 27.8 Hz   (b)   41.7 Hz;   (c)   139 Hz;   (d)   333 Hz
      (e)   556 Hz;   (f)   2.04 kHz;   (g)   4.58 kHz

7.   (a) ωt = 2 π ft = .314 rad ωt = 360° ft = 18°   18° $\times \pi$ / 180° = .314 rad
      (b) ωt = .785 rad = 45°   (c) ωt = 3.14 rad = 180°   (d) ωt = 8.8 rad = 504°

9. (a) $\omega t = 2\pi$ ft = 1.6 rad $\omega t = 360°$ ft = 91.8°   91.8° × π / 180° = .1.6 rad

(b) $\omega t = 4.01$ rad = 230°   (c) $\omega t = 16$ rad = 918°   (d) $\omega t = 44.9$ rad = 2570°

11. (a) f = ωt / (2π t) = 14.3 kHz   (b)   f = 1.03 kHz   (c)   f = 9.26 kHz   (d)   f = 62.2 kHz

13. (a) f = ωt / (360° t) = 175 Hz   (b)   f = 1.72 kHz   (c)   f = 61.1 kHz   (d)   f = 1.67 MHz

15. (a) t = ωt / (2π f) = 31.8 μ sec   (b)   t = 3.98 μ sec   (c)   t = 151 μ sec

(d) t = ωt / (360° f) = 11.1 μ sec   (e)   t = 50 μ sec   (f)   t = 167 μ sec

17. (a) t = ωt / (2π f) = 10.6 μ sec   (b)   t = 1.33 μ sec   (c)   t = 50.2 μ sec

(d) t = ωt / (360° f) = 3.70 μ sec   (e)   t = 16.7 μ sec   (f)   t = 55.6 μ sec

End of Chapter Problems 18–3

Note To Student: The formulas use V_{pk} and I_{pk}, not V or I.
   If in degrees, use $\omega t = 360°$ ft which is in degrees/sec
   If in radians, use $\omega t = 2\pi$ ft which is in radians / sec
   Basic formulas are: $v = V_{pk} \sin(\omega t \pm \theta)$ and $i = I_{pk} \sin(\omega t \pm \theta)$

1. (a) e = 3.91 V_t;   (b)   e = 9.57 V_t;   (c)   e = 17.7 V_t;   (d)   e = –9.57 V_t;

(e) e = –25 V_t;   (f)   e = –9.57 V_t

3. (a) e = 8.59 V_t;   (b)   e = 10.9 V_t;   (c)   e = –6.75 V_t;   (d)   e = –9.37 V_t;

(e) e = –11.2 V_t;   (f)   e = –12.0 V_t

5. (a) i = 700 μA_t;   (b)   i = 0 μA_t;   (c)   i = –700 μA_t;   (d)   i = 0 A_t;

(e) i = 700 μA_t;   (f)   i = 0 μA_t

7. (a) i = 86.7 μA_t;   (b)   i = 173 μA_t;   (c)   i = –260 μA_t;   (d)   i = 346 μA_t;

(e) i = 432 μA_t;   (f)   i = 518 μA_t

End of Chapter Problems 18–4

Note To Student: Be sure to use correct subscripts on these units. The subscript rms and can be
   omitted or included. Both ways are correct.

1. (a) 65 V × $\sqrt 2$ = 91.9 V_{pk};   91.9 V_{pk} × 2 = 184 V_{p-p}

(b) 110 V × $\sqrt 2$ = 156 V_{pk};   156 V_{pk} × 2 = 311 V_{p-p}

3. (a) 220 V × $\sqrt 2$ = 311 V_{pk};   311 V_{pk} × 2 = 622 V_{p-p}

(b) 440 V × $\sqrt 2$ = 622 V_{pk};   622 V_{pk} × 2 = 1244 V_{p-p}

5. (a) 600 μA × $\sqrt 2$ = 848 μA_{pk};   848 μA_{pk} × 2 = 1.70 mA_{p-p}

(b) 1.2 mA × $\sqrt 2$ = 1.70 mA_{pk};   1.70 mA_{pk} × 2 = 3.39 mA_{p-p}

7. (a) 37.8 mA × $\sqrt 2$ = 53.5 mA_{pk};   53.5 mA_{pk} × 2 = 107 mA_{p-p}

(b) 3 A = 3 A × $\sqrt 2$ = 4.24 A_{pk};   4.24 mA_{pk} × 2 = 8.48 A_{p-p}

9. (a) 350 μV_{pk} × 2 = 700 μA_{p-p};   350 μV_{pk} / $\sqrt 2$ = 247 μV_{rms}

(b) 400 mV_{pk} × 2 = 800 mV_{p-p};   400 mV_{pk} / $\sqrt 2$ = 283 mV

11. (a) 80 V$_{pk}$ × 2 = 160 V$_{p-p}$;   80 V$_{pk}$ / √2 = 56.6 V$_{rms}$ = 56.6 V

  (b) 200 V$_{pk}$ × 2 = 400 V$_{p-p}$;   200 V$_{pk}$ / √2 = 141 V$_{rms}$ = 141 V

13. (a) 200 μA$_{pk}$ × 2 = 400 μA$_{p-p}$;   200 μA$_{pk}$ / √2 = 141 μA$_{rms}$

  (b) 9.45 mA$_{pk}$ × 2 = 18.19 mA$_{p-p}$;   9.45 mA$_{pk}$ / √2 = 6.68 mA

15. (a) 500 mA$_{pk}$ × 2 = 1.00 A$_{p-p}$;   500 mA$_{pk}$ / √2 = 354 mA$_{rms}$

  (b) 1.75 A$_{pk}$ × 2 = 3.50 A$_{p-p}$;   1.75 A$_{pk}$ / √2 = 1.24 A$_{rms}$ = 1.24 A

17. (a) 320 μV$_{p-p}$ / 2 = 160 μV$_{pk}$;   160 μV$_{pk}$ / √2 = 113 μV

  (b) 70 mV$_{p-p}$ / 2 = 35 mV$_{pk}$;   35 mV$_{pk}$ / √2 = 24.7 mV

19. (a) 17 V$_{p-p}$ / 2 = 8.5 V$_{pk}$;   8.5 μV$_{pk}$ / √2 = 6.01 V$_{rms}$ = 6.01 V

  (b) 283 V$_{p-p}$ / 2 = 142 V$_{pk}$;   142 V$_{pk}$ / √2 = 100 V

21. (a) 50 μA$_{p-p}$ / 2 = 25 μA$_{pk}$;   25 μA$_{pk}$ / √2 = 17.7 μA

  (b) 700 μA$_{p-p}$ / 2 = 350 μA$_{pk}$;   350 μA$_{pk}$ / √2 = 247 μA

23. (a) 9.38 mA$_{p-p}$ / 2 = 4.69 mA$_{pk}$;   4.69 mA$_{pk}$ / √2 = 3.32 mA

  (b) 650 mA$_{p-p}$ / 2 = 325 mA$_{pk}$;   325 mA$_{pk}$ / √2 = 230

End of Chapter Problems 18–5

Note To Student: Remember to use correct mode [degrees or radians]

  Basic formulas are: $v = V_{pk} \sin(\omega t \pm \theta)$ and $i = I_{pk} \sin(\omega t \pm \theta)$

1. ωt = 360° ft   i = 4 mA$_{pk}$ sin (ωt)   e = 10 V$_{pk}$ sin (ωt + θ)

  (a) ωt = 36°;   i = 4 mA$_{pk}$ sin 36° = 2.35 mA$_t$;   e = 10 V$_{pk}$ sin (36° + 25°) = 8.75 V$_t$

  (b) ωt = 86.4°; i = 4 mA$_{pk}$ sin 86.4° = 3.99 mA$_t$;   e = 10 V$_{pk}$ sin (86.4° + 25°) = 9.31 V$_t$

  (c) ωt = 180°; i = 4 mA$_{pk}$ sin 180° = 0 mA$_t$;   e = 10 V$_{pk}$ sin (180° + 25°) = –4.23 V$_t$

  (d) ωt = 288°; i = 4 mA$_{pk}$ sin 288° = –3.80 mA$_t$;   e = 10 V$_{pk}$ sin (288° + 25°) = –7.31 V$_t$

3. ωt = 360° ft   i = 25 mA$_{pk}$ sin (ωt + θ)   e = 9 V$_{pk}$ sin (ωt –30°)

  (a) ωt = 36°;   i = 25 mA$_{pk}$ sin (36° + 35°) = 23.6 mA$_t$;   e = 28.3 V$_{pk}$ sin 36° = 16.6 V$_t$

  (b) ωt = 90°;   i = 25 mA$_{pk}$ sin (90° + 35°) = 20.5 mA$_t$;   e = 28.3 V$_{pk}$ sin 90° = 28.3 V$_t$

  (c) ωt = 115°; i = 25 mA$_{pk}$ sin (115° + 35°) = 12.4 mA$_t$;   e = 28.3 V$_{pk}$ sin 115° = 25.6 V$_t$

  (d) ωt = 299°; i = 25 mA$_{pk}$ sin (299° + 35°) = –11.0 mA$_t$;   e = 28.3 V$_{pk}$ sin 299° = –24.8 V$_t$

5. ωt = 360° ft   i = 25 mA$_{pk}$ sin (ωt)   e = 80 V$_{pk}$ sin (ωt + θ)

  (a) ωt = 13.5°; i = 600 μA$_{pk}$ sin 13.5° = 140 μA$_t$;   e = 80 V$_{pk}$ sin (13.5° –55°) = –53 V$_t$

  (b) ωt = 54°;   i = 600 μA$_{pk}$ sin 54° = 485 μA$_t$;   e = 80 V$_{pk}$ sin (54° –55°) = –1.40 V$_t$

  (c) ωt = 162°; i = 600 μA$_{pk}$ sin 180° = 185 μA$_t$;   e = 80 V$_{pk}$ sin (162° –55°) = 76.5 V$_t$

  (d) ωt = 270°; i = 600 μA$_{pk}$ sin 270° = –600 μA$_t$;   e = 80 V$_{pk}$ sin (270° –55°) = –45.9 V$_t$

7. $\omega t = 360°$ ft $i = 25\ mA_{pk}\ \sin(\omega t + \theta)$ $e = 65\ V_{pk}\ \sin(\omega t)$

   (a) $\omega t = 21.2°$; $i = 25\ mA_{pk}\ \sin(21.2° + 40°) = 21.9\ mA_t$; $e = 65\ V_{pk}\ \sin 21.2° = 23.5\ V_t$

   (b) $\omega t = 59.2°$; $i = 25\ mA_{pk}\ \sin(59.2° + 40°) = 24.7\ mA_t$; $e = 65\ V_{pk}\ \sin 59.2° = 55.8\ V_t$

   (c) $\omega t = 169°$; $i = 25\ mA_{pk}\ \sin(169° + 40°) = -12.2\ mA_t$; $e = 65\ V_{pk}\ \sin 169° = 12.2\ V_t$

   (d) $\omega t = 508°$; $i = 25\ mA_{pk}\ \sin(508° + 40°) = -3.31\ mA_t$; $e = 65\ V_{pk}\ \sin 508° = 34.8\ V_t$

END OF CHAPTER 19 PROBLEMS

End of Chapter Problems 19–1

1. $\theta = \tan^{-1}(V_C / V_R) = \tan^{-1}(-20\text{ V} / 20\text{ V}) = -45°$; $E = V_C / \sin \theta = 28.3$ V

3. $\theta = \tan^{-1}(V_C / V_R) = \tan^{-1}(-8\text{ V} / 12\text{ V}) = -33.7°$; $E = V_C / \sin \theta = 14.4$ V

5. $\theta = \cos^{-1}(V_R / E) = \cos^{-1}(6.35\text{ V} / 10\text{ V}) = -50.6°$; $V_C = E \sin \theta = -7.73$ V

7. $\theta = \cos^{-1}(V_R / E) = \tan^{-1}(21\text{ V} / 40\text{ V}) = -58.3°$; $V_C = E \sin \theta = -34$ V

9. $E = V_R / \cos \theta = 15\text{ V} / \cos -40° = 19.6$ V; $V_C = V_R \tan \theta = -12.6$ V

11. $E = V_R / \cos \theta = 5.5\text{ V} / \cos -25° = 6.07$ V; $V_C = V_R \tan \theta = -2.56$ V

13. $V_R = E \cos \theta = 18\text{ V} \times \cos -35.6° = 14.6$ V; $V_C = E \sin \theta = -10.5$ V

15. $V_R = E \cos \theta = 70\text{ V} \times \cos -27° = 62.4$ V; $V_C = E \sin \theta = -31.8$ V

17. $\theta = \sin^{-1}(V_C / E) = \sin^{-1}(-20/30) = -41.8°$; $V_R = E \cos \theta = 22.4$ V

19. $\theta = \sin^{-1}(V_C / E) = \sin^{-1}(-40/50) = -53.1°$; $V_R = E \cos \theta = 30$ V

21. $E = V_C / \sin \theta = -5.5\text{ V} / \sin -32° = 10.4$ V; $V_R = V_C / \tan \theta = 8.82$ V

23. $E = V_C / \sin \theta = -30\text{ V} / \sin -70° = 31.9$ V; $V_R = V_C / \tan \theta = 10.9$ V

End of Chapter Problems 19–2

$X_C = 1 / (2 \pi f C)$ $Z = R / \cos \theta = X_C / \sin \theta$ $V_R = E \cos \theta$

$\theta = \tan^{-1}(X_C / R)$ $I = E / Z$ $f = 1 / (2 \pi X_C C)$ $V_C = E \sin \theta$

1. $X_C = -6.37\ \Omega$; $\theta = -32.5°$; $Z = 11.9$ kΩ

3. $X_C = -796\ \Omega$; $\theta = -48.7°$; $Z = 1.06$ kΩ

5. $X_C = -3.18$ kΩ; $\theta = -57.9°$; $Z = 3.76$ kΩ

7. $X_C = -20.5$ kΩ; $\theta = -37.3°$; $Z = 33.9$ kΩ

9. $X_C = -692\ \Omega$; $\theta = -11.8°$; $Z = 3.37$ kΩ

11. $X_C = -1.33$ kΩ; $\theta = -33.6°$; $Z = 2.40$ kΩ; $V_R = 25$ V $V_C = -16.6$ V $I = 12.5$ mA

13. $X_C = -15.9$ kΩ; $\theta = -57.9°$; $Z = 18.8$ kΩ; $V_R = 5.32$ V $V_C = -8.47$ V $I = 532\ \mu$A

15. $X_C = -5.31$ kΩ; $\theta = -58.1°$; $Z = 6.25$ kΩ; $V_R = 15.8$ V $V_C = -25.5$ V $I = 4.8$ mA

17. $X_C = -49.0$ kΩ; $\theta = -78.5°$; $Z = 50.0$ kΩ; $V_R = 4.00$ V; $V_C = -19.6$ V; $I = 400\ \mu$A

19. $X_C = -398\ \Omega$; $\theta = -40.3°$; $Z = 616\ \Omega$; $V_R = 76.3$ V; $V_C = -64.6$ V; $I = 162$ mA

21. $X_C = -8.76$ kΩ; $\theta = -46.9°$; $f = 90.8$ kHz; $V_R = 27.3$ V $V_C = -29.2$ V $I = 3.33$ mA

23. $X_C = -937$ kΩ; $\theta = -51.3°$; $f = 17$ kHz; $V_R = 9.38$ V; $V_C = -11.7$ V; $I = 12.5$ mA

25. $X_C = -2.23$ kΩ; $\theta = -39.5°$; $f = 2.38$ kHz; $V_R = 23.1$ V $V_C = -19.1$ V $I = 8.57$ mA

27. $X_C = -31.8\ \Omega$; $\theta = -29.6°$; $f = 200$ Hz; $V_R = 6.52$ V $V_C = -3.70$ V $I = 116\ \mu$A

29. $X_C = -802\ \Omega$; $\theta = -44.7°$; $f = 198$ Hz; $V_R = 8.53$ V $V_C = -8.44$ V; $I = 10.5$ mA

End of Chapter Problems 19–3

$\theta = \tan^{-1}(V_L / V_R) = \sin^{-1}(V_L / E) = \cos^{-1}(V_R / E)$ $V_R = E \cos \theta$

$E = V_L / \sin \theta = V_R / \cos \theta$ $V_L = E \sin \theta$

1.	$\theta = 51.3°$;	$E = 12.8$ V	3.	$\theta = 55°$;	$E = 24.4$ V
5.	$E = 7.52$ V;	$V_L = 3.41$ V	7.	$E = 71.3$ V;	$V_L = 65.8$ V
9.	$\theta = 45.9°$;	$V_L = 8.62$ V	11.	$\theta = 43.3°$;	$V_L = 41.1$ V
13.	$\theta = 30.0°$;	$V_R = 26$ V	15.	$\theta = 36.0°$;	$V_R = 13.8$ V
17.	$E = 3.4$ V;	$V_R = 1.60$ V	19.	$E = 31$ V;	$V_R = 26.8$ V
21.	$V_R = 4.77$ V;	$V_L = 7.63$ V	23.	$V_R = 35.4$ V;	$V_L = 35.4$ V

End of Chapter Problems 19–4

$X_L = 2 \pi f L$ $\theta = \tan^{-1}(X_L / R)$ $Z = X_L / \sin \theta$ $V_R = E \cos \theta$

$f = X_L / (2 \pi L)$ $V_L = E \sin \theta$

1.	$X_L = 3.77$ kΩ;	$\theta = 44°$;	$Z = 5.43$ kΩ	3.	$X_L = 3.77$ Ω;	$\theta = 37°$; $Z = 626$ Ω
5.	$X_L = 13.4$ kΩ;	$\theta = 26.3°$;	$Z = 30$ kΩ	7.	$X_L = 1.26$ kΩ;	$\theta = 34.9°$; $Z = 2.2$ kΩ
9.	$X_L = 785$ Ω;	$\theta = 38.1°$;	$Z = 1.27$ kΩ		$V_R = 11.8$ V	$V_L = 9.27$ V $I = 11.8$ mA
11.	$X_L = 471$ Ω;	$\theta = 57.5°$;	$Z = 559$ Ω		$V_R = 26.9$ V	$V_L = 42.2$ V $I = 89.4$ mA
13.	$X_L = 19.9$ kΩ;	$\theta = 36.5°$;	$Z = 33.6$ kΩ		$V_R = 16.1$ V	$V_L = 11.9$ V $I = 595$ mA
15.	$X_L = 78.5$ Ω;	$\theta = 38.1°$;	$Z = 127$ Ω;		$V_R = 9.44$ V	$V_L = 7.41$ V $I = 94.4$ mA
17.	$X_L = 3.73$ kΩ;	$\theta = 38.4°$;	$f = 913$ Hz		$E = 12.1$ V;	$V_R = 9.46$ V; $I = 2.02$ mA
19.	$X_L = 26.5$ Ω;	$\theta = 55.8°$;	$f = 56.2$ kHz		$E = 4.47$ V	$V_R = 2.51$ V $I = 140$ μA
21.	$X_L = 28.1$ kΩ;	$\theta = 52.0°$;	$f = 5.59$ kHz		$E = 21.6$ V	$V_R = 13.3$ V $I = 605$ μA
23.	$X_L = 1.60$ kΩ;	$\theta = 64.9°$;	$f = 2.55$ kHz		$E = 29.8$ V;	$V_R = 12.6$ V $I = 16.9$ mA
25.	$X_L = 8.65$ kΩ;	$\theta = 51.8°$;	$L = 320$ mH;		$E = 7.63$ V;	$V_R = 4.72$ V; $I = 694$ μA
27.	$X_L = 4.27$ kΩ;	$\theta = 62.7°$;	$L = 90.5$ mH;		$V_R = 2.32$ V;	$E = 5.06$ V $I = 1.05$ mA
29.	$X_L = 68.4$ kΩ;	$\theta = 55.5°$;	$L = 1.98$ H;		$V_R = 13.8$ V;	$E = 24.3$ V $I = 293$ μA
31.	$X_L = 5.51$ kΩ;	$\theta = 54.7°$;	$L = 73.1$ mH		$V_R = 6.01$ V;	$E = 10.4$ V $I = 1.54$ m

End of Chapter Problems 19–5

1.	$Z_r = 20.7$ kΩ + j23 kΩ;	$Z_p = 30.9$ /48° kΩ
3.	$Z_r = 599$ Ω – j740 Ω;	$Z_p = 9526$ /–51° Ω
5.	$Z_r = 820$ Ω – j251 Ω;	$Z_p = 857$ /–17° Ω
7.	$Z_r = 4.49$ kΩ – j4.49 kΩ;	$Z_p = 6.35$ /–45° kΩ
9.	$Z_r = 40$ kΩ – j30 kΩ;	$Z_p = 50$ /–36° kΩ
11.	$Z_r = 180$ kΩ + j120 kΩ;	$Z_p = 216$ /33.7° kΩ
13.	$Z_r = 3.49$ kΩ – j3 kΩ;	$Z_p = 4.6$ /–40.7° kΩ

15. $Z_r = 3.82$ kΩ $+ j3.75$ kΩ; $Z_p = 5.35 \underline{/44.5°}$ kΩ

17. $Z_r = 10$ kΩ $+ j18$ kΩ; $Z_p = 20.6 \underline{/61.0°}$ kΩ

19. $Z_r = 1.8$ kΩ $- j1.45$ kΩ; $Z_p = 2.31 \underline{/-38.9°}$ kΩ

21. $E_r = 10$ V $+ j12.7$ V; $E_p = 16.2 \underline{/51.8°}$ V

23. $E_r = 4.32$ V $- j6.25$ V; $E_p = 7.60 \underline{/-55.4°}$ V

25. $E_r = 10.6$ V $- j5.7$ V; $E_p = 12 \underline{/-28.4°}$ V

27. $E_r = 12.4$ V $+ j8.5$ V; $E_p = 15 \underline{/35.5°}$ V

29. $E_r = 11.5$ V $- j9.64$ V; $E_p = 15 \underline{/-40°}$ V

31. $E_r = 11.5$ V $+ j7.93$ V; $E_p = 14 \underline{/34.6°}$ V

33. $E_r = 120$ V $- j64$ V; $E_p = 136 \underline{/-28°}$ V

35. $E_r = 2.6$ V $+ j4.27$ V; $E_p = 5 \underline{/58.7°}$ V

37. $E_r = 25.4$ V $+ j16$ V; $E_p = 30 \underline{/32.2°}$ V

39. $E_r = 8$ V $- j6$ V; $E_p = 10 \underline{/-36.9°}$ V

End of Chapter Problems 19–6

Note To Student: Convert polar to rectangular. Then add in rectangular form. Convert rectangular answer back to polar.

1. $Z_1 = 2 \underline{/20°}$ kΩ = 1879 Ω $+ j684.0$ Ω
   $Z_2 = 3 \underline{/65°}$ kΩ = 1268 Ω $+ j2719$ Ω
   $Z_T = 4.64 \underline{/27.2°}$ kΩ = 3147 Ω $+ j3403$ Ω

3. $Z_1 = 11 \underline{/-20°}$ kΩ = 10.3 kΩ $- j3.76$ kΩ
   $Z_2 = 15 \underline{/-30°}$ kΩ = 13 kΩ $- j17.5$ kΩ
   $Z_T = 25.9 \underline{/-25.8°}$ kΩ = 23.3 kΩ $- j11.3$ kΩ

5. $Z_1 = 7.3 \underline{/-25°}$ kΩ = 6.62 kΩ $- j3.09$ kΩ
   $Z_2 = 3 \underline{/40°}$ kΩ = 2.30 kΩ $+ j1.93$ kΩ
   $Z_T = 9.00 \underline{/-7.41°}$ kΩ = 8.92 kΩ $- j1.16$ k

7. $Z_1 = 78 \underline{/38°}$ kΩ = 61.5 kΩ $+ j48.0$ kΩ
   $Z_2 = 50 \underline{/-65°}$ kΩ = 21.1 kΩ $- j45.3$ kΩ
   $Z_T = 82.6 \underline{/1.87°}$ kΩ = 82.6 kΩ $+ j2.7$ kΩ

9. $Z_1 = 270 \underline{/30°}$ kΩ = 234 kΩ $+ j135$ kΩ
   $Z_2 = 150 \underline{/30°}$ kΩ = 130 kΩ $+ j75$ kΩ
   $Z_T = 420 \underline{/30°}$ kΩ = 364 kΩ $+ j210$ kΩ
   j2.44 kΩ

11. $Z_1 = 7.5 \underline{/-90°}$ kΩ = 0 kΩ $- j7.5$ kΩ
    $Z_2 = 13.5 \underline{/22°}$ kΩ = 12.5 kΩ $+ j5.06$ kΩ
    $Z_T = 12.8 \underline{/-11.0°}$ kΩ = 12.5 kΩ $-$

End of Chapter Problems 19–7

1. $Z = 1.76$ kΩ $+ j3$ kΩ $= 3.48 \underline{/59.6°}$ kΩ
3. $Z = 1.15$ kΩ $+ j1.3$ kΩ $= 1.47 \underline{/48.5°}$ kΩ

5. $X_C = 1 / (2fC) = 1 / (2\pi \times 1.2$ kHz $\times 100$ nF$) = 1.33$ kΩ

$X_L = 2\pi fL = 2\pi \times 1.2$ kHz $\times 800$ mH $= 6.03$ kΩ; $Z_r = 3.4$ kΩ $+ j4.70$ kΩ$Z_p = 5.80 \underline{/54.1°}$ kΩ

In the ESC: R = 3.4 kΩ and L = $X_L / (2\pi f) = 4.7$ kΩ $/ (2\pi \times 1.2$ kHz$) = 623$ mH

7. $X_C = 1 / (2\pi fC) = 1 / (2\pi \times 500 \text{ Hz} \times 350 \text{ nF}) = 909 \ \Omega$

$X_L = 2\pi fL = 2\pi \times 500 \text{ Hz} \times 200 \text{ mH} = 628 \ \Omega$; $Z_r = 200 \ \Omega - j281\Omega$; $Z_p = 345 \ \underline{/-54.5°} \ \Omega$

In the ESC: $R = 200 \ \Omega$ and $C = 1 / (2fX_C) = 1 / (2\pi \times 500 \text{ Hz} \times 281 \ \Omega) = 1.13 \ \mu\text{F}$

$$I = \frac{E}{Z} = \frac{25 \text{ V}}{345 \ \Omega} = 72.5 \text{ mA}; \ V_R = IR = 72.5 \text{ mA} \times 200 \ \Omega = 14.5 \text{ V}$$

$V_C = IX_C = 72.5 \text{ mA} \times 909 \ \Omega = -65.9 \text{ V}; \ V_L = IX_L = 72.5 \text{ mA} \times 628 \ \Omega = 45.5 \text{ V}$

End of Chapter Problems 19–8

1. $f_r = 1 / (2\pi[LC]^{1/2}) = 1 / (2\pi \times [750 \text{ mH} \times 5 \text{ nF}]^{1/2}) = 2.60 \text{ kHz}$

at f_r: $X_C = 1 / (2fC) = 1 / (2\pi \times 2.60 \text{ kHz} \times 5 \text{ nF}) = 12.2 \text{ k}\Omega$

$X_L = 2\pi fL = 2\pi \times 2.60 \text{ kHz} \times 750 \text{ mH} = 12.2 \text{ k}\Omega$

$Z = 470 \ \Omega + j12.2 \text{ k}\Omega - j12.2 \text{ k}\Omega = 470 \ \Omega + j0 = 470 \ \underline{/0°} \ \Omega$

$I = E / Z = 10 \text{ V} / 470 = 21.3 \text{ mA}; \ V_R = IR = 21.3 \text{ mA} \times 470 \ \Omega = 10 \text{ V}$

$V_C = IX_C = 21.3 \text{ mA} \times 12.2 \text{ k}\Omega = -260 \text{ V}; \ V_L = IX_L = 21.3 \text{ mA} \times 12.2 \text{ k}\Omega = 260 \text{ V}$

The ESC is: $R = 470 \ \Omega$

at $f = 2.3 \text{ kHz}$: $X_C = 1 / (2fC) = 1 / (2\pi \times 2.30 \text{ kHz} \times 5 \text{ nF}) = 13.8 \text{ k}\Omega$;

$X_L = 2\pi fL = 2\pi \times 2.30 \text{ kHz} \times 750 \text{ mH} = 10.8 \text{ k}\Omega$

$Z = 470 \ \Omega + j10.8 \text{ k}\Omega - j13.8 \text{ k}\Omega = 470 \ \Omega - j3.00 \text{ k}\Omega = 3.04 \ \underline{/-81.1°} \text{ k}\Omega$

$I = E / Z = 10 \text{ V} / 3.04 \text{ k}\Omega = 3.29 \text{ mA}; \ V_R = IR = 3.29 \text{ mA} \times 470 \ \Omega = 1.55 \text{ V}$

$V_C = IX_C = 3.29 \text{ mA} \times 13.8 \text{ k}\Omega = -45.4 \text{ V}; \ V_L = IX_L = 3.29 \text{ mA} \times 10.8 \text{ k}\Omega = 35.5 \text{ V}$

The ESC is: $R = 470 \ \Omega$ and $C = 1 / (2\pi \times 2.3 \text{ kHz} \times 3.04 \text{ k}\Omega) = 23.1 \text{ nF}$ at $f = 2.7 \text{ kHz}$:

$X_C = 1 / (2fC) = 1 / (2\pi \times 2.70 \text{ kHz} \times 5 \text{ nF}) = 11.8 \text{ k}\Omega$

$X_L = 2\pi fL = 2\pi \times 2.70 \text{ kHz} \times 750 \text{ mH} = 12.7 \text{ k}\Omega$

$Z = 470 \ \Omega + j12.7 \text{ k}\Omega - j11.8 \text{ k}\Omega = 470 \ \Omega + j900 \ \Omega = 1.02 \ \underline{/62.4°} \text{ k}\Omega$

$I = E / Z = 10 \text{ V} / 1.02 \text{ k}\Omega = 9.80 \text{ mA}; \ V_R = IR = 9.80 \text{ mA} \times 470 \ \Omega = 4.61 \text{ V}$

$V_C = IX_C = 9.80 \text{ mA} \times 11.8 \text{ k}\Omega = -116 \text{ V}; \ V_L = IX_L = 9.80 \text{ mA} \times 12.7 \text{ k}\Omega = 125 \text{ V}$

The ESC is: $R = 470 \ \Omega$ and $L = 900 \ \Omega / (2\pi \times 2.7 \text{ kHz}) = 53.1 \text{ mH}$

3. $f_r = 1 / (2\pi[LC]^{1/2}) = 1 / (2\pi \times [1\text{ H} \times 500\text{ nF}]^{1/2}) = 225\text{ Hz}$

    at f_r: $X_L = 2\pi fL = 2\pi \times 225\text{ Hz} \times 1\text{ H} = 1.41\text{ k}\Omega$

    $X_C = 1 / 2\pi fC = 1 / (2\pi \times 225\text{ Hz} \times 500\text{ nF}) = 1.41\text{ k}\Omega$

    $Z = 300\ \Omega + j1.41\text{ k}\Omega - j1.41\text{ k}\Omega = 300\ \Omega + j0 = Z = 300\ \underline{/0°}\ \Omega$

    $I = E / Z = 25\text{ V} / 300\ \Omega = 83.3\text{ mA}$; $V_R = IR = 83.3\text{ mA} \times 300\ \Omega = 25\text{ V}$

    $V_C = IX_C = 83.3\text{ mA} \times 1.41\text{ k}\Omega = -118\text{V}$; $V_L = IX_L = 83.3\text{ mA} \times 1.41\text{ k}\Omega = 118\text{ V}$

    The ESC is: $R = 300\ \Omega$

    at $f = 200\text{ Hz}$: $X_C = 1 / (2fC) = 1 / (2\pi \times 200\text{ Hz} \times 500\text{ nF}) = 1.59\text{ k}\Omega$

    $X_L = 2\pi fL = 2\pi \times 200\text{ Hz} \times 1\text{ H} = 1.26\text{ k}\Omega$

    $Z = 300\ \Omega + j1.26\text{ k}\Omega - j1.59\text{ k}\Omega = 300\ \Omega - j330\text{ k}\Omega = 446\ \underline{/-47.7°}\ \Omega$

    $I = E / Z = 25\text{ V} / 446\ \Omega = 56.1\text{ mA}$; $V_R = IR = 56.1\text{ mA} \times 300\ \Omega = 16.8\text{ V}$

    $V_C = IX_C = 56.1\text{ mA} \times 1.59\text{ k}\Omega = -89.1\text{ V}$; $V_L = IX_L = 56.1\text{ mA} \times 1.26\text{ k}\Omega = 70.6\text{ V}$

    The ESC is: $R = 300\ \Omega$ and $C = 1 / (2\pi \times 200\text{ Hz} \times 330\ \Omega) = 2.41\ \mu\text{F}$

    at $f = 300\text{ Hz}$: $X_C = 1 / (2fC) = 1 / (2\pi \times 300\text{ Hz} \times 500\text{ nF}) = 1.06\text{ k}\Omega$

    $X_L = 2\pi fL = 2\pi \times 300\text{ Hz} \times 1\text{ H} = 1.88\text{ k}\Omega$

    $Z = 3000\ \Omega + j1.88\text{ k}\Omega - j1.06\text{ k}\Omega = 300\ \Omega + j819\ \Omega = 872\ \underline{/69.9°}\ \Omega$

    $I = E / z = 25\text{ V} / 872\ \Omega = 28.7\text{ mA}$; $V_R = IR = 28.7\text{ mA} \times 300\ \Omega = 8.60\text{ V}$

    $V_C = IX_C = 28.7\text{ mA} \times 1.06\text{ k}\Omega = -30.4\text{ V}$; $V_L = IX_L = 28.7\text{ mA} \times 1.88\text{ k}\Omega = 53.9\text{ V}$

    The ESC is: $R = 300\ \Omega$ and $L = 819\ \Omega / (2\pi \times 300\text{ Hz}) = 434\text{ mH}$

END OF CHAPTER 20 PROBLEMS

End of Chapter Problems 20–1

1. $I_r = 23.5 \text{ mA} + j32.4 \text{ mA}$; $I_p = 40 \underline{/54°} \text{ mA}$ 3. $I_r = 1.05 \text{ mA} + j2.54 \text{ mA}$; $I_p = 2.75 \underline{/76.4°} \text{ mA}$

5. $I_r = 162 \mu A + j65.6 \mu A$; $I_p = 175 \underline{/22°} \mu A$ 7. $I_r = 350 \mu A + j270 \mu A$; $I_p = 442 \underline{/37.6°} \mu A$

9. $I_r = 4.77 \text{ mA} + j7.05 \text{ mA}$; $I_p = 8.51 \underline{/55.9°} \text{ mA}$ 11. $I_r = 100 \mu A + j100 \mu A$; $I_p = 141 \underline{/45°} \mu A$

13. $I_r = 1 \text{ mA} + j649 \text{ mA}$; $I_p = 1.19 \underline{/33°} \text{ mA}$ 15. $I_r = 640 \mu A + j239 \mu A$; $I_p = 683 \underline{/20.5°} \mu A$

17. $I_r = 25.3 \text{ mA} + j47.6 \text{ mA}$; $I_p = \underline{/53.9°} \text{ mA}$ 19. $I_r = 15.5 \text{ mA} + j45 \text{ mA}$; $I_p = 47.6 \underline{/71°} \text{ mA}$

21. $I_r = 3.2 \text{ mA} + j5.44 \text{ mA}$; $I_p = 6.31 \underline{/59.5°} \text{ mA}$ 23. $I_r = 188 \mu A + j275 \mu A$; $I_p = 333 \underline{/55.7°} \mu A$

25. $I_r = 7.5 \text{ mA} + j9.37 \text{ mA}$; $I_p = 12 \underline{/51.3°} \text{ mA}$ 27. $I_r = 650 \mu A + j760 \mu A$; $I_p = 1 \underline{/49.5°} \mu A$

29. $I_r = 2.55 \text{ mA} + j1.85 \text{ mA}$; $I_p = 3.15 \underline{/36.0°} \text{ mA}$ 31. $I_r = 35 \text{ mA} + j25 \text{ mA}$; $I_p = 43 \underline{/35.5°} \text{ mA}$

33. $I_r = 346 \mu A + j200 \mu A$; $I_p = 400 \underline{/30°} \mu A$ 35. $I_r = 4.94 \text{ mA} + j3.55 \text{ mA}$; $I_p = 6.08 \underline{/35.7°} \text{ mA}$

End of Chapter Problems 20–2

1. $B_C = 2\pi fC = 2\pi \times 2 \text{ kHz} \times 30 \text{ nF} = 377 \mu S$; $G = 1 / R = 1 / 3.3 \text{ k}\Omega = 303 \mu S$

   $V = I_T / Y = 4 \text{ mA} / 484 \mu S = 8.26 \text{ V}$; $Y_r = 303 \mu S + j377 \mu S$; $Y_p = 484 \underline{/51.2°} \mu S$

   $I_r = 2.51 \text{ mA} + j3.12 \text{ mA}$;

3. $B_C = 2\pi fC = 2\pi \times 60 \text{ kHz} \times 5 \text{ nF} = 1.88 \text{ mS}$; $G = 1 / R = 1 / 750 \Omega = 1.33 \text{ mS}$

   $I_r = 577 \mu A + j816 \mu A$; $Y_r = 1.33 \text{ mS} + j1.88 \text{ mS}$; $Y_p = 2.31 \underline{/54.7°} \text{ mS}$

   $V = I_T / Y = 1 \text{ mA} / 2.31 \text{ mS} = 433 \text{ mV}$

5   $B_C = 2\pi fC = 2\pi \times 1.56 \text{ kHz} \times 10 \text{ nF} = 9.42 \mu S$; $G = I / R = 1 / 6.8 \text{ k}\Omega = 147 \mu S$

   $V = I_T / Y = 115 \text{ V}$; $Y_r = 147 \mu S + j94.2 \mu S$; $Y_p = 175 \underline{/32.7°} \mu S$

   $I_r = 166.8 \text{ mA} + j10.8 \text{ mA}$

7   $B_C = 2\pi fC = 2\pi \times 1 \text{ kHz} \times 30 \text{ nF} = 188 \mu S$; $G = I / R = 1 / 10 \text{ k}\Omega = 100 \mu S$

   $V = I_T / Y = 10 \text{ mA} / 213 \mu S = 46.9 \text{ V}$; $Y_r = 100 \mu S + j188 \mu S$; $Y_p = 213 \underline{/62.1°} \mu S$

   $I_r = 4.69 \text{ mA} + j8.83 \text{ mA}$

9   $B_C = 2\pi fC = 2\pi \times 35 \text{ kHz} \times 300 \text{ pF} = 66.0 \mu S$; $G = I / R = 1 / 15 \text{ k}\Omega = 66.7 \mu S$

   $V = I_T / Y = 2.13 \text{ V}$; $Y_r = 66.7 \mu S + j66.0 \mu S$; $Y_p = 93.83 \underline{/44.7°} \mu S$

   $I_r = 1.42 \text{ mA} + j1.441 \text{ mA}$;

11. $G = \dfrac{B_C}{\tan \theta} = \dfrac{200\ \mu S}{\tan 50°} = 168\ \mu S;$ $R = \dfrac{1}{G} = \dfrac{1}{168\ \mu S} = 5.96\ k\Omega$

 $f = \dfrac{B_C}{\tan \theta} = \dfrac{200\ \mu S}{2\pi \times 25\ nF} = 1.27\ kHz$ $I_r = \dfrac{I_R}{\cos\theta} = \dfrac{3\ mA}{\cos 50°} = 4.67\ mA$

 $V = I_R R = 3\ mA \times 5.96\ k\Omega = 17.9\ V$

End of Chapter Problems 20–3

1. 3.29 mA – j1.9 mA = 3.8 $\underline{/-30°}$ mA   3. 163 μA – j132 μA = 210 $\underline{/-39°}$ μA

5. 1.23 mA – j532 μA = 1.34 $\underline{/-23.3°}$ mA   7. 12 mA – j180 mA = 41.8 $\underline{/-73.3°}$ mA

9. 30 mA – j40 mA = 50 $\underline{/-53.1°}$ mA   11. 150 μA – j180 μA = 234 $\underline{/-50.2°}$ μA

13. 2 mA – j1.09 mA = 2.28 $\underline{/-28.5°}$ mA   15. 1.3 mA – j4.25 mA = 4.45 $\underline{/-73°}$ mA

17. 37.6 μA – j19.5 μA = 42.4$\underline{/-27.4°}$ μA   19. 730 μA – –j730 μA = 1.03 $\underline{/-45°}$ μA

21. 10.7 mA – j9 mA = 14 $\underline{/-40°}$ mA   23. 501 μA – j475 μA = 690 $\underline{/-43.53°}$ μA

25. 18.1 mA – j20 mA = 27 $\underline{/-47.8°}$ mA   27. 260 μA – j150 μA = 300 $\underline{/-30°}$ μA

29. 1.58 mA – j925 μA = 1.83 $\underline{/-30.4°}$ mA   31. 4.7 mA – j4.77 mA = 6.7 $\underline{/-45.5°}$ mA

33. 825 μA – j1.07 mA = 1.35 $\underline{/-52.3°}$ mA   35. 73.8 mA – j76.5 mA = 100 $\underline{/-42.4°}$ mA

End of Chapter Problems 20–4

With this GL circuit, the answers will be in the format of

 $Y = G - jB_L = Y\ \underline{/-\theta}$ $I = I_G - jI_L = I_T\ \underline{/-\theta}$

where $I_G = I_T \cos \theta$ $I_L = I_T \sin \theta$

 $G = 1/R$ in Siemens $B_L = 1 / (2\pi fL)$ in Siemens

 $Y = \sqrt{(G^2 + B^2)}\ \underline{/arctan\ (B/G)}$ in Siemens

If this were a GC circuit, the angle and j would be +, and $B_C = 2\pi fC$ in Siemens.

Fill in the values given in the problem and then rearrange these equations to solve for the missing values.

1. Y = 50 μS – j39.8 μS = 63.9 $\underline{/-38.5°}$ μS   I = 31.3 mA – j24.9 mA = 40 $\underline{/-38.5°}$ mA

3. Y = 100 μS – j132.6 μS = 166 $\underline{/-53.0°}$ μS   I = 120 mA – j160 mA = 200 $\underline{/-53.0°}$ mA

5. Y = 213 μS – j159 μS = 63.9 $\underline{/-36.7°}$ μS   I = 80.1 μA – j59.8 μA = 100 $\underline{/-36.7°}$ μA

7. Y = 37 μS – j31.8 μS = 48.8 $\underline{/-40.7°}$ μS   I = 303 μA – j261 μA = 400 $\underline{/-40.7°}$ μA

9. Y = 1333 μS – j663 μS = 1489 $\underline{/-26.4°}$ μS   I = 26.9 mA – j13.3 mA = 30 $\underline{/-26.4°}$ mA

End of Chapter Problems 20–5

Note To Student: The easiest way to handle a parallel circuit is to convert Ohms values to Siemens values, then add up the Siemens values. Remember that polar values must be changed to rectangular form before you can add.

1. $Z_T = 269 \; \underline{/-27°} \; \Omega$　　　　　　　　3.　$Z_T = 158 \; \underline{/40°} \; \mu S$

5.　$Y_1 = 1 / Z_1 = 1 / 700 \; \underline{/70°} \; k\Omega = 1.43 \; \underline{/-70°} \; \mu S = 489 \; nS - j1.34 \; \mu S$

　　$Y_2 = 1 / Z_2 = 1 / 1.5 \; \underline{/-25°} \; k\Omega = 667 \; \underline{/25°} \; \mu S = 604 \; \mu S + j282 \; \mu S$

　　$Y_T = Y_1 + Y_2 = 605 \; \mu S + j280 \; \mu S = 667 \; \underline{/24.9°} \; \mu S; \; Z_T = 1 / Y_T = 1500 \; \underline{/-24.9°} \; \Omega = 1361 \; \Omega - j631 \; \Omega$

7.　$Y_1 = 1 / Z_1 = 1 / 35 \; \underline{/20°} \; k\Omega = 28.63 \; \underline{/-20°} \; \mu S = 26.8 \; \mu S - j9.77 \; \mu S$

　　$Y_2 = 1 / Z_2 = 1 / 10 \; \underline{/-40°} \; k\Omega = 100 \; \underline{/+40°} \; \mu S = 76.6 \; \mu S + j64.3 \; \mu S$

　　$Y_T = Y_1 + Y_2 = 103 \; \mu S + j54.5 \; \mu S = 117 \; \underline{/27.8°} \; \mu S; \; Z_T = 1 / Y_T = 8552 \; \underline{/-27.8°} \; \Omega = 7566 \; \Omega - j3986 \; \Omega$

9.　$Y_1 = 1 / Z_1 = 1 / 3.3 \; \underline{/0°} \; k\Omega = 303 \; \underline{/0°} \; \mu S = 303 \; \mu S + j0$

　　$Y_2 = 1 / Z_2 = 1 / 1.42 \; \underline{/-90°} \; k\Omega = 238 \; \underline{/90°} \; \mu S = 0 + j238 \; \mu S$

　　$Y_T = Y_1 + Y_2 = 303 \; \mu S + j238 \; \mu S = 385 \; \underline{/38.2°} \; \mu S$

　　$Z_T = 1 / Y_T = 2.59 \; \underline{/-38.2°} \; k\Omega = 2.04 \; k\Omega - j1.60 \; k\Omega$

End of Chapter Problems 20–6

Note To Student: Remember that in a DC circuit I = GE and in an AC circuit I = VY

1.　$B_C = 2\pi fC = 2\pi \times 35 \; kHz \times 400 \; PF = 88.0 \; \mu S; \; G = 1 / R = 1 / 15 \; k\Omega = 66.7 \; \mu S$

　　$Y = 66.7 \; \mu S - j88.0 \; \mu S = 110 \; \underline{/52.8°} \; \mu S; \; I_R = 1.21 \; mA; \; I_C = 1.59 \; mA$

　　$Z_p = 1 / Y_p = 9.06 \; \underline{/-52.8°} \; k\Omega = 5.47 \; k\Omega - j7.22 \; k\Omega; \; V = I / Y_T = 2 \; mA / 110 \; \mu S = 18.1 \; V$

　　In the ESC: $R = 5.47 \; k\Omega; \; C = 1 / (2\pi fX_C) = 1 / (2\pi \times 35 \; kHz \times 7.22 \; k\Omega) = 630 \; pF$

3.　$B_C = 2\pi fC = 2\pi \times 3 \; kHz \times 150 \; nF = 2.83 \; mS; \; G = 1 / R = 1 / 470 \; \Omega = 2.13 \; mS$

　　$Y = 2.13 \; mS + j2.83 \; mS = 3.54 \; \underline{/53.0°} \; mS; \; I_R = 24.1 \; mA; \; I_L = 32.0 \; mA$

　　$Z_p = 1 / Y_p = 283 \; \underline{/-53°} \; \Omega = 170 \; \Omega - j226 \; \Omega; \; V = I_T / Y = 40 \; mA / 3.54 \; \mu S = 11.3 \; V$

　　In the ESC: $R = 170 \; \Omega; \; C = 1 / (2\pi fX_C) = 1 / (2\pi \times 3 \; kHz \times 226 \; \Omega) = 236 \; nF$

5.　$B_L = C = 1 / (2\pi fL) = 1 / (2\pi \times 150 \; kHz \times 60 \; mH) = 17.7 \; \mu S; \; G = 1 / R = 1 / 47 \; k\Omega = 21.3 \; \mu S$

　　$Y = 21.3 \; \mu S - j17.7 \; \mu S = 3.54 \; \underline{/53.0°} \; mS; \; I_R = 192 \; \mu A; \; I_L = 160 \; \mu A$

　　$Z = 36.1 \; \underline{/39.7°} \; k\Omega = 27.8 \; k\Omega + j23.1 \; k\Omega; \; V = I_T / Y = 250 \; \mu A / 27.7 \; \mu S = 9.04 \; V$

　　In the ESC: $R = 27.8 \; k\Omega$ and $C = X_L / (2\pi f) = 23.1 \; k\Omega / (2\pi \times 150 \; kHz) = 24.5 \; mH$

7.　$B_L = 1 / (2\pi fL) = 1 / (2\pi \times 5 \; kHz \times 30 \; mH) = 1.06 \; mS; \; G = 1/ R = 1 / 680 \; \Omega = 1.47 \; mS$

　　$Y = 1.47 \; mS - j1.06 \; mS = 1.81 \; \underline{/35.8°} \; mS; \; I_R = 4.06 \; mA; \; I_L = 2.92 \; mA$

　　$Z = 552 \; \underline{/35.8°} \; k\Omega = 447 \; \Omega + j323 \; \Omega; \; V = I_T / Y = 5 \; mA / 1.81 \; mS = 2.76 \; V$

　　In the ESC:　$R = 447 \; \Omega$ and $L = X_L / (2\pi f) = 323 \; \Omega / (2\pi \times 5 \; kHz) = 10.3 \; mH$

9. $B_L = 1 / (2\pi fL) = 1 / (2\pi \times 25 \text{ kHz} \times 30 \text{ mH}) = -212 \ \mu S$

    $B_C = 2\pi fC = 2\pi \times 25 \text{ kHz} \times 300 \text{ pF} = 47.1 \ \mu S$

    $G = 1 / R = 1 / 10 \text{ k}\Omega = 100 \ \mu S$; $Y = 100 \ \mu S - j165 \ \mu S = 193 \ \underline{/-58.8°} \ \mu S$

    $I_R = VG = 104 \text{ V} \times 100 \ \mu S = 10.4 \text{ mA}$; $I_C = VB_C = 104 \text{ V} \times 47.1 \ \mu S = 4.88 \text{ mA}$

    $Z = 5.18 \ \underline{/58.8°} \text{ k}\Omega = 2.68 \text{ k}\Omega + j4.43 \text{ k}\Omega$; $V = I_T / Y = 20 \text{ mA} / 193 \ \mu S = 104 \text{ V}$

    $I_L = VB_L = 104 \text{ V} \times -212 \ \mu S = -22.0 \text{ mA}$

    In the ESC: $R = 2.68 \text{ k}\Omega$ and $L = X_L / (2\pi f) = 4.43 \text{ k}\Omega / (2\pi \times 25 \text{ kHz}) = 28.2 \text{ mH}$

11. $B_L = 1 / (2\pi fL) = 1 / (2\pi \times 125 \text{ kHz} \times 4 \text{ mH}) = 2.65 \text{ mS}$

    $B_C = 2\pi fC = 2\pi \times 15 \text{ kHz} \times 30 \text{ nF} = 2.83 \text{ mS}$

    $G = 1 / R = 1 / 6.8 \text{ k}\Omega = 147 \ \mu S$; $Y = 147 \ \mu S - j175 \ \mu S = 228 \ \underline{/49.9°} \ \mu S$

    $I_R = VG = 1.75 \text{ V} \times 147 \ \mu S = 257 \ \mu A$; $I_C = VB_C = 1.75 \text{ V} \times 2.83 \text{ mS} = 4.95 \text{ mA}$

    $Z = 4.38 \ \underline{/-49.9°} \text{ k}\Omega = 2.82 \text{ k}\Omega - j3.35 \text{ k}\Omega$; $V = I_T / Y = 400 \ \mu A / 228 \ \mu S = 1.75 \text{ V}$

    $I_L = VB_L = 1.75 \text{ V} \times 265 \text{ mS} = -4.64 \text{ mA}$

    In the ESC: $R = 2.82 \text{ k}\Omega$ and $C = 1 / (2\pi fX_C) = 1 / (2\pi \times 15 \text{ kHz} \times 3.35 \text{ k}\Omega) = 3.17 \text{ nF}$

End of Chapter Problems 20–7

1. $X_C = 1 / (2\pi fC) = 1 / (2\pi \times 4 \text{ kHz} \times 50 \text{ nF}) = 796 \ \Omega$

    $G = R / \left(R^2 + X_C^2 \right) = 680 \ \Omega / (680 \ \Omega^2 + 796 \ \Omega^2) = 621 \ \mu S$

    $B_C = X_C / \left(R^2 + X_C^2 \right) = 796 \ \Omega / (680 \ \Omega^2 + 796 \ \Omega^2) = 726 \ \mu S$

    $Y_r = 621 \ \mu S + j726 \ \mu S$; $C = B_C / (2\pi f) = 726 \ \mu S / (2\pi \times 4 \text{ kHz}) = 28.9 \text{ nF}$

3. $X_C = 1 / (2\pi fC) = 1 / (2\pi \times 120 \text{ kHz} \times 100 \text{ pF}) = 13.3 \text{ k}\Omega$

    $G = R / \left(R^2 + X_C^2 \right) = 15 \text{ k}\Omega / (15 \text{ k}\Omega^2 + 13.3 \text{ k}\Omega^2) = 37.4 \ \mu S$

    $B_C = X_C / \left(R^2 + X_C^2 \right) = 13.3 \text{ k}\Omega / (15 \text{ k}\Omega^2 + 13.3 \text{ k}\Omega^2) = 33.1 \ \mu S$

    $Y_r = 37.4 \ \mu S + j33.1 \ \mu S$; $C = B_C / (2\pi f) = 33.1 \ \mu S / (2\pi \times 120 \text{ kHz}) = 43.9 \text{ pF}$

5. $X_L = 2\pi fL = 2\pi \times 2.65 \text{ kHz} \times 100 \text{ mH} = 1.67 \text{ k}\Omega$

    $G = R / \left(R^2 + X_C^2 \right) = 2.2 \text{ k}\Omega / (2.2 \text{ k}\Omega^2 + 1.67 \text{ k}\Omega^2) = 289 \ \mu S$

    $B_L = X_L / \left(R^2 + X_L^2 \right) = 1.67 \text{ k}\Omega / (2.2 \text{ k}\Omega^2 + 1.67 \text{ k}\Omega^2) = 219 \ \mu S$

    $Y_r = 289 \ \mu S - j219 \ \mu S$; $L = 1 / (2\pi fB_L) = 1 / (2\pi \times 2.65 \text{ k} \times 219 \ \mu S) = 274 \text{ mH}$

7. $X_L = 2\pi fL = 2\pi \times 10 \text{ kHz} \times 200 \text{ mH} = 12.6 \text{ k}\Omega$

    $G = R / \left(R^2 + X_L^2 \right) = 15 \text{ k}\Omega / (15 \text{ k}\Omega^2 + 12.6 \text{ k}\Omega^2) = 39.2 \ \mu S$

    $B_L = X_L / \left(R^2 + X_L^2 \right) = 12.6 \text{ k}\Omega / (15 \text{ k}\Omega^2 + 12.6 \text{ k}\Omega^2) = 32.8 \ \mu S$; $Y_r = 39.2 \ \mu S - j32.8 \ \mu S$

    $L = 1 / (2\pi fB_L) = 1 / (2\pi \times 10 \text{ kHz} \times 32.8 \ \mu S) = 485 \text{ mH}$

9. $B_C = 2\pi fC = 2\pi \times 10\ \text{kHz} \times 2\ \text{nf} = 126\ \mu S$

$R = G / \left(G^2 + B_C^2\right) = 256\ \mu S / (256\ \mu S^2 + 126\ \mu S^2) = 3.15\ k\Omega$

$X_C = B_C / \left(G^2 + B_C^2\right) = 126\ \mu S / (256\ \mu S^2 + 126\ \mu S^2) = 1.55\ k\Omega;\ Z_r = 3.15\ k\Omega - j1.55\ k\Omega$

$C = 1 / (2\pi fX_C) = 1 / (2\pi \times 10\ \text{kHz} \times 1.55\ k\Omega) = 10.3\ \text{nF}$

11. $B_C = 2\pi fC = 2\pi \times 3.25\ \text{kHz} \times 100\ \text{nf} = 2.04\ \text{mS}$

$R = G / \left(G^2 + B_C^2\right) = 1.22\ \text{mS} / (1.22\ \text{mS}^2 + 2.04\ \text{mS}^2) = 216\ \Omega$

$X_C = B_C / \left(G^2 + B_C^2\right) = 2.04\ \text{mS} / (1.2\ \text{mS}^2 + 2.04\ \text{mS}^2) = 361\ \Omega;\ Z_r = 216\ \Omega - j361\ \Omega$

$C = 1 / (2\pi fX_C) = 1 / (2\pi \times 3.25\ \text{kHz} \times 361\ \Omega) = 136\ \text{nF}$

13. $B_L = 1 / (2\pi fC) = 1 / (2\pi \times 100\ \text{Hz} \times 200\ \text{mH}) = 7.96\ \text{mS}$

$R = G / \left(G^2 + B_L^2\right) = 14.7\ \text{mS} / (14.7\ \text{mS}^2 + 7.96\ \text{mS}^2) = 52.6\ \Omega$

$X_L = B_L / \left(G^2 + B_L^2\right) = 7.96\ \text{mS} / (14.7\ \text{mS}^2 + 7.96\ \text{mS}^2) = 28.5\ \Omega;\ Z_r = 52.6\ \Omega + j28.5\ \Omega$

$L = X_L / (2\pi f) = 28.5\ \Omega / (2\pi \times 100\ \text{Hz}) = 45.3\ \text{mH}$

15. $B_L = 1 / (2\pi fL) = 1 / (2\pi \times 8.1\ \text{kHz} \times 30\ \text{mH}) = 655\ \mu S$

$R = G / \left(G^2 + B_L^2\right) = 110\ \mu S / (110\ \mu S^2 + 655\ \mu S^2) = 249\ \Omega$

$X_L = B_L / \left(G^2 + B_L^2\right) = 655\ \mu S / (110\ \mu S^2 + 655\ \mu S^2) = 1.48\ k\Omega;\ Z_r = 249\ \Omega + j1.48\ k\Omega$

$L = X_L / (2\pi f) = 1.48\ k\Omega / (2\pi \times 8.1\ \text{kHz}) = 29.2\ \text{mH}$

End of Chapter Problems 20–8

1. Convert the RL series circuit to its parallel equivalent:

$G = 4.99\ \mu S$ and $B_L = 99.8\ \mu S$ so $Y_r = G + jB_C - jB_L = 4.99\ \mu S + j50\ \mu S - j99.8\ \mu S = 4.99\ \mu S - j49.8\ \mu S$

(equivalent circuit is GL) $Z_r = 2.00\ k\Omega + j19.9\ k\Omega$

3. Convert the RL series circuit to its parallel equivalent: $G = 60\ \mu S$ and $B_L = 20\ \mu S$

Convert the RC series circuit to its parallel equivalent: $G = 860\ \mu S$ and $B_C = 40\ \mu S$

$Y_r = G_1 + G_2 + jB_C - jB_L = 140\ \mu S + j20\ \mu S$ (equivalent circuit is GC); $Z_r = 7.00\ k\Omega - j1.00\ k\Omega$

5. Convert the RL series circuit to its parallel equivalent: $G = 13.8\ \mu S$ and $B_L = 17.9\ \mu S$

$Y_r = G + jB_C - jB_L = 13.8\ \mu S + j32.1\ \mu S$ (equivalent circuit is GC)

R series $= 11.3\ k\Omega$ and $X_C = 26.3\ k\Omega;\ Z_T = R_1 + R_s - jX_C = 16.9\ k\Omega - j26.3\ k\Omega$

7. Convert the RL series circuit to its parallel equivalent: $G_1 = 41.7\ \mu S$ and $B_L = 41.7\ \mu S$

Convert the RC series circuit to its parallel equivalent: $G_2 = 91.7\ \mu S$ and $B_C = 27.5\ \mu S$

$Y_r = G_1 + G_2 + jB_C - jB_L = 133\ \mu S - 14.2\ \mu S$ (equivalent circuit is RL)

Z_r (of the equivalent circuit) $= 7.41\ k\Omega + j789\ \Omega;\ Z_r = R_1 + R_s + X_L - X_{C1} = 8.61\ k\Omega - 9.21\ k\Omega$

9. $B_C = 2\pi fC = 2\pi \times 1$ kHz $\times 3$ nf $= 18.8$ μS; $X_L = 2\pi fL = 2\pi \times 1$ kHz $\times 500$ mH $= 3.14$ kΩ

    Convert the series RL to its parallel equivalent: $G = 92.0$ μS and $B_L = 289$ μS

11. $X_C = X_L / (2\pi fC) = 1 / (2\pi \times 5$ kHz $\times 3$ nF$)$ $= 10.6$ kΩ

    $X_L = 2\pi fL = 2\pi \times 5$ kHz $\times 250$ mH $= 7.85$ kΩ

    Convert the series RL circuit to its parallel equivalent: $G = 8.07$ μS and $B_L = 127$ μS

    Convert the series RC circuit to its parallel equivalent: $G_2 = 1.78$ μS and $B_C = 94.2$ μS

    $Y_r = 9.85$ μS $- j32.8$ μS (equivalent circuit is GL); $Z_r = 7.41$ kΩ $+ j789$ Ω

    $Z_r = 8.45$ kΩ $+ j28.1$ kΩ; $R = 8.45$ kΩ; $\theta = 73.2°$; $L = X_L / (2\pi f) = 28.1$ kΩ $/ (2\pi \times 5$ kHz$) = 895$ mH

13. Find the ESC of the series parallel circuit: $X_{C2} = 1 / (2\pi \times 1$ kHz $\times 8$ nF$) = 19.9$ kΩ;

    $X_L = 2\pi \times 1$ kHz $\times 3.5$ H $= 22.0$ kΩ

    Convert the series RL circuit to its parallel equivalent: $G_1 = 22.6$ μS and $B_L = 24.9$ μS

    Convert the series RC circuit to its parallel equivalent: $G_2 = 15.4$ μS and $B_C = 45.0$ μS

    $Y_r = 38.0$ μS $+ j20.0$ μS (equivalent circuit is GC); $Z_r = 20.6$ kΩ $+ j10.9$ Ω

    circuit $Z_r = 3.3$ kΩ $+ 20.6$ kΩ $- j10.9$ kΩ $- j7.97$ kΩ $= 23.9$ kΩ $- j18.9$ kΩ

    $R = 23.9$ kΩ; $\theta = -38.3°$; $C = 1 / (2\pi fX_C) = 1 / (2\pi \times 1$ kHz $\times 18.9$ k$\Omega) = 8.42$ nF

15. $X_L = 2\pi fL = 2\pi \times 6.7$ kHz $\times 150$ mH $= 6.31$ kΩ; $B_C = 2\pi fC = 2\pi \times 6.7$ kHz $\times 10$ nF $= 421$ μS

    Convert the series RL circuit to its parallel equivalent: $G = 45.6$ μS and $B_L = 144$ μS

    $Y_r = 45.6$ μS $- j144$ μS $+ j421$ μS $= 45.6$ μS $+ j277$ μS; $Z_r = 583$ Ω $- j3.52$ kΩ

    circuit $Z_r = 583$ Ω $+ 5.6$ kΩ $- j3.52$ kΩ $= 6.18$ kΩ $- j3.52$ kΩ; $R = 6.18$ kΩ

    $\theta = -29.7°$; $C = 1 / (2\pi fX_C) = 1 / (2\pi \times 6.7$ kHz $\times 10$ nF$) = 6.75$ nF

END OF CHAPTER 21 PROBLEMS

End of Chapter Problems 21–1

1. $I_{max} = \dfrac{V_{in}}{R} = \dfrac{15\text{ V}}{470\ \Omega} = 31.9$ mA, $P_{max} = \dfrac{V_{in}^2}{R} = \dfrac{(15\text{ V})^2}{470\ \Omega} = 479$ mW, $V_{c(max)} = V_{in} = 15$ V

    at f_{co} : $X_c = R = 470\ \Omega$, $Z = R - jX_c = 665\ \underline{/-45°}\ \Omega$

    $I = V_{in} / Z = 15$ V $/ 665\ \Omega = 22.6$ mA, $P = I^2\ R = (22.6\text{ mA})^2 \times 470\ \Omega = 239$ mW

    $V_o = IX_c = 22.6$ mA $\times 470\ \Omega = 10.6$ V

3. $I_{max} = V_{in} / R = 300$ mV $/ 5.6$ kΩ $= 53.6\ \mu$A, $P_{max} = V_{in}^2 / R\ (300\text{ mV})^2 / 5.6$ kΩ $= 16.1\ \mu$W

    $V_{c(max)} = V_{in} = 300$ mV

    at f_{co} : $X_c = 5.6$ kΩ, $Z = R - jX_c = 7.92\underline{/-45°}\ \Omega$; $I = V_{in} / Z = 300$ mV $/ 7.92$ kΩ $= 37.9\ \mu$A,

    $P = I^2R = 8.03\ \mu$W; $V_o = IX_c = 37.9\ \mu$A $\times 5.6$ kΩ $= 212$ mV

5. $f_{co} = 1 / (2\pi RC) = 1 / (2\pi \times 1.2$ kΩ $\times 500$ nF$) = 265$ Hz

    $X_c = R = 1.2$ kΩ, $Z = R - jX_c = 1.70\underline{/-45°}$ kΩ, $I = V_{in} / Z = 11.8$ mA

    $P = I^2R = (11.8\text{ mA})^2 \times 1.2$ kΩ $= 166$ mW, $V_c = V_{in} \sin\theta = 14.1$ V

7. $f_{co} = 1 / (2\pi RC) = 1 / (2\pi \times 2.2$ kΩ $\times 200$ nF$) = 362$ Hz

    $X_c = R = 2.2$ kΩ, $Z = R - jX_c = 3.11\underline{/-45°}$ kΩ, $I = V_{in} / Z = 12.9$ mA

    $P = I^2R = (12.9\text{ mA})^2 \times 2.2$ kΩ $= 364$ mW, $V_c = V_{in} \sin\theta = 28.3$ V

End of Chapter Problems 21–2

1. C is the load. $R_{TH} = R_3 + R_1 \| R_2 = 1$ kΩ $+ 1.16$ kΩ $= 2.16$ kΩ

    $f_{co} = 1 / (2\pi R_{TH}C) = 1 / (2\pi \times 2.16$ kΩ $\times 500$ nF$) = 147$ Hz

    $V_{oc} = V_2 = ER_2 / (R_1 + R_2) = 10$ V $\times 3.3$ kΩ $/ (1.8$ kΩ $+ 3.3$ kΩ$) = 6.47$ V

    $V_c = V_{co} \sin 45° = 4.57$ V, $I_c = I_3 = V_c / X_c = 4.58$ V $/ 2.16$ kΩ $= 2.11$ mA

    $V_o = V_3 = I_3R_3 = 2.12$ mA $\times 1$ kΩ $= 2.12$ V

3. $R_{TH} = R_2 = 2$ kΩ and $E = 20$ V

    $f_{co} = 1 / (2\pi R_{TH}C) = 1 / (2\pi \times 2$ kΩ $\times 2\ \mu$F$) = 39.8$ Hz, $V_o = V_{co} \sin 45° = 14.1$ V

5. $R_{TH} = R_1 + R_2 \| R_3 = 2.7$ kΩ $+ 2.3$ kΩ $= 5.00$ kΩ, $V_{co} = E = 10$ V

    $f_{co} = 1 / (2\pi R_{TH}C) = 1 / (2\pi \times 5$ kΩ $\times 1\ \mu$F$) = 31.8$ Hz

    $V_{o(max)} = ER_X / (R_1 + R_X)$ where $R_X = R_2 \| R_3$, $V_{o(max)} = 10$ V $\times 2.3$ kΩ $/ (2.3$ kΩ $+ 2.7$ kΩ$) = 4.6$ V

    V_o at $f_{co} = V_{c(max)} \sin 45° = 3.25$ V

7. $R_{TH} = R_1 + R_2 \| R_3 = 2 \text{ k}\Omega + 2.08 \text{ k}\Omega = 4.08 \text{ k}\Omega;$

$V_{oc} = ER_3 / (R_2 + R_3) = 9 \times 5.6 \text{ k}\Omega / (8.9 \text{ k}\Omega) = 5.66 \text{ V};$

$f_{co} = 1 / (2\pi R_{TH}C) = 1 / (2\pi \times 4.08 \text{ k}\Omega \times 1 \text{ }\mu\text{F}) = 39 \text{ Hz}$

9. $I_{sc} = E / R_1 = 15 \text{ V} / 470 \text{ k}\Omega = 31.9 \text{ mA}; G_N = G_1 + G_2 = 2.13 \text{ mS} + 833 \text{ }\mu\text{S} = 2.96 \text{ mS}$

$f_{co} = G_N / (2\pi C) = 9.43 \text{ kHz}, V_{o(max)} = I_{sc} / G_N = 10.8 \text{ V}; V_o \text{ at } f_{co} = 10.8 \text{ V} \times \sin 45° = 7.62 \text{ V}$

11. $I_{sc} = E / R_1 = 10 \text{ V} / 2 \text{ k}\Omega = 5 \text{ mA}, G_N = G_1 + G_2 + G_3 = 891 \text{ }\mu\text{S}$

$f_{co} = G_N / (2\pi C) = 891 \text{ }\mu\text{S} / (2\pi \times 1 \text{ nF}) = 142 \text{ kHz}$

$V_{c(max)} = I_{sc} / G_N = 5 \text{ mA} / 891 \text{ }\mu\text{S} = 5.61 \text{ V}, V_o \text{ at } f_{co} = 5.61 \text{ V} \times \sin 45° = 3.97 \text{ V}$

End of Chapter Problems 21–3

1. $R_{TH} = R_1 + R_2 = 1.88 \text{ k}\Omega, f_1 = 1 / (2\pi R_{TH}C_1) = 1 / (2\pi \times 1.88 \text{ k}\Omega \times 500 \text{ nF}) = 169 \text{ Hz}$

$G_N = G_1 + G_2 = 1.47 \text{ mS} + 833 \text{ }\mu\text{S} = 2.30 \text{ mS}$

$f_2 = G_N / (2\pi R_{TH}C_2) = 2.30 \text{ mS} / (2\pi \times 2 \text{ nF}) = 183 \text{ kHz}$

$V_o \text{ at } f_{oc} = ER_2 / (R_1 + R_2) = 9 \text{ V} \times 1.2 \text{ k}\Omega / (680 \text{ }\Omega + 1.2 \text{ k}\Omega) = 5.74 \text{ V}$

$V_o \text{ at } f_{co} = V_{c(max)} \times \sin 45° = 4.06 \text{ V}$

3. $R_{TH} = R_1 + R_2 = 5.3 \text{ k}\Omega, f_1 = 1 / (2\pi R_{TH}C_1) = 1 / (2\pi \times 5.38 \text{ k}\Omega \times 2 \text{ }\mu\text{F}) = 15 \text{ Hz}$

$G_N = G_1 + G_2 = 803 \text{ }\mu\text{S}, f_2 = G_N / (2\pi C_2) = 803 \text{ }\mu\text{S} / (2\pi \times 1 \text{ nF}) = 128 \text{ kHz}$

$V_o \text{ at } f_{oc} = ER_2 / (R_1 + R_2) = 5.66 \text{ V}, V_o \text{ at } f_{co} = 5.66 \text{ V} \times \sin 45° = 4 \text{ V}$

5. $R_{TH} = R_1 + R_2 = 6.1 \text{ k}\Omega, f_1 = 1 / (2\pi R_{TH}C_1) = 1 / (2\pi \times 6.1 \text{ k}\Omega \times 1.2 \text{ }\mu\text{F}) = 21.7 \text{ Hz}$

$G_N = G_1 + G_2 = 711 \text{ }\mu\text{S}, f_2 = G_N / (2\pi C_2) = 7113 \text{ }\mu\text{S} / (2\pi \times 20 \text{ nF}) = 5.66 \text{ kHz}$

$V_o \text{ at } f_{oc} = ER_2 / (R_1 + R_2) = 1.28 \text{ V}, V_o \text{ at } f_{co} = 1.28 \text{ V} \times \sin 45° = 904 \text{ mV}$

7. $R_{TH} = R_1 + R_2 = 1.15 \text{ k}\Omega, f_1 = 1 / (2\pi R_{TH}C_1) = 1 / (2\pi \times 1.15 \text{ k}\Omega \times 200 \text{ nF}) = 692 \text{ Hz}$

$G_N = G_1 + G_2 = 4.25 \text{ mS}, f_2 = G_N / (2\pi C_2) = 4.25 \text{ mS} / (2\pi \times 500 \text{ pF}) = 1.35 \text{ mHz}$

$V_o \text{ at } f_{oc} = ER_2 / (R_1 + R_2) = 2.14 \text{ V}, V_o = 2.14 \text{ V} \times \sin 45° = 1.51 \text{ V}$

9. $R_{TH} = R_3 + R_1 \| R_2 = 1.8 \text{ k}\Omega + 1.82 \text{ k}\Omega = 3.62 \text{ k}\Omega$

$f_1 = 1 / (2\pi R_{TH}C_1) = 1 / (2\pi \times 3.62 \text{ k}\Omega \times 1 \text{ }\mu\text{F}) = 43.9 \text{ Hz}$

$G_N = G_1 + G_2 + G_3 = 1.10 \text{ mS}, f_2 = G_N / (2\pi C_2) = 1.10 \text{ mS} / (2\pi \times 2 \text{ nF}) = 87.9 \text{ kHz}$

11. $R_{TH} = R_3 + R_1 \| R_2 = 6.8 \text{ k}\Omega + 938 \text{ }\Omega = 7.74 \text{ k}\Omega$

$f_1 = 1 / (2\pi R_{TH}C_1) = 1 / (2\pi \times 7.74 \text{ k}\Omega \times 2 \text{ }\mu\text{F}) = 10.3 \text{ Hz}$

$G_N = G_1 + G_2 + G_3 = 1.21 \text{ mS}, f_2 = G_N / (2\pi C_2) = 1.21 \text{ mS} / (2\pi \times 800 \text{ pF}) = 241 \text{ kHz}$

13. $BW = f_r / Q = 2 \text{ kHz} / 25 = 80 \text{ Hz}; f_1 = f_r - BW / 2 = 2 \text{ kHz} - 40 \text{ Hz} = 1.96 \text{ kHz}$

$f_2 = f_1 + BW / 2 = 2 \text{ kHz} + 40 \text{ Hz} = 2.04 \text{ kHz}$

at f_1: $V_R = V_{in} = 20 \text{ V}, I = V_{in} / R = 20 \text{ V} / 1 \text{ k}\Omega = 20 \text{ mA}; P = V_{in} \times I = 400 \text{ mW}$

at f_1 and f_2: $V_R = V_{R(max)} \sin 45° = 20 \text{ V} \times \sin 45° = 14.1 \text{ V}; I = V_R / R = 14.1 \text{ V} / 1 \text{ k}\Omega = 14.1 \text{ mA}$

$P = IV_R = 14.1 \text{ mA} \times 14.1 \text{ V} = 200 \text{ mW}$

15. $BW = f_r / Q = 5.5 \text{ kHz} / 14 = 393 \text{ Hz}$

$f_1 = f_r - BW / 2 = 5.30 \text{ kHz}, f_2 = f_r + BW / 2 = 5.70 \text{ kHz}$

at f_1: $V_R = V_{in} = 5 \text{ V}, I = V_{in} / R = 5 \text{ V} / 120 \text{ }\Omega = 41.7 \text{ mA}; P = V_{in} \times I = 5 \text{ V} \times 41.7 \text{ mA} = 208 \text{ mW}$

at f_1 and f_2: $V_R = V_{R(max)} \sin 45° = 5 \text{ V} \times \sin 45° = 3.54 \text{ V}; I = V_R / R = 3.54 \text{ V} / 120 \text{ }\Omega = 29.5 \text{ mA}$

$P = V_R \ \ I = 3.54 \text{ V} \times 29.5 \text{ mA} = 104 \text{ mW}$

17. $f_r = 1 / [2\pi(LC)^{1/2}] = 1 / [2\pi(100 \text{ mH} \times 250 \text{ nF})^{1/2}] = 1.01 \text{ kHz}$

$X_L = 2\pi fL = 2\pi \times 1.01 \text{ kHz} \times 100 \text{ mH} = 632 \text{ }\Omega; Q = X_L / R = 632 \text{ }\Omega / 45 \text{ }\Omega = 14.1$

$BW = f_r / Q = 1.01 \text{ kHz} / 14.1 = 71.9 \text{ Hz}$

$f_1 = f_r - BW / 2 = 974 \text{ Hz}. f_2 = f_r + BW / 2 = 1.05 \text{ kHz}$

19. $f_r = 1 / [2\pi(LC)] = 3.56 \text{ kHz}, X_L = 2\pi fL = 447 \text{ }\Omega$

$Q = X_L / R = 447 \text{ }\Omega / 75 \text{ }\Omega = 5.96, BW = \dfrac{f_r}{Q} = 597 \text{ Hz}$

$f_1 = f_r - BW / 2 = 3.56 \text{ kHz} - 299 \text{ Hz} = 3.26 \text{ kHz}.$

$f_2 = f_r - BW / 2 = 3.56 \text{ kHz} + 299 \text{ Hz} = 3.86 \text{ kHz}$

END OF CHAPTER 22 PROBLEMS

End of Chapter Problems 22–1

Note To Student: Remember that $\log_B N = L$ is logarithmic form and $B^L = N$ is exponential form for the same fact. When no Base is specified, the B is considered to be 10 for common log.

Logarithmic Form	Exponential Form		Logarithmic Form	Exponential Form
1. $\log 1000 = 3$	$10^3 = 1000$	3.	$\log 1 = 0$	$10^0 = 1$
5. $\log 10\ 000\ 000 = 7$	$10^7 = 10\ 000\ 000$	7.	$\log 0.1 = -1$	$10^{-1} = 0.1$
9. $\log 0.000001 = -6$	$10^{-6} = 0.000001$			

End of Chapter Problems 22–2

Note To Student: Although only 3 significant digits are required, working with logarithms often requires use of 5 significant digits, so it is often a good idea to use 4 or 5 or even 6 significant digits in the middle of problems using logs to improve accuracy. It is easier to record 5 digits and ignore 2 of them than to have to redo problem. Sometimes logs are used to obtain very accurate answers to many significant digits.

On the calculator, use 10^x rather than y^x key for exponential form. Usually the 10^x is second level function on the same key as log.

Logarithmic Form	Exponential Form		Logarithmic Form	Exponential Form
1. $\log 3.42 = 0.534$	$10^{0.534} = 3.42$	3.	$\log 4.05 = 0.608$	$10^{0.608} = 1$
5. $\log 6.44 = 0.809$	$10^{0.809} = 6.44$	7.	$\log 9.45 = 0.975$	$10^{0.975} = 9.45$
9. $\log 2.50 = 0.398$	$10^{0.398} = 2.50$			

End of Chapter Problems 22–3

Logarithmic Form	Exponential Form		Logarithmic Form	Exponential Form
1. $\log 14 = 1.15$	$10^{1.15} = 14$	3.	$\log 743 = 2.87$	$10^{2.87} = 743$
5. $\log 1,070 = 3.03$	$10^{3.03} = 1,070$	7.	$\log 43.4 = 1.64$	$10^{1.64} = 43.4$
9. $\log 10\ 000 = 4.00$	$10^{4.00} = 10\ 000$	11.	$\log 23\ 400 = 4.37$	$10^{4.37} = 23\ 400$
13. $\log 47\ 000 = 4.68$	$10^{4.68} = 47\ 000$	15.	$\log 14.6 = 1.16$	$10^{1.16} = 14.6$
17. $\log 37\ 000 = 4.57$	$10^{4.57} = 37\ 000$	19.	$\log 2\ 000\ 000 = 6.30$	$10^{6.30} = 2\ 000\ 000$

End of Chapter Problems 22–4

		Logarithmic Form	*Exponential Form*			*Logarithmic Form*	*Exponential Form*

1. $\log 0.00377 = -2.42$ $\quad 10^{-2.42} = 0.00377$ $\qquad$ 3. $\log 0.037 = -1.43$ $\qquad 10^{-1.43} = 0.037$

5. $\log 0.746 = -0.127$ $\quad 10^{-0.127} = 0.746$ $\qquad$ 7. $\log 0.407 = -0.390$ $\qquad 10^{-0.390} = 0.407$

9. $\log 0.000614 = -3.21$ $\quad 10^{-3.21} = 0.000614$ $\qquad$ 11. $\log 0.49 = -0.310$ $\qquad 10^{-0.310} = 0.49$

13. $\log 0.00814 = -2.09$ $\quad 10^{-2.09} = 0.00814$ $\qquad$ 15. $\log 0.301 = -0.521$ $\qquad 10^{-0.521} = 0.301$

17. $\log 0.975 = -0.011$ $\quad 10^{-0.011} = 0.975$ $\qquad$ 19. $\log 0.0275 = -1.56$ $\qquad 10^{-1.56} = 0.0275$

End of Chapter Problems 22–5

1. $\begin{aligned} \log 27 &= 1.4314 \\ + \log 56 &= + \underline{1.7482} \\ &3.1796 \end{aligned}$

   $10^{3.1796} = 1512 = 27(56)$

3. $\begin{aligned} \log 107 &= 2.0294 \\ + \log 243000 &= + \underline{5.3856} \\ &7.4150 \end{aligned}$

   $10^{7.4150} = 26.0 \times 10^6 = 107(243000)$

5. $\begin{aligned} \log 43 &= 1.6335 \\ + \log .143 &= - \underline{.8447} \\ &.7888 \end{aligned}$

   $10^{.7888} = 6.149 = 43(.143)$

7. $\begin{aligned} \log .043 &= -1.3665 \\ + \log .0106 &= - \underline{1.9747} \\ &-3.3412 \end{aligned}$

   $10^{-3.3412} = 455.8 \times 10^{-6} = .043(.0106)$

9. $\begin{aligned} \log .0000176 &= -4.7545 \\ + \log .000357 &= - \underline{3.4473} \\ &-8.2018 \end{aligned}$

   $10^{-8.2018} = 6.2832 \times 10^{-9} = .0000176(.000357)$

11. $\begin{aligned} \log 256 &= 2.4082 \\ + \log .00246 &= - \underline{2.6091} \\ &-.2008 \end{aligned}$

   $10^{-.2008} = .62976 = 256(.00246)$

13. $\begin{aligned} \log 78 &= 1.8921 \\ + \log .473 &= - \underline{.3251} \\ &1.5670 \end{aligned}$

   $10^{1.5670} = 36.894 = 78(.473)$

15. $\begin{aligned} \log 4730 &= 3.67486 \\ + \log .000\ 506 &= - \underline{3.29584} \\ &.37902 \end{aligned}$

   $10^{.37902} = 2.39338 = 4730(.000\ 506)$

17. $\begin{aligned} \log 760 &= 2.8808 \\ + \log 7360 &= + \underline{3.8669} \\ &6.7477 \end{aligned}$

   $10^{6.7477} = 5.5936 \times 10^6 = 760(7360)$

19. $\begin{aligned} \log 2560 &= 3.4082 \\ + \log .00457 &= + \underline{2.3400} \\ &1.0682 \end{aligned}$

   $10^{1.0682} = 11.6992 = 2560(.00457)$

End of Chapter Problems 22–6

1. $\begin{aligned} \log 1760 &= 3.2455 \\ - \log 43 &= - \underline{1.6335} \\ &1.6120 \end{aligned}$

   $10^{1.6120} = 40.93 = 1760/43$

3. $\begin{aligned} \log 65 &= 1.8129 \\ - \log 467 &= - \underline{2.6693} \\ &-0.8564 \end{aligned}$

   $10^{-0.8564} = .13919 = 65/467$

5. $\begin{aligned} \log .00273 &= -2.56384 \\ - \log 172 &= - \underline{2.23553} \\ &-4.79937 \end{aligned}$

   $10^{-4.79937} = 15.87 \times 10^{-6} = .00273/172$

7. $\begin{aligned} \log 4300 &= 3.63347 \\ - \log 0.15 &= + \underline{.82391} \\ &4.45738 \end{aligned}$

   $10^{4.45738} = 28667 = 4300/.15$

9. $\log .0675 = -1.17070$
    $\underline{-\log .00103 = +\ 2.98716}$
    1.81647

    $10^{1.81647} = 65.53 = .0675/.00103$

11. $\log .00467 = -2.33068$
    $\underline{-\log 73.2 = -\ 1.86463}$
    -4.19531

    $10^{-4.19531} = 63.79 \times 10^{-6} = .00467/73.2$

13. $\log .147 = -0.83268$
    $\underline{+\log .0432 = +\ 1.36452}$
    $.53183$

    $10^{.53183} = 3.4028 = .147/.0432$

15. $\log 4730 = 3.67486$
    $\underline{-\log .443 = +\ 0.35360}$
    4.02846

    $10^{4.02846} = 10677 = 4730/.443$

17. $\log 0.445 = -0.35164$
    $\underline{-\log 635 = -\ 2.80277}$
    -3.15441

    $10^{-3.15441} = .000\ 700\ 787 = .445/635$

19. $\log 0.00275 = -2.56067$
    $\underline{-\log 4.35 = -\ 0.63849}$
    -3.19916

    $10^{-3.19916} = .000\ 63218 = .00275/4.35$

End of Chapter Problems 22–7

1. $3 \log 3.4 = 3\ (.53148) = 1.5944$ $10^{1.5944} = 39.3 = 3.4^3$

3. $-1.3 \log 6 = -1.3\ (.77815) = -1.01160$ $10^{-1.01160} = .097365 = 6^{-1.3}$

5. $2.5 \log .43 = 2.5\ (-.36653) = -.91632$ $10^{-.91632} = .121247 = .43^{2.5}$

7. $4.3 \log 6 = 4.3\ (.77815) = 3.34605$ $10^{3.34605} = 2218.45 = 6^{4.3}$

9. $-4.4 \log .27 = 4.4\ (-.56864) = 2.5020$ $10^{2.5020} = 317.687 = .27^{-4.4}$

11. $6.3 \log 8.7 = 6.3\ (.93952) = 5.9190$ $10^{5.9190} = 829796 = 8.7^{6.3}$

13. $3.2 \log 3.4 = 3.2\ (.53148) = 1.70073$ $10^{1.70073} = 50.203 = 3.4^{3.2}$

15. $2.3 \log 6.35 = -2.3\ (.80277) = -1.84638$ $10^{-1.84638} = .01424 = 6.35^{-2.3}$

17. $3.6 \log .045 = 3.6\ (-1.34679) = -4.8484$ $10^{-4.8484} = 14.176 \times 10^{-6} = .045^{3.6}$

19. $2.5 \log 0.00735 = -2.5\ (-2.13371) = 5.3343$ $10^{5.3343} = 215914 = .00735^{-2.5}$

End of Chapter Problems 22–8

Note To Student: Remember that $\log_B N = L$ is logarithmic form and $B^L = N$ is exponential form for the same fact. When $B = e = 2.718281828$, then $\ln N = L$ and $e^L = N$. ln can be read as natural log or as Naperian log. On the calculator, use e^x rather than y^x key for exponential form. Usually the e^x is second level functions on the same key as ln or lnX.

Logarithmic Form	*Exponential Form*		*Logarithmic Form*	*Exponential Form*
1. $\ln 2 = 0.6931$	$e^{0.6931} = 2$	3. $\ln 0.932 = -0.07042$	$e^{-0.07042} = 0.932$
5. $\ln 60 = 4.094$	$e^{4.094} = 60$	7. $\ln 0.073 = -2.617$	$e^{-2.617} = 0.073$
9. $\ln 247 = 5.509$	$e^{5.509} = 247$	11. $\ln 0.00146 = -6.529$	$e^{-6.529} = 0.00146$
13. $\ln 1100 = 7.003$	$e^{7.003} = 1100$	15. $\ln 0.00027 = -8.217$	$e^{-8.217} = 0.00027$
17. $\ln 8.43 = 2.132$	$e^{2.132} = 8.43$	19. $\ln 0.346 = -1.061$	$e^{-1.061} = 0.346$
21. $\ln 3.67 = 1.30$	$e^{1.30} = 3.67$	23. $\ln 0.107 = -2.235$	$e^{-2.235} = 0.107$
25. $\ln 176 = 5.170$	$e^{5.170} = 176$	27. $\ln 0.293 = -1.228$	$e^{-1.228} = 0.293$
29. $\ln 873 = 6.772$	$e^{6.772} = 873$	31. $\ln 10.38 = 2.34$	$e^{2.34} = 10.38$

33. $\ln 43.38 = 3.77$ $e^{3.77} = 43.38$ 35. $\ln 70.11 = 4.25$ $e^{4.25} = 70.11$

37. $\ln 200.3 = 5.3$ $e^{5.3} = 200.3$ 39. $\ln 4.711 = 1.55$ $e^{1.55} = 4.711$

41. $\ln 1.537 = .43$ $e^{.43} = 1.537$ 43. $\ln 0.9955 = -.0045$ $e^{-.0045} = 0.9955$

45. $\ln 1.162 = .15$ $e^{.15} = 1.162$ 47. $\ln 0.7298 = -.315$ $e^{-.315} = 0.7298$

49. $\ln 0.8676 = -.142$ $e^{-.142} = 0.8676$

END OF CHAPTER 23 PROBLEMS

End of Chapter Problems 23–1

Note To Student: Remember that $\log_B N = L$ is logarithmic form and $B^L = N$ is exponential form for the same fact.

1.	$10^x = 340$	3.	$10^x = 14$	5.	$10^x = 7.4$	7.	$10^y = .014$
9.	$10^y = .734$	11.	$10^y = -.00178$	13.	$x = 10^{-2.43}$	15.	$x = 10^{-3.64}$
17.	$x = 10^{-.143}$	19.	$y = 10^{1.44}$	21.	$y = 10^{2.83}$	23.	$y = 10^{4.14}$
25.	$\log y = 3.6$	27.	$\log y = 4.73$	29.	$\log y = 2.73$	31.	$\log 732 = a$
33.	$\log 47.3 = a$	35.	$\log 276 = a$	37.	$\log .043 = y$	39.	$\log .177 = y$
41.	$\log .00178 = y$	43.	$\log x = -3.4$	45.	$\log x = -2.76$	47.	$\log x = -1.17$

End of Chapter Problems 23–2

Note To Student: Remember that $\log_B M^N = N \log_B M$

1. $y = 2.291 \times 10^7$

3. $x = 1.002$

5. $a = 0.3776$

7. $x = 0.9917$

9. $x = 2.665$

11. $x = -1.762$

13. $y = -2.602$

15. $y = 4.668$

17. $x = 1.445 \times 10^4$

19. $x = 1.079$

21. $y = 2.512 \times 10^{-4}$

23. $y = 0.6714$

25. $x = 2.873$

27. $x = -2.145$

29. $x = 2.778 \times 10^3$

31. $x \log 0.026 = \log 7; \; x = \dfrac{\log 7}{\log 0.026} = -.533$

33. $4.3 \log x = \log 7300$

$\log x = \dfrac{\log 7300}{4.3} = 0.8984; \; 10^{0.8984} = x = 7.915$

35. $3 \log y = 9$

$\log y = \dfrac{9}{3} = 3; \; y = 10^3 = 1 \times 10^3$

37. $10^{7.36} = y = 2.291 \times 10^7$

39. $7 \log x = \log 14$

$\log x = \dfrac{\log 14}{7} = 0.1637$

41. $x \log 70 = \log 12$

$x = \dfrac{\log 12}{\log 70} = 0.5849$

End of Chapter Problems 23-3

1. $(2 - y) \log 6 - \log 68$; $2 - y = \dfrac{\log 68}{\log 6} = 2.355$

3. $\dfrac{y}{4} \log 75 = \log 3.54$; $\dfrac{y}{4} = \dfrac{\log 3.54}{\log 75} = 0.2928$; $y = 1.171$

5. $10^{1.7} = x / 42$; $x = 42 \times 10^{1.7} = 2.105 \times 10^3$

7. $10^6 = 100 / x$; $x = 100 / 10^6 = 1 \times 10^{-4}$

9. $(x - 2) \log 3 = \log 50$; $x - 2 = \dfrac{\log 50}{\log 3} = 3.561$

11. $\dfrac{3}{x} \log 16 = \log 200$; $\dfrac{3}{x} = \dfrac{\log 200}{\log 16} = 1.911$; $\dfrac{3}{1.911} = x$, $x = 1.570$

13. $10^6 = \dfrac{x}{100}$; $x = 100 \times 10^6 = 1 \times 10^8$

15. $10^{-4} = \dfrac{20}{x}$; $x = \dfrac{20}{10^{-4}} = 2 \times 10^5$

17. $\dfrac{x}{2} \log 14 = \log 43$; $\dfrac{x}{2} = \dfrac{\log 43}{\log 14} = 1.425$; $x = 2.850$

19. $(3 - x) \log 35 = \log 470$; $3 - x = \dfrac{\log 470}{\log 35} = 1.731$; $3 - 1.731 = x$, $x = 1.269$

21. $10^3 = \dfrac{0.005}{x}$; $x = \dfrac{0.005}{10^3} = 5 \times 10^{-6}$

23. $10^{4.3} = \dfrac{y}{9}$; $9 \times 10^{4.3} = y$; $y = 1.796 = 10^5$

25. $(x - 2) \log 45 = \log 3.75$; $x - 2 = \dfrac{\log 3.75}{\log 45} = 0.3472$; $x = 2.347$

27. $(x + 2) \log 8.7 = \log 150$; $x + 2 = \dfrac{\log 150}{\log 8.7}$; $x = 0.3162$

29. $\dfrac{y}{3} \log 60 = \log 1.78$; $\dfrac{y}{3} = \dfrac{\log 1.78}{\log 60}$; $\dfrac{y}{3} = 0.1408$, $y = 0.4225$

End of Chapter Problems 23–4

1. $x = 2.398$

3. $x = 2.708$

5. $x = 5.298$

7. $x = -7.824$

9. $x = -2.708$

11. $x = 14.88$

13. $y = 3.829$

15. $y = 1.832 \times 10^{-2}$

End of Chapter Problems 23–5

Note To Student: Remember that $\log_B B^A = A$ which means that $\log 10^A = A$ and $\ln e^A = a$. Read A as Anything.

1. $e^{-x} = 1 - .625 = .375; \ -x = \ln .375; \ x = .9819$ $-.470$

3. $e^{-x} = \dfrac{50}{80} = .625; \ -x = \ln .625; \ x =$

5. $x = 25(1 - e^{-.75}) = 25(.52763) = 13.19$

7. $x = \dfrac{30}{1 - e^{-3}} = \dfrac{30}{.95021} = 31.57$

9. $e^{-x/3} = \dfrac{10}{25} = .40; \ \dfrac{-x}{3} = \ln .40; \ x = -3 \ln .40 = 2.749$

11. $e^{-4/x} = \dfrac{3}{9} = .3333; \ \dfrac{-4}{x} = \ln .3333; \ x = \dfrac{-4}{\ln .3333} = 3.641$

13. $e^{-2x/3} = 0.176; \ -2x / 3 = \ln .176; \ x = -3 / 2 \ln .176 = 2.606$

15. $e^{-2/x} = 0.5; \ -2 / x = \ln .5; \ x = -2 / \ln .5 = 2.885$

17. $x = 1 - e^{-3} = .9502$

19. $e^{-x} = 1 - .376 = .624; \ -x = \ln .624; \ x = 4.716$

21. $e^{-x/2} = 0.76; \ -x / 2 = \ln .76; \ x = -2 \ln .76 = .5489$

END OF CHAPTER 24 PROBLEMS

End of Chapter Problems 24–1

Note To Student: Practice rearranging equations $A_{PdB} = 10 \log \left(\dfrac{P_{out}}{P_{in}} \right)$ and $A_{VdB} = 20 \log \left(\dfrac{V_{out}}{V_{in}} \right)$ to solve for P_{out}, P_{in}, V_{out}, V_{in} in letters. Then insert numbers into the equations. You will have many equations to rearrange like this in your electronics career.

1. $A_{PdB} = 10 \log \left(\dfrac{P_{out}}{P_{in}} \right) = 60$ dB

3. $A_{PdB} = 10 \log \left(\dfrac{20}{1 \text{ m}} \right) = 43$ dB

5. $A_{PdB} = 10 \log \left(\dfrac{50}{2 \text{ m}} \right) = 44$ dB

7. $P_{in} = \dfrac{P_{out}}{10^{A_P/10}} = 3.79$ mW

9. $P_{in} = \dfrac{100 \text{ W}}{10^{20/10}} = 1$ W

11. $P_{in} = \dfrac{5 \text{ W}}{10^{3.2}} = 3.15$ mW

13. $P_{out} = 10 \text{ mW} \times 10^{2.2} = 1.58$ W

15. $P_{out} = 500 \ \mu\text{W} \times 10^{3.8} = 3.15$ W

17. $P_{out} = 10 \text{ mW} \times 10^{1.5} = 316$ mW

19. $P_{out} = 1 \text{ mW} \times 10^{2} = 100$ mW

21. $P_{out} = 1 \text{ mW} \times 10^{3.2} = 1.58$ W

23. $P_{out} = 1 \text{ mW} \times 10^{5} = 100$ W

25. $A_{vdB} = 20 \log \left(\dfrac{2.7 \text{ V}}{100 \ \mu\text{V}} \right) = 88.6$ dB

27. $A_{vdB} = 20 \log \left(\dfrac{3}{10 \text{ m}} \right) = 49.5$ dB

29. $A_{vdB} = 20 \log \left(\dfrac{10}{50 \ \mu} \right) = 106$ dB

31. $V_{out} = V_{in} \times 10^{Av/20} = 5 \text{ mV} \times 10^{40/20} = 500$ mV

33. $V_{out} = 2 \text{ mV} \times 10^{22.7/20} = 27.3$ mV

35. $V_{out} = 23 \text{ mV} \times 10^{73/20} = 103$ V

37. $V_{in} = V_{out} / 10^{A_v/20} = 126 \ \mu\text{V}$

39. $V_{in} = 15 \text{ V} / 10^{75/20} = 2.67$ mV

41. $V_{in} = 600 \text{ mV} / 10^{4} = 60 \ \mu\text{V}$

43. $V_{in} = 500 \text{ mV} / 10^{-3/20} = 706$ mV

45. $V_{in} = 1 \text{ V} / 10^{-6/20} = 2$ V

47. $V_{in} = 5 \text{ V} / 10^{-3/20} = 7.06$ V

49. $V_{in} = 100 \text{ mV} / 10^{-30/20} = 3.16$ V

End of Chapter Problems 24–2

Note To Student: Remember that for a circuit with Rs and Cs, $f_{co} = \dfrac{1}{2\pi CR}$.

You need to include the points f_{co}, f_{co}, $10\, f_{co}$ on Bode plot = 3 cycles.

Cycle lines themselves must always be multiples of 10.

1. $f_{co} = 1 / (2\pi \times 1\ k\Omega \times 0.3\ \mu F) = 531$ Hz;3 cycles; cycle lines at 10 Hz, 100 Hz, 1 kHz, 10 kHz.
3. $f_{co} = 1 / (2\pi \times 470\ \Omega \times 1\ \mu F) = 339$ Hz;3 cycles; cycle lines at **10 Hz,** 100 Hz, 1 kHz, 10 kHz.

1 & 3.

5. $f_{co} = 1 / (2\pi \times 3.9 \text{ k}\Omega \times 300 \text{ nF}) = 136 \text{ Hz}$;3 cycles; cycle lines at 10 Hz, 100 Hz, 1 kHz, 10 kHz.

7. $f_{co} = 1 / (2\pi \times 2 \text{ k}\Omega \times 50 \text{ nF}) = 1.59 \text{ kHz}$;3 cycles; cycle lines at 100 Hz, 1 kHz, 10 kHz, 100 kHz.

5 & 7.

9. $f_{co} = 1 / (2\pi \times 750 \text{ }\Omega \times 200 \text{ nF}) = 1.06 \text{ kHz}$;3 cycles; cycle lines at 100 Hz, 1 kHz, 10 kHz, 100 kHz.

11. $f_{co} = 1 / (2\pi \times 2 \text{ k}\Omega \times 40 \text{ nF}) = 1.99 \text{ kHz}$;3 cycles; cycle lines at 100 Hz, 1 kHz, 10 kHz, 100 kHz.

End of Chapter Problems 24–3

Note To Student: Remembers that for a circuit with Rs and Cs, $f_{co} = f_1 = \dfrac{1}{2\pi C_1 (R_1 + R_2)}$

and $f_{co} = f_2 = \dfrac{1}{2\pi C_2 (R_1 \| R_2)}$. You need to include the points $\dfrac{f_1}{10}$, f_1, $10\, f_1$ if f_1 is on Bode

plot. You need to include the points $\dfrac{f_2}{10}$, f_2, $10\, f_2$ if f_2 is on Bode plot. Cycle lines must

always be multiples of 10.

Note To Student: Remember that $A_{VdBMax} = 20 \log \left(\dfrac{R_2}{R_1 + R_2} \right)$

All values on Bode plot will then be relative to A_{VdBMax}

1. $f_1 = \dfrac{1}{2\pi (R_1 + R_2) C_1} = \dfrac{1}{2\pi \times 1.88\ \text{k}\Omega \times 250\ \text{nF}} = 339\ \text{Hz};\ 4\ \text{cycles}$

$f_2 = \dfrac{1}{2\pi (R_1 \| R_2) C_2} = \dfrac{1}{2\pi \times 434\ \Omega \times 40\ \text{nF}} = 9.17\ \text{kHz};\ \text{cycle lines at 10, 100, 1 k, 10 k, 100 kHz}$

3. $f_1 = \dfrac{1}{2\pi (R_1 + R_2)\, C_1} = \dfrac{1}{2\pi \times 2.27\ \text{k}\Omega \times 500\ \text{nF}} = 140\ \text{Hz; 4 cycles}$

$f_2 = \dfrac{1}{2\pi (R_1 \| R_2)\, C_2} = \dfrac{1}{2\pi \times 373\ \Omega \times 50\ \text{nF}} = 8.54\ \text{kHz; cycle lines at 10, 100, 1 k, 10 k, 100 kHz}$

5. $f_1 = \dfrac{1}{2\pi (R_1 + R_2)\, C_1} = \dfrac{1}{2\pi \times 5.5\ \text{k}\Omega \times 200\ \text{nF}} = 145\ \text{Hz; 4 cycles}$

$f_2 = \dfrac{1}{2\pi (R_1 \| R_2)\, C_2} = \dfrac{1}{2\pi \times 1.32\ \text{k}\Omega \times 30\ \text{nF}} = 4.02\ \text{kHz; cycle lines at 10, 100, 1 k, 10 k, 100 kHz}$

7. 6 cycles; cycle lines at 1, 10, 100, 1 k, 10 k, 100 k, 1 MHz

At 40 Hz (gen. case): $A_v = 20 \log \dfrac{1}{[1 + (f_1/f)^2]^{1/2}} = 20 \log \dfrac{1}{1.60} = -4.09$ dB

$A_v = 20$ dB $- 4.09$ dB $= 15.9$ dB

At 25 kHz (gen. case): $A_v = 20 \log \dfrac{1}{[1 + (f/f_2)^2]^{1/2}} = 20 \log \dfrac{1}{1.71} = -4.67$ dB

$A_v = 20$ dB $- 4.67$ dB $= 15.3$ dB

9.   5 cycles; cycle lines at 1, 10, 100, 1 k, 10k, 100 kHz

At 40 Hz (gen. case): $A_v = 20 \log \dfrac{1}{[1 + (f_1/f)^2]^{1/2}} = 20 \log \dfrac{1}{2.24} = -6.99 \text{ dB}$

$A_v = 10 \text{ dB} - 6.99 \text{ dB} = 3.01 \text{ dB}$

At 12 kHz (gen. case): $A_v = 20 \log \dfrac{1}{[1 + (f/f_2)^2]^{1/2}} = 20 \log \dfrac{1}{3.16} = -10 \text{ dB}$

$A_v = 10 \text{ dB} - 10 \text{ dB} = 0 \text{ dB}$

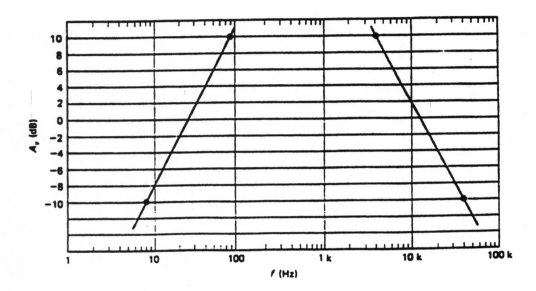

11. $f_1 = \dfrac{1}{2\pi (R_1 + R_2) C_1} = \dfrac{1}{2\pi \times 1.15 \text{ k}\Omega \times 1 \text{ }\mu\text{F}} = 138 \text{ Hz; 5 cycles}$

$f_2 = \dfrac{1}{2\pi (R_1 \| R_2) C_2} = \dfrac{1}{2\pi \times 278 \text{ }\Omega \times 20 \text{ nF}} = 28.6 \text{ kHz; cycle lines at 10, 100, 1 k, 10 k, 100 k, 1 M}$

$A_{VM} = 20 \log \dfrac{R_2}{R_1 + R_2} = 20 \log \dfrac{680}{1.15 \text{ k}\Omega} = -4.56 \text{ dB}$

At 30 Hz (gen. case): $A_v = -4.65 \text{ dB} + 20 \log \dfrac{1}{[1 + (f_1/f)^2]^{1/2}} = -4.56 \text{ dB} + 20 \log \dfrac{1}{4.71}$

$= -4.56 \text{ dB} - 13.5 \text{ dB} = -18.1 \text{ dB}$

At 50 kHz: $A_v = -4.56 \text{ dB} + 20 \log \dfrac{1}{[1 + (f/f_2)^2]^{1/2}} = -4.56 \text{ dB} + 20 \log \dfrac{1}{2.01}$

$= -4.56 \text{ dB} - 6.08 \text{ dB} = -10.6 \text{ dB}$

$TC = RC = 47 \text{ k}\Omega \times 50 \text{ nF} = 2.35 \text{ ms. } I_{MAX} = \dfrac{100 \text{ V}}{47 \text{ k}\Omega} = 2.13 \text{ mA}$

End of Chapter Problems 24–4

Note To Student: These equations refer to the Universal Time Constant Chart which was given in the text in chapter 14.

For an RC circuit, one time constant (TC) = RC and $E = v_R + v_C$

For an RL circuit, one time constant (TC) = L/R and $E = v_R + v_L$

1. $v_R = Ee^{-t/RC} = 65.3$ V; $v_C = E(1 - e^{-t/RC}) = 34.7$ V

3. $v_C / E = 1 - e^{-t/RC}$; $e^{-t/RC} = 1 - \dfrac{v_c}{E}$; $t = -RC \ln\left(1 - \dfrac{v_c}{E}\right)$; $t = 2.47$ m sec

5. $I = \dfrac{E}{R} = 2.13$ mA; $I = Ie^{-t/RC}$; $e^{-t/RC} = \dfrac{i}{I}$; $t = -RC \ln\left(\dfrac{i}{I}\right) = 145 \mu$ sec.

7. $e^{-t/RC} = \dfrac{v_R}{E}$; $t = -RC \ln\left(\dfrac{v_R}{E}\right) = 5.41$ m sec

9. $e^{-t/RC} = \dfrac{v_R}{E}$; $-t/RC = \ln\left(\dfrac{v_R}{E}\right)$; $R = \dfrac{-t}{C \ln(v_R / E)} = 9.79$ kΩ

11. $v_C = E(1 - e^{-t/RC})$; $\dfrac{v_c}{E} = 1 - e^{-t/RC}$; $e^{-t/RC} = 1 - \dfrac{v_c}{E}$; $\dfrac{-t}{RC} = \ln\left(1 - \dfrac{v_c}{E}\right)$;

$C = \dfrac{-t}{R \ln(1 - v_c / E)} = 9.53$ nF

END OF CHAPTER 25 PROBLEMS

End of Chapter Problems 25–1

Note To Student: Decimal numbers may use or omit the subscript 10.
Use spaces in binary numbers to make them easier to read.

1. 7	3. 10	5. 13	7. 23	9. 38
11. 56	13. 101	15. 119_{10}	17. 240	19. 195
21. 101_2	23. 1100_2	25. 10101_2	27. 101101_2	29. 111011_2
31. 1000100_2	33. 1100000_2	35. 10000111_2	37. 11010010_2	

End of Chapter Problems 25–2

1. 12_{10}	3. 63_{10}	5. 190_{10}	7. 2174_{10}	9. 5068_{10}
11. 24_8	13. 120_8	15. 550_8	17. 2611_8	19. 7315_8

End of Chapter Problems 25–3

Note To Student: Both 16 and H are correct subscripts for Hexadecimal Numbers.

1. 26_{10}	3. 76_{10}	5. 512_{10}	7. 4522_{10}	9. $41,033_{10}$
11. 16_{16}	13. 61_{16}	15. 2000_{16}	17. $A8C_{16}$	19. $17BB_{16}$

End of Chapter Problems 25–4

1. $312_8 = CA_{16}$	3. $233_8 = 9B_{16}$	5. $201_8 = 81_{16}$	7. $6311_8 = CC9_{16}$
9. $5303_8 = AC3_{16}$	11. 1111_2	13. 100100_2	15. 10000000_2
17. 101110000_2	19. 1000000000_2	21. 1100_2	23. 100100_2
25. 1001111_2	27. 11100011_2	29. 110011010_2	

End of Chapter Problems 25–5

Note To Student: Use spaces with binary numbers to make nybbles of 3 bits each to read in
octal nybbles and nybbles of 4 bits each to read in hexadecimal nybbles. A byte contains 8
bits, and a nybble is a little byte.

1. $111101_2 = 61_{10} = 3D_{16}$	3. $1100000_2 = 96_{10} = 60_{16}$
5. $101010_2 = 52_8 = 42_{10}$	7. $110100111_2 = 647_8 = 423_{10}$
9. $46_8 = 38_{10} = 26_{16}$	11. $705_8 = 453_{10} = 1C5_{16}$
13. $1010_2 = 12_8 = A_{16}$	15. $100100010_2 = 442_8 = 122_{16}$

End of Chapter Problems 25–6

1. 357_8	3. 775_8	5. 776_8	7. 1423_8	9. 1107_8

End of Chapter Problems 25–7

1. ED_{16}	3. $CA5_{16}$	5. $D56_{16}$	7. $179D_{16}$	9. $1DA6C_{16}$

End of Chapter Problems 25–8

1. 10101_2 3. 110011_2 5. 101001_2 7. 1100010_2 9. 1101001_2

End of Chapter Problems 25–9

1. 45_8 3. 42_8 5. 245_8 7. 337_8 9. 1515_8

End of Chapter Problems 25–10

1. $1A_H$ 3. $3E1_H$ 5. $5F1_H$ 7. AFD_H 9. FDC_H

End of Chapter Problems 25–11

1. 101_2 3. 10_2 5. 10_2 7. 11_2 9. 10110_2

End of Chapter Problems 25–12

Note To Student: You will have an easy time reading binary numbers if you nybble off the bits into octal nybbles of 3 bits each using spaces. You can then do the problem in octal on the side.

1. $1111_2 - 1010_2 + 1 = 0101_2 + 1 = 0110_2$

3. $111\ 111_2 - 101\ 101_2 + 1 = 010\ 010_2 + 1 = 10\ 011_2$

5.
$$\begin{array}{lll} 11\ 001_2 = & 11\ 000 & = \quad 31_8 \\ \underline{-\ 01\ 100_2} \Rightarrow & +\ \underline{10\ 011} & = \quad \underline{-14_8} \\ & 101\ 100 & \\ & \llcorner\!\!\rightarrow +\ 1 & \\ & 01\ 101_2 = & 15_8 \end{array}$$

7.
$$\begin{array}{lll} 101\ 101_2 = & 101\ 101 & = \quad 55_8 \\ \underline{-\ 001\ 010_2} \Rightarrow & +\ \underline{110\ 101} & = \quad \underline{-\ 12_8} \\ & 1\ 100\ 010 & \\ & \llcorner\!\!\rightarrow +\ 1 & \\ & 100\ 011_2 = & 43_8 \end{array}$$

Note To Student: Notice that the two's complement is equal to one's complement plus one; you still need to remove leftmost 1 from the sum after you add the two's complement to the original number. Be sure the complement is at least as long as the first number. It is a good idea to add extra leading 1's to complement the finish nybble. Always nybble off in octal and do in octal on the side as extra proof.

9.
$$\begin{array}{lll} 10\ 110_2 = & 010\ 110_2 & = \quad 26_8 \\ \underline{-\ 01\ 011_2} \Rightarrow & +\ \underline{110\ 101_2} & = \quad \underline{-\ 13_8} \\ & 1\ 001\ 011_2 & \\ & 1\ 0111_2 & = \quad 13_8 \end{array}$$

11.
$$\begin{array}{lll} 1\ 011\ 001_2 = & 1\ 011\ 001_2 & = \quad 131_8 \\ \underline{-\quad 010\ 110_2} \Rightarrow & +\ \underline{111\ 101\ 010_2} & = \quad \underline{-\ 26_8} \\ & 1\ 001\ 000\ 011_2 & \\ & 1\ 000\ 011_2 & = \quad 103_8 \end{array}$$

End of Chapter Problems 25–13

1. $77_8 - 64_8 + 1 = 13_8 + 1 = 14_8$ 3. $777_8 - 635_8 + 1 = 142_8 + 1 = 143_8$

5. $FF_H - A3_H + 1 = 5C_H + 1 = 5D_H$ 7. $FFF_H - C1E_H + 1 = 3E1_H + 1 = 3E2_H$

9. $63_8 - 25_8 = 63_8 + 77_8 - 25_8 + 1 - 100_8 = 63_8 + 53_8 - 100_8 = 36_8$

11. $626_8 - 377_8 = 626_8 + 777_8 - 377_8 + 1 - 1000_8 = 626_8 + 401_8 - 100_8 = 227_8$

13. $A2_H - 8C_H = A2_H + FF_H - 8C_H + 1 - 100_H = A2_H + 74_H - 100_H = 16_H$

15. $6A2_H - 4FF_H = 6A2_H + FFF_H - 4FF5_H + 1 - 1000_H = 6A2_H + B01_H - 1000_8 = 1A3_H$

END OF CHAPTER 26 PROBLEMS

End of Chapter Problems 26–1

1.

3.

5.

7.

9.

11.

13.

15.

17.

19.

21. $A\overline{B} + \overline{B}C$

23. $\overline{\overline{\overline{XYZ}}}$

25. $\overline{\overline{AB}} + C$

27. $(A + B)\overline{(A + B)}D$

29. $Z(X + Y)$

31. $\overline{\overline{AB}(A + B)}$

33. $\overline{X + \overline{\overline{Y}} \cdot \overline{Y} + Z}$

35. $\overline{\overline{A + B}(B + C)(C + D)}$

37. $\overline{XY + \overline{YZ}}$

39. $\overline{A\overline{B} + \overline{B}C}$

End of Chapter Problems 26–2

1.   A ((A + B) (B)) original

   = A (B (A + B)   ) commutative 6a says Anything and Other = Other and anything

   = A (B   ) absorption 15a says Anything (Anything or other) = Anything

   = AB   simplified result which is equivalent to original

A	B	A+B	(A+B)(B)	A ((A+B)(B)	AB
0	0	0	0	0	0
0	1	1	0	0	0
1	0	1	1	0	0
1	1	1	1	1	1

3.

$\left(\overline{A} + B + C\right) + \left(\overline{A} + B\right) + C$ original

$= \overline{A} + B + C + \overline{A} + B + C$ associate 7b

$= \overline{A} + \overline{A} + B + B + C + C$ associate 7b rearrange alphabetically

$= \overline{A} + B + C$ = 11b   since Anything + Anything = Anything

A

$\overline{A}$

B
C

$\overline{A} + B + C$

A	B	C	$\overline{A}$	$\overline{A} + B$	$\overline{A} + B + C$	$(\overline{A} + B + C) + (\overline{A} + B) + C$
0	0	0	1	1	1	1
0	0	1	1	1	1	1
0	1	0	1	1	1	1
0	1	1	1	1	1	1
1	0	0	0	0	0	0
1	0	1	0	0	1	1
1	1	0	0	1	1	1
1	1	1	0	1	1	1

$\left((A\,B)(\overline{B} + C)\right) C$ original equation

5. $= \left(AB\overline{B} + ABC\right) C$ distributive property 8a

$= (0\quad + ABC)\,C$ anything and not – anything = 0 by 12a

$= (ABC)\,C$ 0 + anything = anything 9b

$= ABCC$ associative property 7a

$= ABC$ anything and anything = anything 11a

A	B	C	AB	$\overline{B}$	$\overline{B} + C$	$(AB)(\overline{B} + C)$	$((AB)(\overline{B} + C))C$	ABC
0	0	0	0	1	1	0	0	0
0	0	1	0	1	1	0	0	0
0	1	0	0	0	0	0	0	0
0	1	1	0	0	1	0	0	0
1	0	0	0	1	1	0	0	0
1	0	1	0	1	1	0	0	0
1	1	0	1	0	0	0	0	0
1	1	1	1	0	1	1	1	1

A
B
C

ABC

End of Chapter Problems 26–3

1.

$\overline{A + \overline{B} \cdot \overline{C}}$ Original expression
$\overline{A}\overline{B}\overline{C}$ 14a

(a)

(b)

A	B	C	Ā	B̄	C̄	A + B	Ā + B̄	Ā + B̄·C̄	ĀB̄C̄
0	0	0	1	1	1	0	1	1	1
0	0	1	1	1	0	0	1	0	0
0	1	0	1	0	1	1	0	0	0
0	1	1	1	0	0	1	0	0	0
1	0	0	0	1	1	1	0	0	0
1	0	1	0	1	0	1	0	0	0
1	1	0	0	0	1	1	0	0	0
1	1	1	0	0	0	1	0	0	0

Equal

(c)

3.

$(A + B)(\overline{\overline{A} + C})D$ Original expression
$(A + B)(\overline{AC})D$ 14a
$A\overline{A}CD + \overline{A}B\overline{C}D$ 7a
$0 + \overline{A}B\overline{C}D$ 12a
$\overline{A}B\overline{C}D$ 9b

(a)

(b)

A	B	C	D	Ā	C̄	A + B	A + C	Ā + C̄	D(A + B)(Ā + C̄)	ĀB̄C̄D
0	0	0	0	1	1	0	0	1	0	0
0	0	0	1	1	1	0	0	1	0	0
0	0	1	0	1	0	0	1	0	0	0
0	0	1	1	1	0	0	1	0	0	0
0	1	0	0	1	1	1	0	1	0	0
0	1	0	1	1	1	1	0	1	1	1
0	1	1	0	1	0	1	1	0	0	0
0	1	1	1	1	0	1	1	0	0	0
1	0	0	0	0	1	1	1	1	0	0
1	0	0	1	0	1	1	1	1	0	0
1	0	1	0	0	0	1	1	0	0	0
1	0	1	1	0	0	1	1	0	0	0
1	1	0	0	0	1	1	1	1	0	0
1	1	0	1	0	1	1	1	1	0	0
1	1	1	0	0	0	1	1	0	0	0
1	1	1	1	0	0	1	1	0	0	0

(c)

5.

$\overline{\overline{A}\overline{B}\cdot\overline{B}\overline{C}}$ 14a

$(\overline{A}+B)(B+\overline{C})$ 14b

$\overline{A}B + BB + \overline{A}\overline{C} + B\overline{C}$ 8a

$\overline{A}B + B + \overline{A}\overline{C} + B\overline{C}$ 11a

$B + \overline{A}\overline{C} + B\overline{C}$ 15b

$B + B\overline{C} + A\overline{C}$ 6b

$B + \overline{A}\overline{C}$ 15b

(a)

(b)

A	B	C	$\overline{A}$	$\overline{B}$	$\overline{C}$	$A\overline{B}$	$\overline{B}C$	$A\overline{B} + \overline{B}C$	$\overline{A\overline{B} + \overline{B}C}$	$\overline{A}\overline{C}$	$B + \overline{A}\overline{C}$
0	0	0	1	1	1	0	0	0	1	1	1
0	0	1	1	1	0	0	1	1	0	0	0
0	1	0	1	0	1	0	0	0	1	1	1
0	1	1	1	0	0	0	0	0	1	0	1
1	0	0	0	1	1	1	0	1	0	0	0
1	0	1	0	1	0	1	1	1	0	0	0
1	1	0	0	0	1	0	0	0	1	0	1
1	1	1	0	0	0	0	0	0	1	0	1

└── Equal ──┘

(c)

7.

$\overline{A + B\overline{C}}$ Original expression

$\overline{\overline{A}}\,\overline{B\overline{C}}$ 14a

$\overline{A}(\overline{B} + C)$ 14b

(a)

B ─▷○─
C ──────
A ─▷○─

(b)

A	B	C	$\overline{A}$	$\overline{B}$	$\overline{C}$	$B\overline{C}$	$A + B\overline{C}$	$\overline{A + B\overline{C}}$	$\overline{B} + C$	$\overline{A}(\overline{B} + C)$
0	0	0	1	1	1	0	0	1	1	1
0	0	1	1	1	0	0	0	1	1	1
0	1	0	1	0	1	1	1	0	0	0
0	1	1	1	0	0	0	0	1	1	1
1	0	0	0	1	1	0	1	0	1	0
1	0	1	0	1	0	0	1	0	1	0
1	1	0	0	0	1	1	1	0	0	0
1	1	1	0	0	0	0	1	0	1	0

└── Equal ──┘

(c)

9.

$\overline{(\overline{B}+C)}(C+D)$	Original expression
$\overline{\overline{B}C}(C+D)$	14a
$\overline{\overline{B}}CC + \overline{\overline{B}}CD$	8a
$\overline{B} \cdot 0 + \overline{\overline{B}}CD$	12a
$0 + \overline{\overline{B}}CD$	9a
$\overline{\overline{B}}CD$	9b

(a)

(b)

B	C	D	$\overline{B}$	$\overline{C}$	B + C	$\overline{\overline{B}+C}$	C + D	$(\overline{\overline{B}+C})(C+D)$	$\overline{\overline{B}}CD$
0	0	0	1	1	0	1	0	0	0
0	0	1	1	1	0	1	1	1	1
0	1	0	1	0	1	0	1	0	0
0	1	1	1	0	1	0	1	0	0
1	0	0	0	1	1	0	0	0	0
1	0	1	0	1	1	0	1	0	0
1	1	0	0	0	1	0	1	0	0
1	1	1	0	0	1	0	1	0	0

(c)

Equal

273

11.

$\overline{AB + CD}$	Original expression
$\overline{\overline{AB} \cdot \overline{CD}}$	14a
$AB \cdot \overline{\overline{CD}}$	13a
$AB(\overline{C} + D)$	14b

(a)

(b)

A	B	C	D	$\overline{C}$	$\overline{D}$	AB	$\overline{AB}$	$C\overline{D}$	$\overline{AB} + C\overline{D}$	$\overline{\overline{AB} + C\overline{D}}$	$\overline{C} + D$	$AB(\overline{C} + D)$
0	0	0	0	1	1	0	1	0	1	0	1	0
0	0	0	1	1	0	0	1	0	1	0	1	0
0	0	1	0	0	1	0	1	1	1	0	0	0
0	0	1	1	0	0	0	1	0	1	0	1	0
0	1	0	0	1	1	0	1	0	1	0	1	0
0	1	0	1	1	0	0	1	0	1	0	1	0
0	1	1	0	0	1	0	1	1	1	0	0	0
0	1	1	1	0	0	0	1	0	1	0	1	0
1	0	0	0	1	1	0	1	0	1	0	1	0
1	0	0	1	1	0	0	1	0	1	0	1	0
1	0	1	0	0	1	0	1	0	1	0	0	0
1	0	1	1	0	0	0	1	0	1	0	1	0
1	1	0	0	1	1	1	0	0	0	1	1	1
1	1	0	1	1	0	1	0	0	0	1	1	1
1	1	1	0	0	1	1	0	1	1	0	0	0
1	1	1	1	0	0	1	0	0	0	1	1	1

└─────── Equal ───────┘

(c)

End of Chapter Problems 26-4

1. Possibilities for ignition key (which must be turned on) are on or off.
   Possibilities for transmission include park and not park.
   Not park includes neutral, reverse, drive, overdrive, and low.

   (ignition key on) AND (transmission in park) = go

3. (power on) AND (the "on" button must be pressed) AND (operating system installed)
   = computer starts up

5. (down arrow key) OR (page down key) OR (mouse pointer in scroll bar and click the left mouse button)
   = can scroll down a document using a word processor

END OF CHAPTER 27 PROBLEMS

End of Chapter Problems 27–1

Note To Student: The headings for columns and rows for Karnaugh maps can be written with numbers 0 and 1 or with $\overline{A}$ for 0 and A for 1 if using A.

You can use headings 0,0   0,1   1,1   1,0 or $\overline{A}\ \overline{B}$, $\overline{A}B$, AB, $A\overline{B}$

Notice that only one variable at a time is complemented within a pair.

1.

   $MAP = \overline{B}$

3.

   $MAP = A\overline{C} + \overline{A}B$

5.

   $MAP = \overline{C}$

7.

   $MAP = B\overline{C} + \overline{B}C$

9. $MAP = B$

11. $\overline{C} + \overline{A}B$

End of Chapter Problems 27–2

1.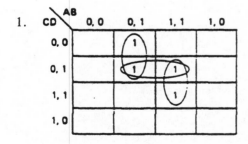

   $MAP = \overline{A}\,B\overline{C} + \overline{B}\,\overline{C}D + ABD$

3.

   $MAP = \overline{C}D + \overline{A}\,\overline{B}\,\overline{C}$

5.

$\text{MAP} = \overline{D} + ABC$

7. $\text{MAP} = D$

9. $\text{MAP} = B\overline{C} + \overline{B}CD$

End of Chapter Problems 28–1

1. 15 scores on a quiz:

```
                            X
                            X
                            X
              X       X     X     X     X
        X     X       X     X     X     X     X
      60(1) 65(2)   70(2) 75(5) 80(2) 85(2) 90(1)
```

3. Scores listed first in ascending order, then counted by range groups:

60 62 65 65 66 70 70 72 73 75 75 75 76 77 78 78 80 80 82 83 85 85 90 94 98

60–64	65–69	70–74	75–79	80–84	85–89	90–94	95–99	= range groups
2	3	4	7	4	2	2	1	= number in that range group
62	67	72	77	82	87	92	97	= interval midpoint

5. 20 amplifiers supposed to be 40 dB each

```
                            X
                            X
                      X     X
          X           X     X     X
          X     X     X     X     X
          X     X     X     X     X     X     X
        37(3) 38(2) 39(4) 40(6) 41(3) 42(1) 43(1)
```

intervals are divided by whole numbers: 37 = 37.00 to 37.99

7. 25 DAYS production

```
                                        X     X
                X                 X     X     X
          X     X     X     X     X     X     X     X     X
          X     X     X     X     X     X     X     X     X
        260(2) 270(3) 280(2) 290(3) 300(3) 310(4) 320(4) 330(2) 340(2)
```

intervals are divided by sets of ten: 260 = 260 to 269

9. 25 samples in kΩ

```
                                  X           X
                            X     X     X     X
                            X     X     X     X
                      X     X     X     X     X     X     X
          X           X     X     X     X     X     X     X
        1.90  1.92  1.94  1.96  1.98  2.00  2.02  2.04  2.06  2.08
        (1)   (0)   (0)   (2)   (4)   (5)   (4)   (5)   (2)   (2)
```

intervals are divided by sets of .02: 1.90 = 1.90 to 1.91

11. 20 day results
     of defective parts
     per hundred:

```
                                    X
                                    X
                                    X
                                    X          X
                        X           X    X           X
              X         X           X    X           X
              X         X           X    X           X          X
            1 (2)     2 (3)       3 (7)  4 (4)      5 (3)      6 (1)
```

13. ten samples in nsec.

     range difference is 4.6 − 2.8 = 1.8, which divides evenly by 9

     to give 0.2 for interval spaces for ten intervals

```
        X
   X    X
   X    X    X
   X    X    X                              X
  2.8  3.0  3.2  3.4  3.6  3.8  4.0  4.2  4.4  4.6
  (3)  (4)  (2)  (0)  (0)  (0)  (0)  (0)  (0)  (1) = ten samples
  2.9  3.1  3.3  3.5  3.7  3.9  4.1  4.3  4.5  4.7 = midpoints of each interval
```
     ten intervals divided by sets of 0.2: 2.8 = 2.80 − 2.99

15. ten samples in MHz.
     range difference is 520 − 475 = 45, which divides evenly by 9
     to give 5 for interval spaces for ten intervals

```
                                 X
   X    X    X         X    X    X    X    X    X
  475  480  485  490  495  500  505  510  515  520
  (1)  (1)  (1)  (0)  (1)  (2)  (1)  (1)  (1)  (1)   = ten samples
  477.5 482.5 487.5 492.5 497.5 502.5 507.5 512.5 517.5 522.5 = midpoints
```
     ten intervals divided by sets of 5: 475 = 475 − 479

End of Chapter Problems 28–2

1. 15 scores on a quiz:
    60 65 65 70 70 75 75 75 75 75 80 80 85 85 90
    mean = 75, median = 75, mode = 75, σ = 7.958

3. 25 scores listed by midrange:
    62(2)   67(3)   72(4)   77(7)   82(4)   87(2)   92(2)   97(1)
    mean = 77, mode = 77, median = 77, σ = 8.36 or 8.50

5. 20 amplifiers supposed to be 40 dB each:

37.0	37.3	37.6	38.2	38.4	39.2	39.2	39.4	39.7	40.2
40.3	40.4	40.7	40.7	40.9	41.3	41.6	41.8	42.6	43.6

    mean = 40.005, median = 40.25, mode = 39.2 and 40.7, σ = 1.72

7. 25 DAYS number of items produced each day:
   260 265 270 276 277 288 288 290 293 295 300 302 306
   310 312 315 315 320 320 325 327 330 332 340 340
   mean = 303.84, median = 306,
   mode = 288 and 315 and 320 and 340, σ = 22.75

9. 25 samples in kΩ:
   1.90   1.96   1.96   1.98   1.98   1.98   1.98   2.00   2.00   2.00
   2.00   2.00   2.02   2.02   2.03   2.03   2.04   2.04   2.04   2.05
   2.05   2.06   2.06   2.08   2.09
   mean = 2.014, median = 2.02, mode = 2.00, σ = .04195

11. 20 days results of defective parts per hundred:
    1 1 2 2 2 3 3 3 3 3 3 4 4 4 4 5 5 5 6
    mean = 3.3, median = 3, mode = 3, σ = 1.308, Sx = 1.342

13. mean is 3.2, mode is 3.0,
    median is 3.1 (3 above this midrange value & 3 below this midrange value)

15. mean is 500, mode is 500,
    median is 502.5 (4 above this value & 4 below this value)

End of Chapter Problems 28–3

1. 60 (1) 65 (3) 70 (5) 75 (7) 80 (5) 85 (4) 90 (2) 95 (1) 100 (1)
   n = 9, mean = 77.4, median = 75, mode = 75,
   range = 100–60 = 40, standard deviation = 9.25

3. 55 (2) 60 (1) 65 (4) 70 (3) 75 (6) 80 (10) 85 (5) 90 (4) 95 (2)
   n = 37, mean = 77.43, median = 80, mode = 80,
   range = 95–55 = 40, standard deviation = 10.04

5. 50–56 (2)   57–63 (5)   64–70 (7)   71–77 (8)   78–84 (6)   85–91 (4)   92–98 (2)
   Use midpoint in any interval as the data value for that interval.
   Use 54 (2)   60 (5)   67 (7)   74 (8)   81 (6)   88 (4)   95 (2)
   n = 34, mean = 73.44, median = 74, mode = 74,
   range = 98–50 = 48, standard deviation = 10.94

7. 50–54 (2) 55–59 (5) 60–64 (5) 65–69 (3) 70–74 (4) 75–79 (6)
   80–84 (8) 85–89 (3) 90–94 (1)
   Use 52 (2)   57 (5)   62 (5)   67 (3)   72 (4)   77 (6)   82 (8)   87 (3)   92 (1)
   n = 37, mean = 71.86, median = 72, mode = 82,
   range = 94–50 = 44, standard deviation = 11.06

9. 300–340 (1)   341–381 (3)   382–422 (5)   423–463 (8)
   464– 504 (12)   505–545 (6)   546–586 (4)   587–627 (2)
   Use 320 (1)   361 (3)   402 (5)   443 (8)   484 (12)   525 (6)   566 (4)   607 (2)
   n = 41, mean = 473, median = 484, mode = 484,
   range = 627–300 = 327, standard deviation = 66.56

11. 500–520 (4)   521–541 (6)   542–562 (11)   563–583 (7)
     584–604 (5)   605–625 (3)   626–646 (1)
     Use 510 (4)   531 (6)   552 (11)   573 (7)   594 (5)   615 (3)   636 (1)
     n = 37, mean = 561.08, median = 552, mode = 552,
     range = 529 – 593 = 64, standard deviation = 31.84

13. standard deviation is 0.488 or 0.5

15. standard deviation is 14

End of Chapter Problems 28–4

1. one σ range is determined by mean 40 mm ± 1 mm.
    34 widgets (68% of 50)   should be in the range of 39mm to 41 mm.
    47 widgets (95% of 50)   should be in the range of 38mm to 42 mm.
    50 widgets (99.7% of 50) should be in the range of 37mm to 43 mm.

3. one σ range is determined by mean 600 parts ± 10 parts
    Assuming round the clock production for 30 days of June,
    68% of 30 = 20 days   should have production of 590 to 610 parts.
    95% of 30 = 29 days   should have production of 580 to 620 parts.
    99.7% of 30 = 30 days   should have production of 570 to 630 parts.

5. one σ range is determined by mean score 73 ± 5.6
    68% of 5000 = 3400 scores   should be between 67.4 and 134.8
    95% of 5000 = 4750 scores   should be between 61.8 and 196.6
    99.7% of 5000 = 4985 scores   should be between 56.2 and 258.4

7. There are many words in this problem, so rewrite the given facts before you look at the size of the number in the batch.
    Premium = microprocessors that operate at greater than (mean + 1 σ)
    Standard = microprocessors that operate within (mean ± 1 σ)
    Economy = microprocessors that operate between (mean – 1 σ) and (mean – 2 σ)
    Test Samples = microprocessors that operate at less than (mean – 2 σ)

    Next study figure 28-38 to find the percentages for each category.

    With normal distribution, 50% of all data will be greater than the mean.
    68% / 2 = 34% of all data will be between mean and (mean + 1 σ).
    Therefore 50% – 34% = 16% will be greater than (mean + 1 σ) for Premium Category.

    Standard Category operates within mean ± 1 σ, so will be 68%.

    With normal distribution, 50% of all data will be less than the mean.
    68% / 2 = 34% of all data will be between mean and (mean – 1 σ).
    95% / 2 = 47.5% of all data will be between mean and (mean – 2 σ).
    Therefore 47.5% – 34% = 13.5% will be between (mean – 1 σ) and (mean – 2 σ) for Economy Category.

    With normal distribution, 95% of all data will be within (mean ± 2 σ).
    Therefore only 5% of all units will operate outside of (mean ± 2 σ).
    Only 2.5% of all units will operate at less than (mean – 2 σ) for Test Samples Category.

For a batch of 1000 microprocessors, normal distribution would be:

Premium = 1000 × 16%   = 160 microprocessors
Standard = 1000 × 68%   = 680 microprocessors
Economy = 1000 × 13.5% = 135 microprocessors
Test Samples = 1000 × 2.5%   =   25 microprocessors

9. For a batch of 800 microprocessors, normal distribution would be:

Premium = 800 × 16%   = 128 microprocessors
Standard = 800 × 68%   = 544 microprocessors
Economy = 800 × 13.5% = 108 microprocessors
Test Samples = 800 × 2.5%   =   20 microprocessors